AMERICAN GEOGRAPHICAL SOCIETY

REPRINT SERIES NO. 5

READINGS IN THE GEOGRAPHY
OF
NORTH AMERICA

A selection of articles from

THE GEOGRAPHICAL REVIEW

AMERICAN GEOGRAPHICAL SOCIETY

BROADWAY AT 156TH STREET

NEW YORK

1952

The articles, maps, and illustrations in this book
are reproduced from copyrighted numbers of the
Geographical Review.

FOREWORD

In 1943, at the request of instructors in the orientation courses being given by the United States government to its armed forces, the American Geographical Society issued two volumes of reprints of articles from its quarterly, the *Geographical Review,* under the titles "Readings in the Geography of France, Germany, Flanders, and the Netherlands" and "Readings in the Geography of the Mediterranean Region." When these volumes were offered for general sale, they were so well received that publication from time to time of similar volumes on other parts of the world seemed in order. In this year of the Society's centennial it is appropriate that, as part of its celebration, it should present a volume of articles on the geography of North America. Such a collection, we feel, will be of interest to foreign geographers attending the Seventeenth Congress of the International Geographical Union, to be held this summer in Washington and New York in honor of the Society's centennial; it will be useful, also, perhaps, to those who participate in the excursions planned in connection with the Congress.

Of a total of 1559 articles that have appeared in the Society's journal since 1916, when its title was changed from *Bulletin of the American Geographical Society* to *Geographical Review,* nearly one-third have dealt with the geography of North America—twenty-two with the continent as a whole and the remainder with the various countries or with parts of them. To select from these the number that could be included in a single volume was no easy task. Various criteria were tried out, and it was finally decided that the articles selected should present as wide a range as possible of the many areas of geographical research of which the results have appeared in the *Geographical Review.* That the compilers would have wished to include many more goes without saying, but it is believed that the articles reprinted give a good cross section as regards both topics and research procedure.

It is a source of great satisfaction that the list can include an article by W. M. Davis so characteristic of his methods of description and exposition and so richly illustrated with fine examples of his famous block diagrams as "The Mission Range, Montana." No less representative of its author's abiding interest in pioneer settlement and his concern with climatic and other risks involved in agricultural ventures in new country is Isaiah Bowman's "Our Expanding and Contracting Desert." Carl O. Sauer's "The Personality of Mexico" is an excellent example of his studies of past cultures as a basis for understanding present relations of land and life and of his enviable maturity of observation and expression. Hugh H. Bennett's "The Geographical Relation of Soil Erosion to Land Productivity," although written at a time when it could be said of soil erosion in North America that farmers were "doing little or nothing to check it and much to accentuate its evil effects," is one of many pioneer articles whose value is by no means diminished with the passage of the years. In much the same class is J. E. Church's "Snow Surveying," which presented for the first time a thorough exposition of the principles and possibilities of a new technique of vital importance to farmers and city dwellers who must depend for their water supply on melt-streams from mountain snow. It is a matter of pride, also, that the *Geographical Review* has been the principal medium in which C. Warren Thornthwaite has published his work on climatic classification. Although perhaps no other article appearing in the *Review* has ever been more widely discussed and put to more practical use than his first statement, "The Climates of North America According to a New Classification," published in 1931, the more recent article selected for this volume is the result of his continued efforts to improve on his original system. An example of the wide acceptance and use of this revised classification is to be found in F. Kenneth Hare's study of the boreal forest formation of eastern Canada. John L. Rich's "Bird's-Eye Cross Section" is not, perhaps, to be classed as a pioneer article, but it merits inclusion as a particularly illuminating example of the use of air photography for geographical reconnaissance, to which the Society has made conspicuous contribution.

From many articles on the geography of agriculture two were selected as representative: John Rose Kerr's on "Corn Yield and Climate," not only because it deals with a region and a crop of high importance in the agricultural economy of the United States but also because it is an example of the use of the statistical method in studies of geographical relationships; and John C. Weaver's on "Barley in the United States," because it sketches the history of the cultivation of a grain that is of particular interest to geographers on account of its wide ecological range. Of articles on the geography of industry, James J. Parsons' "Recent Industrial Development in the Gulf South" seemed of special interest because it treats of the combination of factors responsible for the phenomenal growth of a new industrial area.

No little of the renown of the *Geographical Review* is due to its frequent cumulative review articles. Fortunately, there were two available for this reprint volume that could scarcely have been omitted. To trace the history of the development of modern regional geography of North America there is no one more able than W. L. G. Joerg, and his article on "The Geography of North America" is typical also of his critical mastery of geographical bibliography. Wilma Belden Fairchild's

"The American Scene" offers an alluring sampling of a wide variety of recent books of literary merit that describe and interpret the American countryside and the life of its people.

Selected, also, as representative of many articles giving geographical interpretation to various aspects of the American scene are John K. Wright's on "Voting Habits," Mark Jefferson's on "Great Cities," Richard Hartshorne's on "Racial Maps," and Edward L. Ullman's on "The Railroad Pattern." In this same category may be classed James Walter Goldthwait's classic study of a unique phenomenon in the peopling of the United States—the depopulation of once populous farming country, particularly in New England. Charles B. Hitchcock's report on the area adjacent to New York City originally canvassed for a site for the permanent seat of the United Nations is no less important as a study of a section that, although steadily invaded by increasing numbers of commuters, still retains and even impresses on newcomers much of its own individuality.

The interest of the *Geographical Review* in articles on man's use of his agricultural environment on the fringe of pioneer settlement is reflected in W. D. Albright's "Gardens of the Mackenzie"; and Diamond Jenness' article on "Eskimo Art" is included as representative of the numerous studies of the cultural achievements of primitive man to which the *Review* is always happy to open its pages. Of many articles on exploration in the Far North it seemed appropriate to select the first of several studies of the glaciers of Alaska and British Columbia by William Osgood Field, Jr., a member of the staff of the Society who is responsible for the development of its current Juneau Ice Field Research Project.

CONTENTS

The references in parentheses are to the *Geographical Review*

PAGE

THE MISSION RANGE, MONTANA

By W. M. DAVIS

Location and General Features. The Mission Range, one of the smaller members of the Rocky Mountains in western Montana, has the appearance, as seen from the west, of a gently tilted and moderately dissected fault block, gradually rising southward through its 70 miles of length, and believed to be composed of deformed rocks, mostly quartzites, of so uniform a resistance that no distinct expression of inner structure is recognized in outer form. It occupies the greater part of the distance between the Northern Pacific and the Great Northern Railways on the 114th meridian west of Greenwich. The steeper face of the range, probably representing the battered fault scarp, looks to the west. At the low northern end the moderately uneven crest emerges from beneath the glacial deposits which floor the broad intermont depression thereabouts at an altitude of 3,000 feet and rises slowly southward to a height of 9,800 feet near an abrupt southern descent, there gaining a maximum local relief of nearly 7,000 feet. The eastern side of the range is said to slope gently; the western face is steep. Thus the slowly rising crest and the long eastern slope suggest that the mountain block is an up-faulted fragment of a formerly worn-down mountain region, perhaps of low enough relief to be called a peneplane. Several other mountain masses in the same region exhibit a widespread accordance of summit altitude and thus support the conclusion that the forms of today are carved in the uplifted surface of a worn-down mountain region.

The mountain crest, slowly descending and dwindling away to the north, wedges off the branch intermont depression of the north-flowing Swan River on the east from the much larger and longer intermont depression of the south-flowing Flathead River and Lake on the west (map, Fig. 1). This depression is the southernmost part of the Rocky Mountain Trench, as it has been called by Daly.[1] In the district here concerned, the depression is limited on the east by the strong slope of the Galton and Swan Ranges of the Rocky Mountains and on the west by the more gentle ascent of the Flathead Mountains. On the gravel and silt plains of the depression, north of the lake, lies the flourishing agricultural town of Kalispell (altitude, 2,950 feet), reached by a southwestward, 15-mile spur from the main line of the Great Northern Railway. On the eastern shore

---

[1] R. A. Daly: The Nomenclature of the North American Cordillera Between the 47th and 53rd Parallels of Latitude, *Geogr. Journ.*, Vol. 27, 1906, pp. 586-606; see p. 596.

1

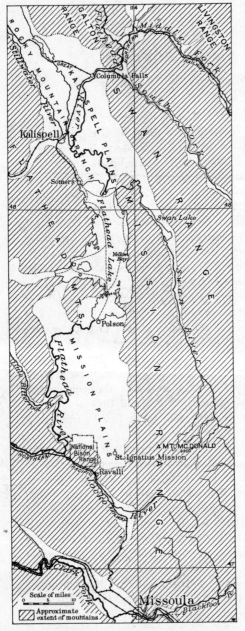

FIG. 1—Sketch-map of the Mission Range region, Montana, with the Flathead intermont depression. Scale, 1:1,100,000.

of Flathead Lake beneath the lower northern part of the Mission Range is the University of Montana Biological Station, the director of which, Professor Morton J. Elrod, has explored the district and published several essays upon it, in which the origin of the range by faulting and its glaciation are briefly mentioned.[2]

My own acquaintance with the Mission Range is brief. In connection with a Shaler Memorial Study in August, 1913, I took a rapid trip 80 miles southward from Kalispell and return and made many notes and sketches of the mountain forms as seen from the lake and plains on the west at distances of one to five or more miles. The diagrams here presented are redrawn from my hurried outlines and represent the range as if it were seen from an elevated point of view several miles to the west. They are roughly generalized figures, suggestive of the kinds of forms there exhibited, rather than sketches of actual details; they undoubtedly exaggerate certain features; they are bare of vegetation; their uncompromising black lines cannot portray the soft-

[2] The Beauties of the Mission Range, *Rocky Mountain Mag.*, 1901, pp. 623-631.

A Biological Reconnaissance in the Vicinity of Flathead Lake, *Bull. Univ. Montana: Biol. Series No. 3*, 1902, pp. 91-182.

The Physiography of the Flathead Lake Region, *ibid.*, No. 5, 1903, pp. 197-203.

ness of the graded slopes; the diagrams are indeed hardly more than cari-
catures of the picturesque **reality**; yet if allowance is made for their limitations they may serve to make the following text and the photographs more
easily intelligible.   The photographs come from the collection of the U. S.
Geological Survey, to which my thanks are hereby rendered; some of them
are by Dr. C. D. Walcott, others by Mr. R. W. Stone.   Their accuracy is
delightful, and the abundance of detail in certain views is extraordinary;
but the relation of the parts that they so well represent to the whole of the
range is nevertheless aided by the rough diagrams.

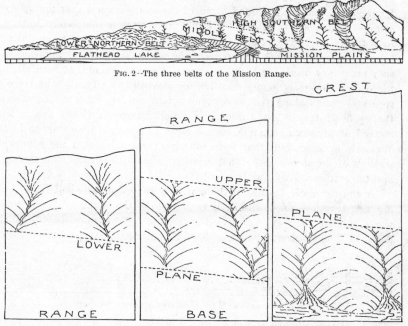

FIG. 2--The three belts of the Mission Range.

FIG. 3—The normal features of the middle belt.

The Three Belts of the Range.   The present features of the Mission
Range, as seen from the intermont depression on the west, may be divided,
in so far as they are due to erosion since uplift, into three oblique belts, as
in Figure 2, by two planes slanting gently to the south and about 1,000
feet apart.   Through the middle of the range where the limiting planes
overlap all three belts are represented.

The Middle Belt.   In the middle belt, confined between the two planes,
the mountain-side forms are all due to the normal erosional forces of
weather and water.   Owing to the overlap of the planes, a continuous
descent cannot be made at any one point within this belt from mountain
crest to mountain base; the overlap is indeed so great that portions of the
belt must be taken, as in Figure 3, at three places in order to show a spur

3

summit and valley heads as on the left, the mid-descent of a spur and
valleys as in the center, and a spur end and piedmont fans as on the right.
The crest of the range here shows rounded, waste-covered summits; the slope
is diversified by maturely graded, large-textured, full-bodied spurs between
the wide-spaced, steep-pitching, apparently consequent valleys of small and
rapid streams. The summits and a good part of the graded spurs are treeless. As is usual in forms of this kind the rarity of rock outcrops makes
outline sketching difficult; there are not enough lines to express the forms.
The concave forward reach of the tapering spurs as they blend into the
piedmont plain is far beyond my power of black-line representation in a
front view. The well-rounded forms of the spurs suggest that the inferred
original fault-scarp of the supposed mountain block is completely destroyed
by retrogressive erosion; and, if so, the upper parts of the streams should
be regarded as obsequent extensions of the original consequents, inasmuch as
they must now discharge to the westward a certain amount of rainfall cap-
tured from formerly longer east-flowing consequents. There is no trace of
spur-end facets along the western mountain border, such as characterize
the up-faulted and less dissected Wasatch Range in Utah; the valleys,
instead of preserving their V cross-section to a simple base line, as in the
Wasatch, open on fans that form re-entrant cusps between the advancing
scallops of the spur ends. What relation exists between the rock structure
and the scalloped base line I cannot say.

A characteristic feature of the maturely carved middle belt is the well-
organized system of down-hill lines by which the descent of water and
waste is made from any point on the slope to the mountain base. All the
paths of descent first follow the down-hill element of a well-graded spur

FIG. 4—Northern end of the range emerging from the plains.

side to a stream; then the down-valley element of a stream course to the
piedmont plain. The spur-side elements are countless; contiguous elements
are nearly parallel to one another, being but slightly convergent or diver-
gent; their declivity changes so slowly and systematically as to insure a
steady though very deliberate progress of the continuous waste cover, as it
creeps and washes toward a stream. The stream lines are comparatively
few, probably not more than eighty or one hundred in the three southern
quarters of the range length where streams are normally developed. The
rock waste, slowly fed from the spur sides into the streams, is rapidly
washed down the channel to the mountain base; for, as well as I could see,
the channels seem to be fairly well graded, though they doubtless still
retain many little rocky rapids and bouldery pools; and their declivity
appears to be such that the streams gain just the velocity that enables

them to do their work of transporting the waste received from the spur sides, with a very small addition supplied by corrasion of beds and banks. The only down-hill lines that do not join a stream are those that follow a spur axis, and these are the lines along which the ascent of the slope is most easily made: their declivity is greatest near mid-height but seldom over 30°, and is much less than that for some distance above the base and below the top.

The Low Northern Belt. In the lower northern belt the smoothly flowing, waste-covered forms of the middle belt are replaced by uneven forms of small texture—bare crags and knobs, cliffs and ledges, channels and hollows—due to recent and severe but immature scouring by a broad and overwhelming glacier of Canadian origin. Similarly immature crags and knobs occur in the glaciated areas of central France[3] and North Wales.[4] Tree growth on the craggy slopes here seen is more abundant than on the waste-covered spurs of the middle belt, and a good share of the surface is thus concealed; but the bare and uneven ledges are so plentifully visible that I felt no doubt of their extending under the tree cover as well. Outline sketching is, however, again difficult because the innumerable rock outcrops now provide details so abundant that there are too many lines to draw; needless to say that the knobs and cliffs shown in my diagrams are not minutely accurate copies of actual forms.

The northern half of this belt forms the northern quarter of the range and lies entirely beneath its limiting plane, as in Figures 4, 5, and 6; it has

FIG. 5—The gradual rise of the scoured northern belt.

an arbitrarily uneven crest, the profile of which lies beneath the northward prolongation of the non-glaciated crest in the middle belt by one or several hundred feet, as if worn down by glacial scouring. The side slope of rubbed and roughened hills and hollows is a medley of unorganized forms; it has no sign of the well-arranged lines of continuous descent by which the middle belt is characterized and no indication of the delicate interdependence of parts that Gilbert long ago, in his classic report on the Henry Mountains, showed to be an essential characteristic of streams and surfaces that had been long enough exposed to the normal processes of subaërial erosion for the development of mature drainage systems: naturally not, for

[3] W. M. Davis: Glacial Erosion in France, Switzerland, and Norway, *Proc. Bost. Soc. Nat. Hist.*, Vol. 29, 1900, pp. 273-322; reference on p. 276.
[4] W. M. Davis: Glacial Erosion in North Wales, *Quart. Journ. Geol. Soc.*, Vol. 65, 1909, pp. 281-350; reference on p. 336.

the irregular slopes here seen are not the work of down-hill washing and creeping by water and weather, but of side-hill scouring and plucking by a huge glacier, moving almost horizontally southward and at so recent a date that small advance toward the development of normally carved forms and toward the establishment of well-organized drainage systems is yet to be seen. There appears, however, as far as I could make out by repeated examination with a field glass, to be some talus at the foot of cliffs and some smooth flooring of detritus gathered in the hollows and there may be small gorges cut in rock sills by the plunging streams. The lines here followed by falling, rolling, and creeping waste are short, irregularly disposed, and of rapidly changing declivity; they radiate in all directions from countless knobs and hillocks, they converge in all directions toward countless channels and hollows: the lines followed by leaping and lagging streams are frequently deflected almost parallel to the range front, in one direction or the other, as if following small troughs worn along the face of the mountain slope; the streams must therefore turn this way and that, they must alternately hurry and loiter, striving to wear down ledges that are too steep and to fill up sags that are too flat, the latter task probably being farther advanced than the former. Streams thus arranged form an elabo-

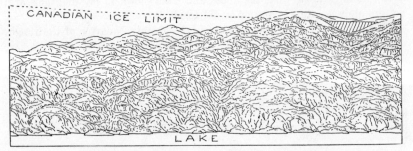

FIG. 6—The scoured northern belt overlapped by the middle belt.

rate branch work; Y-junctions are very frequent, the stems of the smaller upper y's forming the branches of the next lower and larger ones, over and over again. As a result no direct stream lines for the descent of water and waste from the range crest are seen here, and no continuous spur axes to guide paths of direct ascent from the range base. The branch-work stream system thus constituted stands in strong contrast to the single-line streams of the normally eroded middle belt; yet the branch-work streams as well as the single-line streams are consequent, in the sense of following courses offered to them when taking possession of the surfaces that they drain; their differences are chiefly due to difference in the nature of the surfaces offered to their action, and for the rest to differences in their stage of development; for the single-line streams are almost mature, while the branch-work streams are very young: but all this contrast is implied

6

in saying that the northern end of the range shows "uneven forms due to recent and severe but immature scouring by a broad and overwhelming glacier."

Northern End of the Range. If the range is followed farther north, as in Figure 4, its height decreases with a somewhat regular irregularity until the last visible knobs, deeply scoured and channeled and plucked, more or less detached from one another, rise hardly a hundred feet above the surrounding plain of out-washed glacial gravels and silts diversified by low morainic hills, which here occupies the broad intermont depression and presumably covers a farther northward extension of the range crest underground. Some of the knobs lie somewhat west of the line that farther south follows the mountain base, and this suggests that the strong fault by which the central and southern part of the range is thought to be limited, may here, near the least uplifted end of the mountain block, be represented by an up-warped or up-arched mass of which the western limb corresponds to the underground wing of the fault farther south. Low as the range is here, the rocks of the knobs are resistant and apparently of the same nature as those which form the lofty mountain crest to the south. Evi-

Fig. 7—Morainic embankments between normal summits and scoured slopes.

dently, then, the northward diminution of range height cannot be due to degradation of a once much loftier mass in the present cycle of erosion, but rather to the northward decrease in the uplift of a previously worn-down mass. The range rises highest where the uplift, increasing southward along the edge of the supposed fault block, has its greatest value.

A curious feature of the trailing northern end of the range is its transection by the Swan River, which, instead of making a northward detour and avoiding all the rocky knobs, takes a short cut westward through them on its way from its own valley on the back-slope side of the Mission fault block to the larger Flathead valley on the fault-scarp side. This is presumably a persistent consequence of temporary constraint by the waning mass of the Canadian glacier; if so, search should be made in notches at higher levels in the trailing crest for transverse water-worn channels marking temporary outlets of a proglacial lake in the upper Swan River valley; and it is quite possible that the highest channel of all may occur at the head of the valley westward around the southern end of the Mission Range or southward over the neighboring hills directly into the valley of Jocko River.

Truncated Spurs and Morainic Embankments. If we now turn southward to the second fourth of the range, where its crest rises above the limit of glaciation, as in Figure 6, the normally rounded summits and the normally hollowed valley heads of the middle belt make their appearance above the rugged slope of glacial erosion. The valleys are barred across by what I take to be morainic embankments (Figs. 7 and 8), which record the height of glacial action to a nicety; the spurs are imperfectly truncated in irregular cliffs and ledges, strongly scoured along the mountain side.

Below the gently slanting line defined by the moraines, the disorderly tumult of bare cliffs and ledges in the imperfectly truncated spur ends forms a striking contrast with the subdued orderliness of the waste-covered higher slopes; the subdued forms of large texture express a long and suc-

FIG. 8—Normal slopes above scoured slopes.

cessful continuity of degradational processes; the disorderly forms of small texture express a striving and unsuccessful discontinuity. Above, all the local variations of rock structure, such as are determined by the composition, thickness, and attitude of successive beds and by the number and inclination of joints, are practically without influence upon the form of the surface, because local and individual influences are masked by the generalizing effect of the creeping cover of rock waste; below, the masses and planes of structural strength and weakness are strongly expressed in the bared rock faces and fissures of the many cliffs and benches.

The streams in this fourth of the range exhibit a haphazard habit in their plunging courses, for the valleys as well as the spurs are largely obliterated below the line of moraines. Cascades and pools must be frequent in watercourses that are consequent on the smaller forms of so rocky and rugged a mountain side; as far as I could see, little progress towards

8

establishing a graded profile has been accomplished. In the absence of pronounced spurs and valleys, the whole mountain side here descends like a battered wall and dips under the waters of Flathead Lake, of which the eastern shore line is comparatively simple when viewed as a whole but minutely irregular when viewed in detail. The western shore line is much more sinuous. There are, however, two eastern re-entrants of small size, Woods and Yellow Bays, roughly represented in Figures 7 and 8, which appear to occupy scoured hollows between spur remnants, but as to this I am uncertain; the buildings of the Biological Station of the University of Montana are beautifully situated on the north side of Yellow Bay, where a gravel delta, not shown in the diagram, now occupies part of the original re-entrant.

As one advances farther southward, some of the morainic embankments are trenched by the streams from the normal valleys behind them, as in

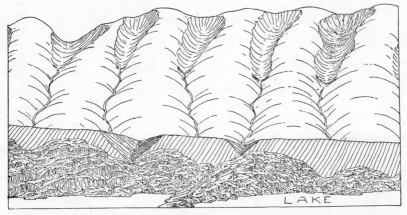

FIG. 9—Small cirques above a continuous moraine.

Figure 9, the spur ends are scoured to less and less height, and their truncation is less and less effective; one of the spurs advances in a low promontory and is continued across the lake by a string of small islands, one of which is shown in Figure 16. The ruggedness of its nearby rocks justifies the generalized details of the glaciated slopes in Figures 7, 8, and 9, although such details are not shown in the photographic view of the range from one of the rocky islands (Fig. 18). Farther on still, the embankments stand at less and less heights above the lake and at the same time become larger and longer, until they ride over the spurs and thus form a long unbroken ridge, which gradually departs from the base of the range, as in Figures 9 and 10. The morainic ridge in this part of its length is truly only about half as high as the 1,500-foot embankment that forms the northern side of the huge morainic amphitheater in which the ancient glacier that followed the valley of the Dora Baltea from the southern side of the Mt.

9

Blanc group ended on the plains of Italy at Ivrea; nevertheless it constitutes a formidable monument of glacial construction, which becomes especially conspicuous as it swings away from the mountains in the noble terminal moraine, dotted with boulders, that sweeps westward across the intermont depression with a relief of 400 or 500 feet—see Figure 2—and a breadth of one or two miles, separating Flathead Lake on its concave northern side from the Mission Plains, chiefly composed of earlier glacial deposits, on its convex southern side. The lake outlet follows a trench sharply cut across the moraine at the southwestern angle of the lake; the town of Polson lies on the morainic slope next east of the outlet, and gives its name to the moraine.

The truncation of mountain-side spurs by a passing glacier is of familiar occurrence in the valley troughs of formerly glaciated mountain ranges; it is less familiar as a feature of ranges that border broad intermont plains.

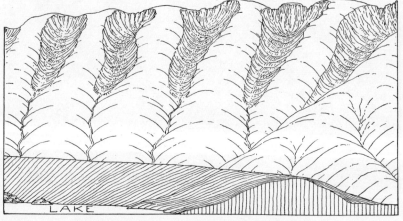

FIG. 10—Larger cirques: the moraine curves westward.

Yet another example of such truncation occurs not far away to the northeast, where the flanks of the Galton and Swan Ranges, the former far northward and the latter for some ten or fifteen miles south of the deep notch by which the Great Northern Railway enters the mountains from the broad intermont depression a short distance east of Columbia Falls station, bear conspicuous marks of scouring by the broad Canadian glacier, similar to but larger than those left upon the flanks of the Mission Range. Near the railway notch the terminal facets of the truncated spurs may well rise a thousand feet over the plain; but they rapidly decrease in height southward, and, beyond the last and lowest one, many other spurs trail away with long concave slopes into the intermont plain: it therefore appears that the farthest effect of the Canadian glacier along the mountain base is seen in the last spur-end facet.

The High Southern Belt. Several miles before the long morainic embankment turns west from the base of the Mission Range at the southern end of the low northern belt, the valley heads show cirque-like enlargement, as in Figures 8 and 9, and thus define the beginning of the third, or high southern belt. Unlike the other two belts, in each of which the sculpture is all of one kind—all normal sculpture in the middle belt, all glacial sculpture in the northern belt—the features of the southern belt are of two kinds, normal and glacial; but here the features of glacial sculpture are the work of separate local glaciers, each in its own valley, and the resulting cirques and troughs alternate with summits and spurs of normal erosion. The first cirque—see Figure 8—is so faintly developed that, were it seen alone, one might remain uncertain as to its nature; but there can be no doubt as to

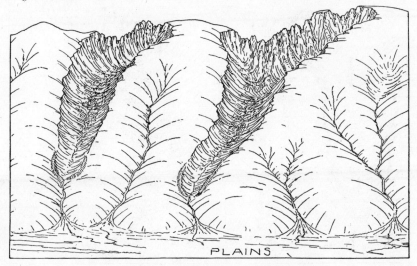

FIG. 11—Sharpened crests between opposing cirques.

its being the slight enlargement of a normal valley head by a small local glacier when it is seen as the northernmost recognizable member of a systematic series of twenty-five or more, of which the southernmost (Fig. 13) is a huge cliff-rimmed excavation in the mountain top, at least 1,000 feet deep, opening into a great rock-walled, hollow-floored trough that descends 5,000 feet to the mountain foot, where it is looped around by a beautiful though small terminal moraine. A line drawn through the lower end of all the troughs separates the middle belt from the high southern belt.

The normal features of the southern belt differ from those of the middle belt only in size and in completeness of development. They are large enough to extend through the entire height of the mountain side. Some of the spurs are subdivided by valleys of normal form that head at half or three-quarters mountain height, and therefore too low for the development

11

of cirques at their head; but other spurs continue undivided from mountain crest to mountain base. With increase of summit height southward, the spurs are more and more encroached upon by the intervening cirques and troughs, but the two classes of forms do not blend; they are separated by well-defined edges where the convex, waste-covered, normal form is suddenly undercut by the steep rock wall of the glacial excavation. The close association in which the two classes of forms are here seen adds force to the objections that I have elsewhere urged[5] against the empirical German phrase-words *Mittelgebirgsformen* and *Hochgebirgsformen*—that is, forms of middle-height mountains and of high mountains—as designations for features of the two classes which are here so intimately associated at the same

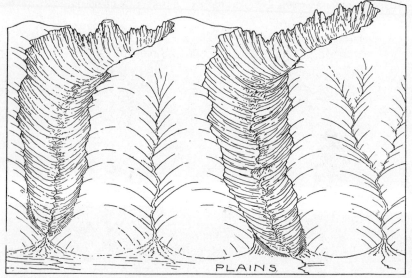

FIG. 12—The cirques are enlarged southward.

altitude; and the confidence with which the two classes are here distinguished gives renewed warrant for preferring explanatory phrases, like forms of normal and of glacial sculpture, to empirical phrases, such as round-topped and sharp-crested mountains.

Cirques and Troughs of Local Glaciers. It has surprised me on various earlier occasions to note the ease with which high-standing cirques can be made out at distances of several miles; from five to twenty miles in the Wasatch Range in Utah[6] and in the Front Range of Colorado,[7] from thirty to forty miles with a field glass in the higher ranges of Turkestan[8]; but

[5] Die erklärende Beschreibung der Landformen, Teubner, Leipzig, 1912, p. 286.

[6] The Wasatch, Canyon, and House Ranges, Utah, *Bull. Mus. Comp. Zool.*, Vol. 49, 1905, pp. 15-58; reference on p. 22.

[7] The Colorado Front Range, *Annals Assoc. Amer. Geogrs.*, Vol. 1, 1912, pp. 21-83; reference on p. 56.

[8] A Journey in Turkestan, pp. 23-119 (reference on p. 91) in R. Pumpelly's Explorations in Turkestan, *Carnegie Inst. Publ. No. 26*, Washington, 1905.

12

only in the Mission Range has the recognition of cirques at a distance been facilitated by their arrangement in a regularly progressive series of two dozen or more, in which larger and larger, stronger and stronger examples follow in regular procession through a stretch of forty miles. The series begins with smooth-contoured, valley-head hollows, perhaps a quarter mile in length and less in breadth, which, as above indicated, hardly deserve the name of cirques. As one's view is turned southward, the size of the hollows gradually increases, the head and side walls become steeper, with a greater exposure of base rock, as in Figure 9; farther on, as in Figure 10,

Fig. 13—An alpine crest and a piedmont lake.

the sky line of the head walls becomes notched, as if two opposing cirques had eaten through the convex crest of the mountain and locally converted it into a sharp and ragged edge, the beginning of maturity in glacial erosion of this kind; at the same time the troughs increase in length. These features characterize the parts of the range shown in Figures 15 and 17, looking across the plains south of Flathead Lake to the east and southeast. As the range increases in height a tendency is noted to the enlargement of the cirques southward, as if in exemplification of the rule that glaciers are best developed on shaded slopes[9]; and as the enlargement becomes more pronounced an extension of the maturely sharpened sky line is perceived through a greater length of mountain crest, as in Figures 11 and 12;

[9] G. K. Gilbert: Systematic Asymmetry of Crest Lines on the High Sierras of California, *Journ. of Geol.*, Vol. 12, 1904, pp. 579-588.

13

here the Alpine term, arête, may be well applied. With the fuller development of the cirques, the troughs gain strongly oversteepened walls and increase so greatly in length as to extend far down toward the foot of the range. The oversteepened walls have, as above noted, a sharply defined edge where they undercut the convex spurs; the bare rock, here and in the cirques exposed to free attack of the weather, is assuming minutely irregular forms and furnishing detritus to talus slopes and fans that are invading the rock floors below, but as far as I could see the change thus accomplished is small as yet. The emphatic definition of the mature cirques is strikingly unlike the vague limitation of the mature normal valley heads, and the acute

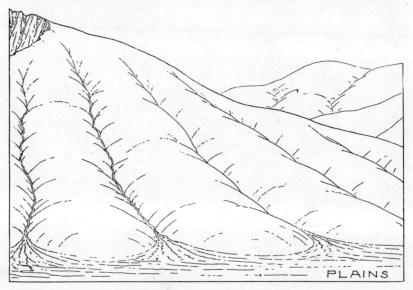

FIG. 14—Normal forms at the southern end of the range.

edge of mature arêtes, where only a narrow belt is exposed to weathering, is strikingly unlike the ample arch of the normally rounded mountain crest, where a broad belt is exposed to weathering; but both these unlikenesses are expectable in view of the fact that a mature glacier is of greatest size close to its high-level source, while a mature stream at its source is of smallest size. The broadly concave form of the troughs is strongly contrasted with the narrow concave of the normal valleys, and this contrast is intensified when one realizes that the proper homology of the large-featured glacial troughs is really found in the minute stream channels that are entrenched within the narrow valley concaves. Here one may realize the contrast between the sluggishness of a heavy glacier that nearly fills its wide and deep trough and the nimbleness of a slender stream that carries away all the ice water in a minute channel; here one may recall the comparison between mountain-

14

side glaciers, which in a temperate climate dwindle and disappear as they creep from snowy reservoirs down into a milder zone, with mountain-side streams, which in an arid climate wither and vanish as they run from the rainier summits down into the drier lower air.

Culmination of the Range. With continued increase in range heights, the southward enlargement of the cirques becomes so great that from a front view a large part of their interior is hidden, as in Figure 12. Finally, at the slowly attained culmination of the range close to its southern end, the largest and last cirque of the entire series is a formidable cavity, excavated half a mile or more southward of its discharging trough; and a small glacier is reported as lying concealed in the cirque head. Here the highest cirque wall, a great mass of bare rock, rises to an acutely serrate crest, forming in Mt. McDonald, 9,800 feet altitude, the loftiest peak of the range, near which the views reproduced in Figures 19, 20, and 21 were taken. The sky line of Figure 19 illustrates the simple crest of the range where it is not narrowed and notched between encroaching cirques, while the great rock face in the same view gives warrant for the steepness and ruggedness of the cirque and trough walls, as shown in the diagrammatic figures. The floor of the McDonald cirque is not in sight from the plain. The trough is a huge channel, rock-walled and rock-floored, with a fairly mature cross-section of catenary pattern. On either side the rounded spurs of normal sculpture are as typically convex as the trough is concave. The hollowed trough floor is not yet much encumbered, as far as I could determine, with talus fans; its longitudinal profile is somewhat broken by rock sills; whether rock basins occur also I could not see. The dimensions of the trough decrease as it descends the mountain side, but it is still well developed to the very foot of the range, where it is extended on the piedmont plain in the form of a terminal basin, rimmed by a well-formed terminal moraine. Farther to the south only normal forms (Fig. 14) are seen as the range rapidly declines toward the Jocko River in a long sunny slope.

The last member in the long succession of forms due to the local action of single glaciers is a fully developed example, beyond which an increase in size is possible but not an increase in completeness of detail; for between the cirque walls which rise to sharpened peaks and the trough which ends at a piedmont moraine is included the whole range of features that a single local glacier can produce. When, in addition to the features due to local glaciation in the high southern belt, are added those due to general glaciation in the low northern belt and both are viewed in their suggestive contrast with the normal features of the middle belt, the Mission Range is seen to be highly flavored with the spice that comes from variety. The concise and systematic combination of these varied features makes the range, as far as I have seen and read, unique.

15

FIG. 15.

FIG. 16.

FIG. 15—Southern part of Mission Range across Mission Plains. (Photo by R. W. Stone.)—Continuous with Figure 17.

FIG. 16—A scoured island in Flathead Lake. (Photo by R. W. Stone.)

16

FIG. 17.

FIG. 18.

FIG. 17—Southern part of Mission Range across Mission Plains. (Photo by R. W. Stone.)—Continuous with Figure 15.

FIG. 18—Glacial troughs in Mission Range over Flathead Lake. (Photo by R. W. Stone.)

17

Cycles and Episodes of Glacial Erosion. Large as the McDonald cirque is, it does not represent the completion of a glacial attack upon a mountain mass; that demands a relatively rapid widening of the cirque floor and its slower lowering until the enclosing walls are consumed—the action of the weather on exposed surfaces here aiding the action of ice on covered surfaces—and the mountain mass is truncated; at the same time the thick-

FIG. 19 –Glaciers on Mission Range, southeast of Mt. McDonald. (Photo by C. D. Walcott.)

ness of the ice on the truncated surface should diminish by reason of lessening mountain height and consequently decreasing snowfall, until the thin and relatively inert glacial veneer almost or quite disappears, the glacial tongues descending from it shorten and vanish, and the truncated mass remains subject only to normal dissection by the retrogressive erosion of its flanks. Here the analogy with stream work in an arid climate may be again recalled; for just as the wearing down of a mountain in a temperate region diminishes the snowfall upon it, so when a mountain range in a desert lowland is worn down the rainfall upon its area will decrease, and eventually, when the range is reduced to low relief, its surface will be about as dry as the lowland around it and subject to further degradation rather by wind than by water action. It was, I believe, Tyndall who first fancifully suggested that deglaciation might be the result of loss of height by

18

glacial erosion;[10] it is now generally agreed that deglaciation was the result of climatic change. Thus two schemes of the life history of a glacier are suggested: one is the highly ideal scheme of a constant climate, during which an upraised mountain mass will, if at first high enough, be glaciated until it is worn so low that its snowfall is lessened and its glaciers disappear, as Tyndall imagined for the actual case of the Alps, and as is above outlined for a supposititious case; this involves a complete "cycle of glacial erosion",[11] in the same sense that the wearing down of an upraised mass by weather and water involves a complete cycle of normal erosion. The other scheme is the more expectable one of a variable climate, in which a mountain mass will be glaciated only as long as the snowfall is sufficient to form glaciers, as was the case with Pleistocene glaciation; glaciers were then extinguished long before their work was completed, and hence, thus limited, the "life history of a glacier" as presented by Russell[12] and the "cycle of mountain glaciation" as presented by Hobbs[13] include only a life history or cycle cut short by climatic change in its prime; that is, a mere episode of glaciation, in which only the earlier stages of a complete cycle, the earlier phases of a full life history are considered. In the Mission Range we evidently have to do only with an episode of glaciation due to climatic changes, introduced upon a mountain already well carved by normal erosion from its initial form; an episode that was closed long before the final stage of an uninterrupted cycle of glacial erosion was reached.

The Explanatory Description of Mountains. The Mission Range forms an admirable subject for close examination by a student of physical geography to whom camping and climbing are exhilarating and to whom the study of land forms is a specialty; all the better if he could go on from the forms to their climate and their inhabitants, and thus make himself a full-fledged geographer. The district is easily accessible; supply stations are abundant near the mountain base. The range is sufficiently separated from its neighbors to form a well-limited field of work. Its rocks, as far as I have learned, have neither paleontological content nor petrographical composition in such variety as to distract a would-be geographer into irrelevant geological complications. The varied physiographic features are developed with remarkable clearness; if accurately described and illustrated they might serve as standards, in terms of which other less simple ranges could be advantageously treated.

---

10 Tyndall wrote: "Given the uplifted land, and we have a glacial epoch; let the ice work down the earth, every foot it sinks necessitates its own diminution; the glaciers shrink as the valleys deepen; and finally we have a state of things in which the ice has dwindled to limits which barely serve as a key to the stupendous operations of a by-gone glacial age. To account for a glacial epoch, then, we need not resort to the hard hypothesis of a change in the amount of solar emission, or of a change in the temperature of space traversed by our system. Elevations of the land, which would naturally accompany the cooling of the earth, are quite competent to account for such an epoch; and the ice itself, in the absence of any other agency, would be competent to destroy the conditions which gave it birth." (The Conformation of the Alps, *Philos. Mag.*, Vol. 24, 1862, pp. 169-173; see pp. 172-173.)

11 See reference in footnote 3, p. 294.

12 I. C. Russell: Glaciers of North America, Ginn, Boston, 1897, Chapter 10.

13 W. H. Hobbs: The Cycle of Mountain Glaciation, *Geogr. Journ.*, Vol. 35, 1910, pp. 146-163 and 268-284.

19

FIG. 20.—Mission Range in vicinity of Mt. McDonald, from head of Swan River. (Photo by C. D. Walcott.)

20

286

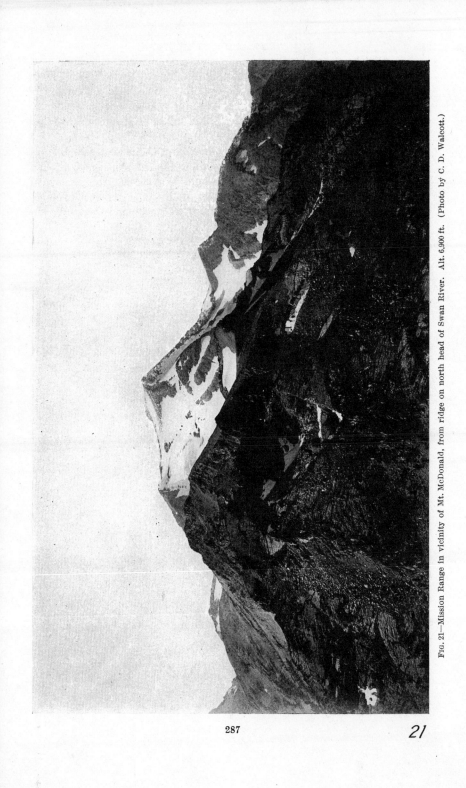

Fig. 21—Mission Range in vicinity of Mt. McDonald, from ridge on north head of Swan River. Alt. 6,900 ft. (Photo by C. D. Walcott.)

21

A spirit of geographical adventure has encouraged me here to set forth the results of a mere reconnaissance; first, because so little is known geographically of the individual ranges of Montana that every contribution to their further description is desirable; again, because the appearance of an incomplete account of the Mission Range may hasten the production of a more thorough study; finally and chiefly, because incomplete as this account is, it has a value in showing that a systematic method of treating land forms is sometimes applicable in rapid work, where conservative geographers of the empirical school think it is inapplicable, their idea being that explanatory description must demand long and intensive study, and therefore cannot be based on brief inspection.

ESKIMO ART *

By Diamond Jenness
Geological Survey of Canada

One of the most fascinating problems in ethnological study is the presence of a highly developed art among races that are in a very low stage of culture. Our paleolithic ancestors in western Europe covered the walls of their cave dwellings with lifelike paintings of the men and animals around them; and in South Africa the primitive Bushmen adorned their rock shelters with equally realistic figures in black and white. So, too, the Eskimos of the Arctic, using only flakes of flint or treasured scraps of iron, carved and engraved on bone and ivory with a skill that excited the admiration of every early explorer. This graphic art was universal among the Eskimos, extending from Alaska on the one side to Greenland on the other; it dates from prehistoric times until the present day. Every large museum in Europe and America is filled with excellent examples of it. There are not only carvings of men and animals, free and in relief, but exquisite engravings, from elaborate representations of hunting and domestic scenes down to simple geometrical patterns. It is true that there are great differences in the artistic ability of different tribes. In southern Alaska it is almost the exception to find an article of bone or ivory without decoration of some kind; even so utilitarian and commonplace an object as a bucket handle often has a row of seals or other animals carved in relief on its surface. Farther east, in Coronation Gulf, the only designs are a few incised lines, even though the beautifully polished bone needle cases and quiver handles would naturally lend themselves to more elaborate ornamentation. Sculpture reappears, however, in Hudson Bay; and in East Greenland, among one of the most barbarous and impoverished of all the Eskimo tribes, it reached almost the same high level as in Alaska. Every branch of the Eskimo race, indeed, seems to possess marked artistic ability, although in some places, owing partly to unfavorable economic conditions, the talent remained more latent than it did elsewhere.

---

* Published by permission of the Director of the Victoria Memorial Museum, Ottawa, Canada.

INFLUENCE OF EUROPEAN CIVILIZATION

This highly developed art of the Eskimos, far from being destroyed by contact with European civilization, as happened so often elsewhere, received a certain stimulus. Thus there are strong grounds for believing that the exceptional development of sculpture and engraving among the Alaskan Eskimos was due to contact with the Indian tribes on the northwest coast and with Russian civilization filtering in through Asia. In more recent times the settlement of Alaska by Americans has led to the creation of a regular industry in ivory work; and though most of the carving and engraving that is now being produced and sold to the outside world is of a much inferior quality, despite the use of modern tools and machinery, now and again some specimen does really attain to, if not actually surpass, the work of previous generations. The same thing has happened, although to a less degree, on the Hudson Bay side of the continent and again in Greenland.

Such unusual artistic talent among a primitive nomadic race of hunters could not fail to attract the notice of scientists, and various writers, Hoffman,[1] Boas,[2] and Thalbitzer,[3] have discussed their work in bone and ivory. One development from it, however, the pencil sketches of the Eskimos, has been altogether neglected in English-speaking countries up to the present, although one or two explorers, notably Peary and MacMillan, have published a few examples of it. The use of pencil and paper is of course quite modern, but it is merely an improvement on the old Eskimo custom of using native graphite for drawing on wood and skin. The ease and freedom of a pencil, however, has made these paper sketches a popular pastime, and amateur artists are everywhere recording their impressions and adventures in notebooks, on the margins of old magazines, and on any scrap of paper that they can find. In Danish Greenland the Eskimos have long run a printing press and published a journal devoted almost entirely to Eskimo topics and illustrated with sketches by native artists. In fact, wherever you wander, if you give a notebook and pencil to an Eskimo, whether he can write or not, he is almost certain to fill the book with drawings of men and animals, hunting scenes, and scenes of social life.

Naturally the average native, even with the pencil, is still bound by his old tradition; his drawings show the same want of perspective, the same lack of detail, and the same conventionality as his engravings and carvings. Nevertheless, under the influence of new ideas inspired by the European sketches which the Eskimos are fond of copying, an artist does occasionally rise above the general level and produce a few drawings that display real imagination and promise. It is not that he departs from the old subjects; his talent is still limited to the delineation of hunting scenes and social life

---

[1] W. J. Hoffman: The Graphic Art of the Eskimos, *Rept. U. S. Natl. Museum for the Year Ending June 30, 1895*, pp. 739–968.

[2] Franz Boas: The Central Eskimo, *6th Ann. Rept. Bur. of Amer. Ethnology for 1884–85*, pp. 399–669; *idem:* Decorative Designs of Alaskan Needlecases, *Proc. U. S. Natl. Museum*, Vol. 34, Washington, D. C., 1908, pp. 321–344.

[3] William Thalbitzer: The Ammassalik Eskimo, *Meddelelser om Grønland*, Vol. 39.

as he knows it; but he develops an impressionistic idea of the scene as a totality, replete with detail and environment, together with a vague notion of perspective and a truer sense of proportion. It does not require much imagination to believe that if one of these Eskimo artists could only receive a little training he might produce something that would be worth hanging in our salons alongside the pen-and-ink sketches from Japan or the drawings of our own impressionistic schools.

Examples of Eskimo Art from Three Different Regions

This new development in Eskimo art aroused the interest of the American Geographical Society, who gathered a number of examples of it from two well-known explorers, Mr. D. B. MacMillan and Mr. R. J. Flaherty. The drawings supplied by Mr. MacMillan were made by Kakotcheea, a nineteen-year old Eskimo of Smith Sound in northern Greenland, where Mr. MacMillan established a base for his explorations. The Smith Sound Eskimos were discovered by Sir John Ross in 1818; since that date they have been visited by many explorers and whalers, some of whom, for example Kane and Peary, remained for two or more years in their midst. Mr. Flaherty's sketches are from an altogether different region. They are the compositions of Wetalltok, an Eskimo from the Great Whale seaboard on the eastern coast of Hudson Bay. Wetalltok had been in the service of the Hudson's Bay Company for about fifteen years and beside these drawings contributed a remarkably accurate sketch map of the Belcher Islands,[4] a map that is itself one of the best examples of the cartographic skill for which the Eskimos have long been famous.

To the sketches from these two regions I have added a few that were drawn for me in the winter of 1913–1914 by an Eskimo from Cape Prince of Wales in northern Alaska. This Eskimo, named Ugiagnak, was a middle-aged man who could neither read nor write, although he had been in contact with white men all his life. The natives of northern Alaska were less advanced in graphic art than those of southern Alaska but far more so than either the Hudson Bay Eskimos or those of Smith Sound. Our three artists, then, from three different regions, are interesting on two quite distinct grounds. In the first place the identity of subject matter in all three bears witness to the remarkable uniformity of Eskimo culture despite the enormous range of territory over which it extends. In the second place, the differences in technique of the three men give us an indication of the direction which this graphic art may take among the Eskimos, if ever they are afforded the opportunity of developing it.

Hunting Scenes

Figures 1–5 illustrate the Eskimo method of hunting the walrus. The season for walrus hunting is the late summer, when the sea is covered with

---

[4] Published in the *Geographical Review*, Vol. 5, 1918, p. 440.

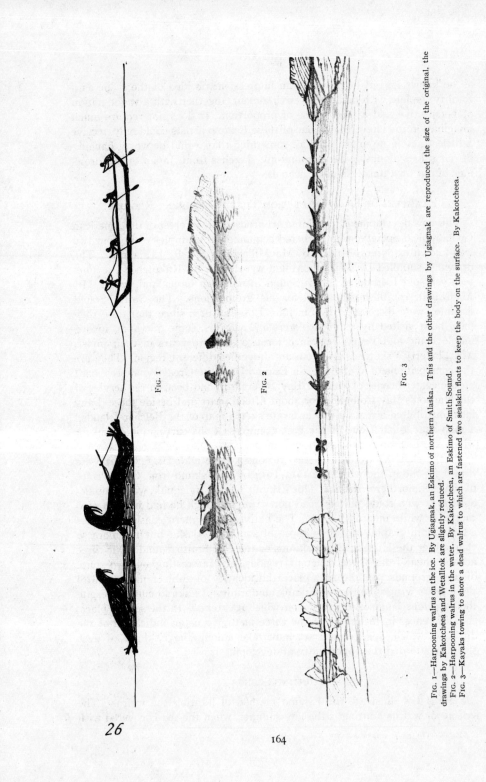

FIG. 1.—Harpooning walrus on the ice. By Ugiagnak, an Eskimo of northern Alaska. This and the other drawings by Ugiagnak are reproduced the size of the original, the drawings by Kakotcheea and Wetalltok are slightly reduced.

FIG. 2.—Harpooning walrus in the water. By Kakotcheea, an Eskimo of Smith Sound.

FIG. 3.—Kayaks towing to shore a dead walrus to which are fastened two sealskin floats to keep the body on the surface. By Kakotcheea.

loose cakes of floating ice that offer very little obstruction to navigation in small boats. The animals are harpooned either while swimming in the water (Fig. 2), or as they bask in the sunshine on some floating ice cake (Fig. 1); the *coup de grâce* is now usually given with the rifle. The carcase is then towed to shore (Figs. 3 and 4) or to the nearest ice floe and immediately cut up (Fig. 5). In Alaska, as we see from Figure 1, the hunter makes use of the large skin boat called umiak, which resembles in shape our whaleboat. Among most Eskimo tribes this is regarded as the woman's boat and is used only for transportation; the hunter's vessel is the smaller one-man kayak, as shown in Figures 2 and 3. But in Alaska the umiak is used for both whale and walrus hunting, the women serving in the latter pursuit as paddlers only. The middle paddler in Figure 1 is plainly a woman, for her hair is tied in a knot on the back of her head.

These five sketches taken together depict a scene which might occur any day in the month of August either off the northwest coast of Alaska or in Hudson Bay or on the coast of Greenland. But there are noticeable differences in the artistic value of the sketches. Figure 1, from Alaska, shows all the hardness and conventionality of the etchings on ivory which are so common in this region; it might easily have been one of these etchings transferred to paper. The artist's imagination is confined to a silhouette outline of the essential features of his subject. There are the two walruses on an ice cake, the boat, the paddlers, the harpooner, and his weapon, every one of which is absolutely essential to the interpretation of the drawing. Beyond this there is nothing, not even an indication of the sea. It is a picture story, a graphic description of an event the details of which are left to the imagination. Conventional as it is, however, it is far from being a mere pictograph; the startled attitudes of the walruses and the vigor with which the women are driving their paddles into the water give character and realism to the drawing that no mere pictograph can ever possess. Figure 4, from Hudson Bay, shows the same limitations, the same silhouette outline and lack of all atmosphere, although the artist has tried to convey a sense of the environment by adding dogs and driftwood. But in Figure 5, from the same region, a new feature is introduced, a dawning sense of perspective. The artist is not quite sure of it, and in consequence his landscape seems divorced from his main subject, the cutting up of the walrus; but he has taken a great step forward and achieved something which his ancestors, for all their skill in carving and etching, never dreamed of. The event is no longer taken out of its setting, but the two are combined into one artistic whole. He has accomplished this, too, without any loss of the old vigor; so that, crude and imperfect as his sketch undoubtedly is, it yet shows possibilities of great development. We can see a growth in Figures 2 and 3, from Smith Sound. In these the artist has a much clearer vision of the details and surroundings of his theme. His kayakers are traveling over a sea full of ripples and reflections. Figure 2 even adds a new feature, the use of shading to give depth and distance. This Smith Sound

FIG. 4

FIG. 5

FIG. 6

FIG. 7

FIG. 4—Dragging a walrus on to the beach. By Wetalltok, an Eskimo of Hudson Bay.
FIG. 5—Skinning a walrus. By Wetalltok.
FIG. 6—Hunter stalking a seal. By Ugiagnak.
FIG. 7—Going after seal (or walrus) in Kayaks. By Wetalltok.

28

artist has certainly traveled far beyond the Alaskan artist of Figure 1, or the engravers on bone and ivory.

Two methods of sealing, both of them common in every part of the Eskimo world, are depicted in Figures 6 and 7. In Figure 6, by the Alaskan artist, the hunter is represented as crawling stealthily over the surface of the ice towards his quarry. This is a method adopted in the spring of the year, when the seals are basking in the sunshine outside their holes. In Figure 7, by Wetalltok, the Hudson Bay Eskimo, the summer method is

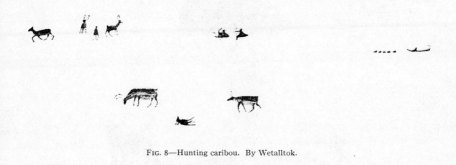

Fig. 8—Hunting caribou. By Wetalltok.

Fig. 9—Caribou scenting hunters. By Kakotcheea.

represented. The seals (and walruses) are then either basking on floating ice cakes or swimming in the water around them. The hunters sometimes harpoon them from their kayaks; more often they paddle over to a small ice cake near by, draw up their kayaks, and fasten the end of the harpoon line round a hummock of ice. They then cautiously work their raft towards the seals and drive in their harpoons. The animals dive but are prevented from escaping by the line fastened to the hummock. This method of hunting has survived even the use of rifles, for in the late summer seals lose much of the blubber that gives them their buoyancy and sink as soon as they are killed.

29

This drawing of Wetalltok illustrates the lack of proportion that is so common in Eskimo drawings. Almost invariably, in depicting men and animals, the head is made out of scale with the rest of the figure; in the present case the seals and the ice cake are much too large. Moreover, the artist, although learning the use of perspective, has not been able to free himself from the old conventionalism. His ice cake is purely a conven-

FIG. 10

FIG. 11

FIG. 12

FIG. 10—Muskox. By Kakotcheea.
FIG. 11—Hunting the polar bear. By Ugiagnak.
FIG. 12—Closing in on a polar bear with a team of dogs. It is the custom upon sighting a bear to release the dogs in order to hold the bear at bay until the driver arrives with the rifle or lance to despatch it. By Kakotcheea.

tional one, and his seals have the traditional impersonality. His sketches of caribou in Figure 8 are far superior. They are depicted in different attitudes, all of them true to life. One is quietly grazing, another walking slowly towards it, a third lying on its side. Near the two hunters, who are armed with the old-fashioned bows and arrows, the caribou have leaped to their feet, startled; and one is running away. Over on the right is the hunters' sled with the dogs lying down in front. Excellent as the individual figures are, there is no background of any kind; they are simply an artist's studies.

Kakotcheea's sketch (Fig. 9) is quite different; it has an impressionistic touch quite new in Eskimo art. There is less variety in the attitudes of the caribou, and the horns are a little too uniform and conventional; but they are true to life, and the background is just sufficiently pronounced to give a sense of realism. It is a curious thing, indeed, that the Eskimos have always been more successful in portraying caribou than anything else; the proportions are more accurate, and the action is more vivid. No doubt it is partly due to the fact that the dependence of the Canadian and Greenland Eskimos upon the caribou for a large portion of their food supply has made

FIG. 13—Shooting geese. By Wetalltok.

them keen students of its actions and attitudes, and this has reflected itself in their art. The same reason would apply also to Alaska, although now the domesticated reindeer has taken the place of the wild caribou, which has been almost exterminated in that region. Yet this explanation alone can hardly be sufficient, otherwise we should expect the same excellence in the representations of the musk ox, which in Smith Sound is almost as important to the Eskimos as the caribou; but, as Figure 10 will illustrate, their drawings of musk oxen show much less fidelity to life. The main reason must surely be that the caribou, so universal once throughout Arctic America and the neighboring portion of Asia and so indispensable to the Eskimos for food and clothing, has been a favorite subject for representation from the very dawn of their art; whereas the musk ox with its more restricted range and lesser economic importance has a far shorter tradition behind it, and artists have not developed the same technique in its portrayal.

31

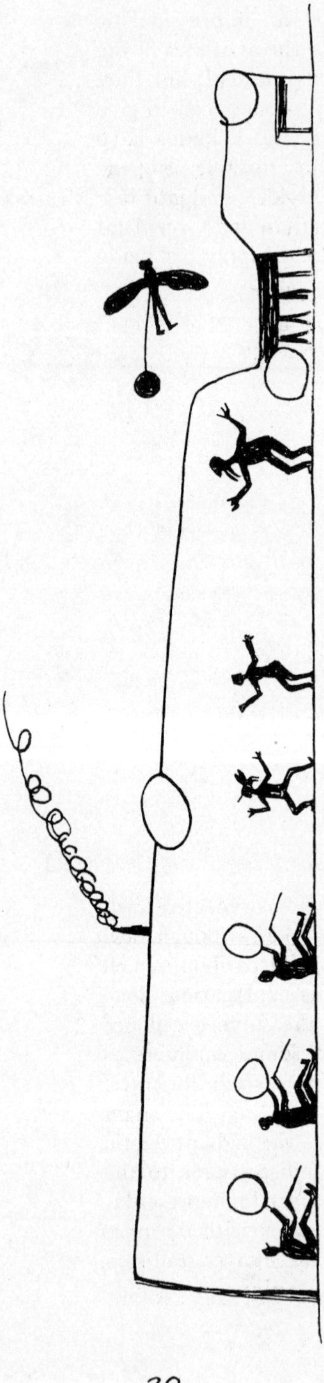

FIG. 14—Scene in a dance house. By Ugiagnak.

Figures 11 and 12 illustrate the hunting of the polar bear, which is common almost everywhere in circumpolar regions. One method is to stalk up cautiously behind ice hummocks and to shoot at close range, formerly with bow and arrow, as in Figure 11, now with the rifle. The polar bear is rather a timid animal until it is brought to bay; even then, in Eskimo estimation, it is less formidable than the Barren Ground grizzly. The method of hunting shown in Figure 12, bringing it to bay with dogs, is more certain of success. During the summer of 1915 a party of Eskimos with whom I was traveling on Victoria Island came upon a polar bear and its cub, the latter nearly full-grown, quietly swimming across a lake. They fled at sight of us; and the Eskimos, loosing the dogs, pursued them on foot. The cub was overtaken after a stiff chase of about three miles, the mother two miles farther on; and both were shot with a rifle. Before rifles came into use, however, the Eskimos used to surround the bear and stab it to death with harpoons and lances, although often one or more of their number was killed or severely wounded.

The last of the hunting scenes in this collection, Figure 13, is also in some ways the most remarkable. Two Eskimos clad in white overshirts, or "dickies," are shooting at a flock of geese flying overhead on their annual migration. Nowhere in Eskimo art have I seen anything approaching the excellence of these birds both in form and detail. The careful shading of the underparts alone would attest European influence. There is still a little stiffness, especially in the foremost bird, but the general effect is remarkably realistic. One can hardly credit the production of this sketch and that of Figure 7 to the same artist.

SOCIAL SCENES

Hunting scenes and game animals are by far the commonest subjects of Eskimo art. However, we do occasionally find, even on bone and ivory, scenes of social life such as that given in Figure 14, where the artist has taken as his subject a dance held inside one of the wooden houses, half buried beneath the snow, in which the Eskimos of Alaska pass the winter. The mingling of ancient and modern elements in their present-day culture comes out in the juxta-position of a skylight of seal intestines sewn together and a chimney belching forth smoke from a sheet-iron stove inside. The figures of the three drummers seated at the back of the room are instinct with vivacity and the *joie de danse*. The prancing attitude of the plume-bedecked man, and the swaying motion of the woman, well illustrate the difference in the methods of dancing of the two sexes. The last figure on the right has a religious significance. It represents a shaman or medicine man inspired by his guardian spirit, the walrus, and simulating the form of that animal by the two tusks that protrude magically from his mouth. The shaman among the Eskimos was a public functionary who gave most of his performances in the dance house. He claimed to control certain of the spirits which were believed to govern the universe, spirits of animals and of mythical beings through which he could regulate the supply of game. One of them is shown in this illustration flying unseen through the air above the dance house in search of caribou, and trailing a large stone with which to kill his enemies. Many other miracles are recorded of them, and even today the natives of Alaska firmly believe in their power, though shamanism is now dead and all the Eskimos in this region have embraced Christianity.

SUMMER ENCAMPMENT

Summer encampments are becoming rather a popular subject for representation among the Eskimos, although comparatively rare in the old engravings. We have two such drawings in this collection, Figures 15 and 16, both by the same Hudson Bay native, Wetalltok. In the latter he has deviated from the old traditional art only in one figure, that of the man peering inside the tent, which shows a little more imagination than is usual in etchings on bone and ivory. The tents, the dogs, and the man standing are as conventional as ever. Figure 15, on the contrary, belongs to the new age that recognizes perspec-

FIG. 15—Eskimo summer camp. By Wetalltok.

tive and shading without as yet mastering either. It is a fair example of the ability of the average Eskimo to depict a landscape. The artist has chosen for his subject an everyday scene in summer, when the Eskimos of both Hudson Bay and Greenland pitch their tents on· the seashore and with their kayaks hunt the seals in the open waters of the bays and fiords. Figure 17, by the same Eskimo, Wetalltok, shows one of their methods of traveling at this period.

SUMMER AND WINTER TRAVEL

As long as the Eskimos remain on the shore they can move from one sealing ground to another in their large skin boats. But summer is also the season for fishing and caribou hunting; the salmon are now migrating

FIG. 16—Eskimo tents. By Wetalltok.

FIG. 17—Eskimos traveling with packs in summer. By Wetalltok.

up the creeks and rivers to spawn, and the caribou have shed their heavy winter coats and are now covered with short-haired fur invaluable for lighter clothing. The rivers are mostly too rapid and too shoal for boats, and moreover the caribou are grazing on the open plains or on the slopes of the hills. So the Eskimo loads all the necessary equipment on his back or on the backs of his dogs and moves away inland. The man always leads on these migrations, for at any moment game may be sighted and he may have to drop his pack and go off hunting; the wife and children follow him, carrying the tent and the household utensils. An Eskimo thinks nothing of traveling 14 or 15 miles with a load of 100 pounds on his back and at the end of the day spending four or five hours in hunting. The women carry almost equal loads, and the children in proportion to their size, while a dog's pack varies from 20 to 50 pounds. Traveling is somewhat easier at other seasons of the year, for the Eskimo can then employ his sled. In Figure 18 our Smith Sound artist has contributed a sketch that partly illustrates this method. It is an impressionistic sketch of a team of dogs dragging a sled, seen from the viewpoint of the driver. Europeans have introduced the custom of driving dogs like horses, singly or in pairs one behind the other, with the most intelligent as the leader; but in many places the Eskimos still cling to the use of a separate trace for each dog, as in the illustration. There are many inconveniences in the method, but it has one advantage; the dogs can all be released simultaneously at the sight of game by simply casting off their traces from the one toggle which holds them.

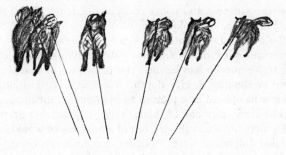

FIG. 18—Dog team viewed from sled. By Kakotcheea.

This little sketch of Kakotcheea is in some ways the most remarkable in the whole collection. In the first place the artistic conception of representing a team of dogs from behind is altogether foreign to ordinary Eskimo art. It is a photographic impression of a momentary scene, not a more or less symbolic representation of a method of traveling, as the old engravers on ivory would have made it. Again, the accuracy with which the dogs are delineated, each with some slight difference, is amazing. These panting animals tugging at their traces are totally unlike the rather lifeless, misshapen creatures of Wetalltok's creation (Figure 17). The one man might seem to have focussed an actual scene on his retina, the other merely conjured up a typical one; but I suspect that the Smith Sound native has simply copied an explorer's photograph, and that the striking individuality of his sketch is due to that source alone.

The Development of Eskimo Art

From these drawings taken from three different regions, Alaska, Hudson Bay, and Smith Sound, we can gather some idea of the course along which Eskimo art has been developing during the last half-century. The Alaska drawings faithfully follow the old tradition; they might have been made

35

on bone or on ivory a hundred years ago. The art is a purely conventional one, everything being represented in silhouette and all details being omitted that are not absolutely essential to the interpretation of the drawings. Its greatest merit lies in the fidelity to life of the figures of men and animals and the vividness with which action is portrayed. But it is essentially a "shadow" art, where figures are merely reflected as on a screen and lack both background and depth; it assumes too readily a symbolic aspect and loses touch with reality altogether—a fate that has overtaken it in many of the ivory etchings, although our artist here has avoided it. The Hudson Bay native is in the awakening stage. He has learned to sense vaguely the crowded world of color and environment and so tends to give more detail to his drawings. Moreover, he has a growing feeling for perspective, of the relation of subject to the surrounding landscape. But the defects in proportion and the stiffness and conventionality of many of his figures mark him as being in the main a follower of the older tradition. The Smith Sound artist, on the other hand, clearly belongs to the new generation. He takes an impressionistic view of his subject, not the symbolic one of the earlier artists. In technique he has learned the principles of perspective to give distance and of shading to give depth. There is a recognition, too, of the necessity for atmosphere in a picture to help out its meaning. He has not mastered completely any one of these things; his sketches are still the productions of a mere novice in the art, but of a novice who would show promise of much higher fulfilment were it not for one great weakness—a weakness that no Eskimo artist to my knowledge has yet tried to overcome—a disregard of individuality that robs a sketch of half its character.

In conclusion one word of warning may be given. Because our Alaskan representative has adhered most closely to the old traditional art of his race, and the Smith Sound one has departed most from it, it must not be assumed that Alaskan artists as a whole are very conservative, whereas those in Smith Sound are more progressive. On the contrary I have seen sketches from both Alaska and the Mackenzie River delta that show as great an advance over the old etchings on ivory as any of the illustrations given in this article. The psychological law that "similar stimuli applied to similar subjects produce similar reactions" is really quite verified, and the type of art common to all branches of the Eskimo race is developing everywhere along the same general lines under the influence of European culture.

A TOWN THAT HAS GONE DOWNHILL

James Walter Goldthwait

Dartmouth College

[With separate map, Pl. IV, facing p. 552]

" AGRICULTURE is, and always will be, the chief business of the people of New-Hampshire, if they attend to their true interest." So wrote Jeremy Belknap, first historian of the state, in 1792.[1] And for thirty years, at least, his words were echoed by authors of successive "gazetteers." Now, for almost a century deserted farms in New Hampshire have been growing up to blueberry pasture, woodland, and forest. The sturdy population that was once evenly distributed over thousands of square miles of the stony upland has slowly and steadily moved down from the hilltops, emigrating to distant places, or lingering yet awhile in the valleys. Large tracts of land have been abandoned or have become the summer homes and playgrounds of well-to-do vacation seekers from the cities.

The downhill movement, particularly, came to my attention a few years ago, while making a topographic map of the township of Lyme. Since the eastern half of this township is deserted country with scarcely an occupied house and very few traveled roads, it became a matter of practical interest to locate all such landmarks as abandoned roads and stone walls, cellar holes, orchards, and other signs of former culture. As this work progressed, comparison with the earliest detailed map then known to me—the map of Grafton County by Walling, in 1860[2]—on which every occupied house is shown with name of occupant, disclosed the fact that certain cellar holes mark sites of houses that were abandoned before 1860. An

---

[1] Jeremy Belknap: The History of New Hampshire, 3 vols., Boston, 1791–1792; reference in Vol. 3, p. 142.

[2] H. F. Walling: Topographical Map of Grafton County, N. H. Scale 1: 70,000. New York, 1860.

FIG. 1

FIG. 2

FIG. 3

FIG. 1—An unoccupied house on the Dorchester road (see Pl. IV, facing p. 552).
FIG. 2—Deserted schoolhouse of the Acorn Hill district.
FIG. 3—On the road to Hardscrabble.   Smart's Mountain in the distance.

FIG. 4

FIG. 5

FIG. 6

FIGS. 4 and 5—The Colonel Selah Beal house, falling to ruin on the Dorchester road under Smart's Mountain.

FIG. 6—An old farmhouse only recently left unoccupied.

39

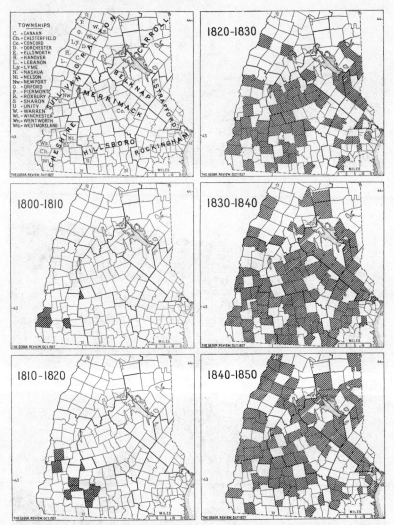

FIG. 7—Maps of central and southern New Hampshire showing losses in population by townships for each decade in the first half of last century. A key map names the counties and the townships referred to in the text. Scale 1:3,250,000.

effort was made, therefore, to discover as many of these pre-1860 cellar holes as possible and thus to obtain data for a map that would show the extent of settlement of the township at the time of its maximum population, which was about 1830. While the results are by no means complete, because many cellar holes or house sites have been erased or lie hidden in a wilderness of forest, they form a basis for comparison with detailed maps of three later dates—the Walling

map of 1860, the map of Lyme in Hurd's Atlas of New Hampshire in
1892,[3] and the new map made in 1925. With these four maps it is
possible to study the shift of population through the township, house
by house, in three successive 30-year periods, or generations: 1830–
1860, 1860–1892, and 1892–1925.

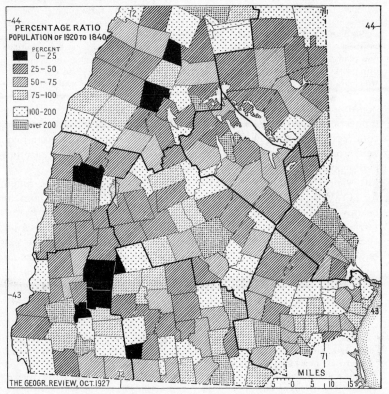

Fig. 8—Map of central and southern New Hampshire showing percentage of losses and gains in
population by townships for the period 1840 to 1920. Scale 1: 1,400,000.

In order more fully to appreciate the movement of which this local
flowage of humanity is a part, its history will first be briefly sketched.

The Incoming Tide of the Eighteenth Century

The interior of New Hampshire, and particularly the upper portion of the Connecticut valley, to which attention is to be drawn, was
settled mainly by farmers from Connecticut just after the close of the
French and Indian wars. According to Belknap the number of people

[3] D. H. Hurd & Co.: Town and City Atlas of the State of New Hampshire. Map of Lyme township on p. 194. Scale approximately 1¼ inches to the mile. Boston, 1892.

41

in this state doubled in less than 19 years, before the year 1790, notwithstanding the fact that seven of these years were years of war.

Where land is cheap, and the means of subsistence may be acquired in such plenty, and in so short a time as is evidently the case in our new plantations, encouragement is given to early marriage. A young man who has cleared a piece of land, and built a hut for his present accommodation, soon begins to experience the truth of that old adage "It is not good for man to be alone." Having a prospect of increasing his substance by labour, which he knows himself able to perform, he attaches himself to a female earlier than prudence would dictate if he had not such a prospect. Nor are the young females of the country averse to a settlement in the new plantations; where, after the second year's labour, by which the land is brought into pasture, there is a necessity for beginning the work of a dairy; an employment which always falls to their lot, and is an object of their ambition, as well as interest.[4]

Abundant evidence remains of the vigor and hopefulness of these pioneers. With their ox teams they cleared incredible areas of hill country. Trees were chopped down or burned, stumps were uprooted, field stone was dragged off to make walls along every road and around every pasture; and crops sprang up on every sunny hillside. Wood lots were left only on north slopes and in tracts absolutely too rough for cultivation. These farmers were bold in their choice of land to occupy and clear. They usually preferred the hillsides to the flat or terraced valleys, because the hills were better drained and because their soil, though more stony, appeared less liable to become exhausted with use than the lighter loam of the valleys. There was no lack of cordwood to warm the houses through the long cold winter; and lumber was to be had without limit, for the sawing. Sawmills and gristmills were built as soon as log huts, and frame houses quickly followed. These were simple but substantial.

Land being easily obtained, and labour of every kind being familiar, there is great encouragement to population. A good husbandman, with the savings of a few years, can purchase new land enough to give his elder sons a settlement, and assist them in clearing a lot and building a hut; after which they soon learn to support themselves. The homestead is generally given to the youngest son, who provides for his parents, when age or infirmity incapacitates them for labour. An unmarried man of thirty years old is rarely to be found in our country towns. The women are grandmothers at forty, and it is not uncommon for a mother and a daughter to have each a child at the breast, at the same time; for a father, son and grandson to be at work together in the same field. Thus population and cultivation proceed together, and a vigorous race of inhabitants grows up, on a soil, which labor vies with nature to render productive.[5]

Every house had a cellar walled with boulders collected from off the place; and doorsteps and hearthstones were carefully selected from flat-splitting blocks or ledges in the neighborhood. Apple orchards, at first wholly for cider but later for "eating apples," were planted

4 Belknap, *op. cit.*, Vol. 3, pp. 237–238.
5 *Ibid.*, pp. 260–261.

FIG. 9

FIG. 10

FIG. 9—The ox team was an essential of the pioneer's equipment.
FIG. 10—Rolling a town road after a snowstorm.

43

around every homestead. Sugar maple orchards were given much care and are still producing quantities of fine syrup.

Altitude and distance from the village seem to have counted little with these settlers. What did it matter if there was a five or six mile journey across the township, in days when the vehicle was an oxcart and when any one in a hurry went on horseback? There was little occasion to go farther than the nearest village store or blacksmith shop. Each neighborhood was practically self-supporting. A journey to a distant city like Boston or Hartford was an unusual event and took days.

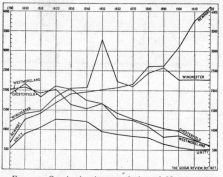

FIG. 11—Graph showing population of Newport and Unity townships and of Winchester, Chesterfield, and Westmoreland townships from 1790 to 1920.

One tramping over these deserted hill farms now is struck with the thought that loneliness was somehow at the root of the process of abandonment. But a consideration of the map shows little basis for that idea. Houses were not far apart. However lonely the country has become, that must not be counted among the original reasons for its abandonment, but rather as a consequence of it. Moreover, life for these people was too earnest to be dull. "The people of New-Hampshire, in general, are industrious, and allow themselves very little time for diversion. One who indulges himself in idleness and play, is stigmatized according to his demerit."[6]

THE TURNING OF THE TIDE TOWARD THE WEST

Early in the nineteenth century the tide of population stopped rising and began at once to subside. By 1840 it was falling generally throughout the state. On the maps in Figure 7 can be seen the way in which this condition of ebb tide spread northward across the upland between 1800 and 1840.

No doubt the country had been somewhat overpopulated, as a result of the processes reviewed by Belknap; for these hill farms were not all productive, and they became less so as successive crops were harvested and fields were not sufficiently fertilized. The discovery of that discouraging fact must have come at an early date, although one finds scarcely an admission of it for several decades in the optimistic gazetteers of the time. It is not until 1860 that we read that "the

---

[6] *Ibid.*, pp. 262–263.

44

FIG. 13

FIG. 14

FIG. 15

FIG. 13—The last occupied house on the Dorchester road.
FIG. 14—A connected "set o' buildings," still occupied, on the side of Plott Hill.
FIG. 15—An old sawmill that still does a small business. Lyme Center.

45

principal occupation of the people is in subduing a hard, silicious
surface, and extorting from its reluctant lap the bread of toil."[7] Accounts of extraordinary crops of maize, wheat, barley, oats, and flax
are offered, in close proximity to derogatory statements about western
farms, which were attracting the New Hampshire farmer as early

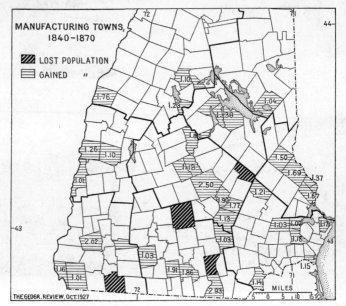

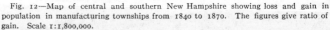

Fig. 12—Map of central and southern New Hampshire showing loss and gain in
population in manufacturing townships from 1840 to 1870. The figures give ratio of
gain. Scale 1:1,800,000.

as 1820 and increasingly for several decades. Hayward's Gazetteer
of 1849, after quoting Dr. Jackson, the state geologist, regarding a
cornfield on one of the islands of Lake Winnepesaukee, where careful
agricultural methods resulted in a yield of 136 bushels to the acre,
remarks:

> One would suppose that the fertility of the western prairie could offer little temp-
> tation to the farmer who might produce such a crop, and remain among his own
> paternal fields; especially when the contrast is made between the healthiness of a
> northern climate, in a high, hilly region, pure water flowing plentifully, all facilities
> for happily training a family; and a country where, indeed, labor is comparatively
> light, land cheap, and winters lose much of their rigor and length; but fever and ague
> sap the constitution, and send back the adventurer a lean, sallow invalid for life, or
> lay him prematurely in the grave.[8]

[7] A. J. Coolidge and J. B. Mansfield: History and Description of New England: New Hampshire,
Boston, 1860, p. 396.

[8] John Hayward: A Gazetteer of New Hampshire, Boston, 1849, p. 22.

46

While this forbidding picture of the emigrant was being held up to readers of the gazetteer, the state continued to pour out farmers into the west at an alarming rate. Where most of them went is shown in Table I.[9]

The tendency for emigrants to go farther and farther west is seen in a comparison of the columns for 1860 and 1870.

TABLE I—NEW HAMPSHIRE IN ACCOUNT WITH OTHER STATES AND TERRITORIES AS REGARDS NATIVE POPULATION

STATE	DR. 1860	CR. 1860	NET LOSS 1860	NET LOSS 1870
Massachusetts . . .	44,035	19,973	24,062	31,269
New York	12,497	2,045	10,452	6,712
Pennsylvania . . .	1,773	227	1,446	1,545
Ohio	4,111	150	3,961	3,117
Indiana	1,072	28	1,044	979
Michigan	3,482	66	3,416	3,544
Illinois	7,868	104	7,764	8,022
Wisconsin	5,907	85	4,822	4,800
Minnesota	2,387	22	2,365	3,216
Iowa	3,287	18	3,269	5,000
California	2,552	15	2,537	2,653
Total, all States and Territories . . .	125,516	47,328	78,188	80,360

This account shows that 124,979 persons who were born in New-Hampshire are now [1870] living in other States in the Union; and that 46,282 who were natives of other States, now reside here—showing an emigration against us of 78,697, or a gain [i. e. increase in emigration] from the last decade of 2172, and probably without a parallel in any State or nation, this side of Ireland.[10]

THE MOVEMENT FROM FARM TO FACTORY

The decline in population in New Hampshire was not due simply to emigration following the discovery of better farms in the west. Another strong influence was at work. New Hampshire with the rest of New England was being transformed into an industrial region. This change began in 1800–1810, so slowly as scarcely to be recognized, but gathered strength and speed, so that by the middle of the century it had become a dominant factor.

To get a closer view of the influence of manufacturing in this early period, we may look again at the maps in Figure 7. Westmoreland and Chesterfield, near the southwest corner of the state, on the Connecticut River, were farming towns of large area and favorable situation which had reached a total population of 2000 by the year 1800. Next to them on the southeast is the township of Winchester, similar

[9] Based on census statistics taken from A. J. Fogg: The Statistics and Gazetteer of New-Hampshire, Concord, N. H., 1874, p. 451.
[10] Ibid., pp. 451–452.

47

to them in size and topography, but crossed diagonally by the swift-flowing Ashuelot River. Although it was mainly a farming town, the mill sites along this stream had come into use at the very first. Between 1800 and 1810 Winchester grew in numbers from 1413 to 1478, while Westmoreland fell from 2066 to 1937 and Chesterfield from 2161 to 1839, starting a decline which has continued until the population is now approximately 35 per cent of what it was.

TABLE II—ECONOMIC CONDITIONS IN NEW HAMPSHIRE IN 1840 AND 1870

	1840	1870
Miles of railway	6	900
Pairs of boots and shoes manufactured . . .	500,000	8,000,000
Cotton goods manufactured	$4,000,000	$30,000,000
Woolen goods manufactured	$800,000	$9,000,000
Total manufactured goods	$13,000,000	$95,000,000
Persons engaged in manufacturing	12,000	46,553
" " " agriculture	78,000	46,573

As the falling wave of population spread northward over New Hampshire, towns like Winchester which had water power came to be oases of prosperity in an otherwise afflicted upland country. The map, which shows losses from 1830 to 1840 in particular, indicates the comparative success and growth of towns along the Merrimack, Contoocook, Ashuelot, and Sugar Rivers. The contrast in the case of Newport and Unity, whose population curves are shown in Figure 11, is the same story in different form.

THE DISTURBING INFLUENCE OF THE RAILWAY

The first railway line to enter New Hampshire came up the Merrimack River in 1838 from Lowell, Mass., to Nashua, ending there within six miles of the border. By 1842 it had been extended up the river to Concord; and before 1850 there were connections northward and northwestward by several routes to the Connecticut valley, where Vermont and New Hampshire vied with each other for the advantages expected to come from rapid transportation. Most of the existing main lines of southern New Hampshire were in operation by 1850; and many branches were built between that date and 1870, linking the smaller towns to the larger by more crooked paths and uneven grades.

In the three decades 1840–1870 the railway was perhaps the strongest single factor affecting life in New Hampshire. Although it might have been expected to encourage farming as well as manufacturing, by putting the farmer within reach of Massachusetts markets, that was not the result. The decline in rural population was not checked but rather intensified. Manufacturing centers grew faster than before. Rising generations of boys and girls felt the urge of the city. The difficulties of earning a livelihood on the small New Hampshire farm became more and more real as the scale of living on the farm rose in response to that of the industrial world. The movement from farm to factory was at last uncontrollable.

The economic transformation of these three decades is shown in Table II. Special attention is called to the last two pairs of figures. While the number of farmers and farm hands fell to about six-tenths the figure of 1840 the number of factory employees rose to almost four times the earlier figure, becoming as large as that of the farming population. Among the contributing factors should be mentioned the introduction of farm machinery which greatly reduced employment on the farm at the time when manufacturing offered abundant opportunity.

The greatest gains were made in the Merrimack valley, where opportunity for power development on a large scale and accessibility to Massachusetts attracted capital; and the cities of Manchester and Nashua, in particular, had phenomenal growth. In several cases industrial growth led to partitioning of old townships into new ones, one mainly industrial and the other agricultural.

The Development of a Summer Migration

The growth of the nation in industry after the seventies, and particularly that of southern New England, brought with it an increasing allotment of time to leisure and recreation. The summer vacation became a vital part of the calendar for hosts of people. Hotels in the White Mountains region grew in number and popularity, and farmhouses began to look for summer boarders. As summer visitors felt the spell of mountains, hills, forest, and lakes, they began to purchase lake-shore lots for camps and cottages, or to buy deserted farms and rehabilitate them. This process is still going on rapidly, after thirty or forty years, without exhausting the supply of desirable places. In fact, there are some townships, like Lyme, in which summer still brings little increase in population. The repairing of the old buildings and clearing up of "the place," though usually without much outlay of money (measured according to city standards), and the occupying of so many farms for even a few months every year have brought employment to a great many year-round inhabitants who act as caretakers, gardeners, painters, and carpenters and furnish fresh vegetables, milk, eggs, and transportation. Country stores that are little more than neighborhood post offices during the winter carry a large and elaborate stock of groceries from late June till mid-September.

49

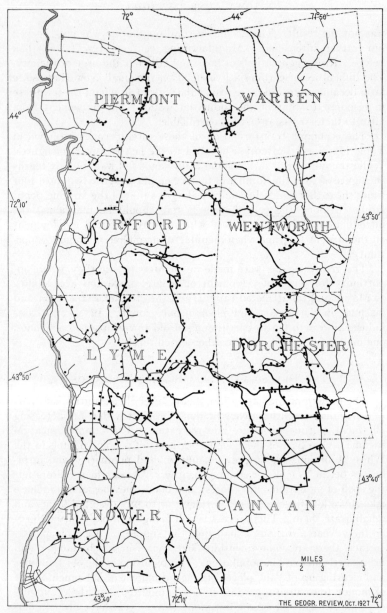

Fig. 16—Map showing the extent of desertion of roads and houses in the region about Lyme, N. H. The dots represent deserted houses, and the heavy lines deserted roads: roads still in use are shown by a light line. On the west the Connecticut River. Compare Figure 17. Scale 1:260,000.

50

During the last fifteen or twenty years the growth of well organized and advertised boys' camps and girls' camps through the state has added still another opportunity to the native population to increase their earnings. Large state and national forests reserves, chiefly in the central and northern parts of the state, trail-cutting, and the establishment of overnight camps and huts by such organizations as the Appalachian Mountain Club have made mountain climbing comfortable and attractive. The scenic features of New Hampshire have come to be regarded as her most precious resource, and countless acres on which serious-minded pioneer farmers and their ox teams toiled a century ago are now delighting a generation of city dwellers.

The latest aspects of the influence of the recreation movement have been the development of overnight stopping places for automobile tourists, the multiplication of small service stations and refreshment stands along all motor routes, and the selling of

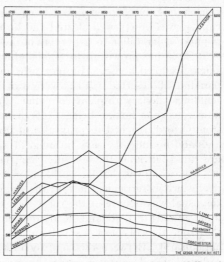

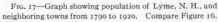

Fig. 17—Graph showing population of Lyme, N. H., and neighboring towns from 1790 to 1920. Compare Figure 16.

vegetables, apples, and other home products at thousands of wayside counters. This business is great in total amount but very widely distributed among the native farming population. It is significant also that summer residents are coming earlier and staying later in the season than formerly; and that efforts of hotel men, railway men, and local merchants to induce people to come up into New Hampshire for mid-winter vacations or holidays are meeting with encouraging response.

FLOOD AND EBB IN THE MIDDLE CONNECTICUT VALLEY

Before looking closely at the town of Lyme we may glance at the block of townships among which Lyme has a central position. The influences reviewed in the foregoing paragraphs have called out differing responses from them, for reasons that will be rather obvious. The map, Figure 16, shows a group of seven towns, namely Hanover, Lyme, Orford, and Piermont along the Connecticut River, and Canaan, Dorchester, and Wentworth adjoining the first four along their eastern borders. These towns were all chartered and settled during the period between 1760 and 1770, with those on the river first to be occupied. On the population curves (Fig. 17) we find Lyme and Orford rising rapidly to a maximum of 1800 population about 1830, then losing strength steadily to 1920, when the population is less than 50 per cent of its old maximum of ninety years ago. Dorchester, high up on the watershed between the Connecticut and Merrimack, has always been a poor town, although, in spite of its handicaps, it was pretty well cleared and farmed by 1840. Since then its population has fallen to 30 per cent of the old figure, and three-quarters of its area has grown up to woodland and forest and contains not a single occupied house. Hunters, fishermen, and campers find here a paradise of deserted roads, overgrown pastures, ruins of old farm buildings, along with plenty of game. Partridges and foxes are more numerous than human beings. Piermont, next township "up-river" from Orford, reached its peak also in 1840, with about 1000 inhabitants and no industry save farming. Its decline has been somewhat less rapid but none the less sure than the others.

The two towns that lie southeast present a marked contrast. Hanover, since its settlement in 1761 the seat of Dartmouth College, shows the usual wave curve of the rural New Hampshire town, with maximum at 2163 in 1840, and steady decline to 1817 in 1890. During all that time the college was small and the township was almost wholly agricultural. Between 1890 and 1900 the rebirth of the college, under a distinguished educator, gave the town new life; and it has risen steadily again to something like its population in the days of profitable agriculture. Even now the land under cultivation (chiefly as dairy farms) reaches farther up the hillsides here than it does in adjoining townships; but the area farmed is only a small part of what was farmed in 1840. The population has gravitated toward the college in the southwestern corner of the town, where it is packed closely into a village precinct.

Lebanon, which lies next southwest of Hanover, on the Connecticut and Mascoma Rivers, has topography and soil as favorable for farming as the surrounding towns, but is far more favorably situated than they for manufacturing. Several really good power sites on the Mascoma River were occupied early, and others have been taken up by manufacturing and power companies. With the coming of the railway in 1847 the town began to gain rapidly and now it is three times the size of its neighbors. Immigration of French Canadians to work in the factories has been considerable; but there has also been a strong draining of the native-born from the farms of the township and those around it. No town in the state, perhaps, offers so good a chance to study in detail the shift from farm to factory.

52

LYME: THE TOWNSHIP AND ITS ACTIVITIES

Like many New Hampshire townships, Lyme is rhomboidal in form and measures six or seven miles on each side. Although in detail its surface is irregular, the broader features are simple and orderly. From the flood lands of the Connecticut River, on its western border, and the somewhat higher terrace of silt that represents the floor of an old glacial lake the upland rises eastward and southeastward over successive ridges and highland areas into a really rugged eastern frontier. Here, at the northeastern corner of the township, Smart's Mountain rises domelike over 3000 feet. To the south, lower hills, yet also fairly rugged and exceeding 2000 feet, break a wooded sky line.

The northeast-southwest trend of the folded metamorphic rocks that pass beneath this township gives to its worn-down surface a strong grain, with ridges and swales parallel to the master feature—the valley of the Connecticut River. But the three streams that drain this township into the Connecticut cross the structure and the ridges squarely, from southeast to northwest. Typical of glaciated New England, these brooks descend by a bewildering series of short rapids, cascades, and still-water stretches, twisting and straightening out as they struggle over ledges or escape around them by cutting through the stony mantle of drift. Midway along the valley of the central stream, Grant's Brook, in the geographic center of the township is the little village of Lyme Center (first called Cook City and then East Lyme), which consists of about twenty houses, a Baptist church, a schoolhouse, a sawmill, and a small but very "general" store. The local post office, as in many a small New England neighborhood, survives in a private house. Two miles down the road, where this valley reaches the upper terrace plains of the Connecticut, is the larger village of Lyme Plain. Two or three stores, a schoolhouse, a large white church of the colonial period, a prosperous village hotel, and a typical old burying ground that looks much too large for the place give distinction to the sides and corners of the village common and indicate that this is certainly the life center of a township.

In the days of its settlement Lyme was reached from the south by road up the Connecticut River, which was passable at least for oxcarts and horseback riders. This old "river road" has never been "thrown up" by the town, but it is so distinctly off the course of modern travel that one may follow it for miles without having to turn out for an automobile. The tourist highway, or "Dartmouth College Road," lies a mile farther in from the river, climbing across low hills from Hanover to Lyme Plain and then descending to the level clay lands of the river valley. This western half of the township is well covered with town roads, in all stages of upkeep or disuse. The eastern half, however, has almost entirely been given over to nature. The road that leads eastward from Lyme Center toward Dorchester is the only

53

FIG. 18

FIG. 19

FIG. 20

FIG. 18—Cellar hole on Dorchester road near Smart's Mountain.

FIG. 19—Old cellar hole near Hardscrabble.

FIG. 20—Cellar hole in a clearing near Smart's Mountain. Birches have grown up out of it. Old apple tree back of plane table.

traveled road in the area and links loosely together a few small farms, which terminate halfway to the Dorchester line.

While Lyme looks like a rich field in which to study at close range the story of decline of population, there is one serious handicap. All the town records prior to 1873 were destroyed by fire, and it boasts no published contemporary early history. The most interesting and informing account available, by far, is an historical sketch of some thirty-five pages written in 1886 by P. H. A. Claflin, a native of the town, for Child's Gazetteer of Grafton County.[11] This draws richly from the memories of old persons then living, from family Bibles, and from other memoranda. The books of the Selectmen and Tax Assessors since 1873 contain interesting material touching area under cultivation, sheep raising, stock farming, poultry raising, dairying, lumber cutting, etc., and show how rich in interest the books of the earlier periods would be if they were available. But records of the late seventies and eighties after all do little more than corroborate

[11] Hamilton Child: Gazetteer of Grafton County, N. H., 1709–1886, Syracuse, N. Y., 1886. Section on Town of Lyme by P. H. A. Claflin, pp. 517–551.

and make more exact the knowledge that one may get from conversation with well preserved octogenarians of today. Records of the local church, which ranked among the largest of the state for many years are of more interest to the antiquarian than the geographer. A complete study of wills and deeds recorded (at Woodsville, N. H.) by early inhabitants of the township would probably supply much information not elsewhere obtainable; but that has not been attempted.

Mill wheels have turned at fifteen or twenty points on brooks in the township. There is no power site here on the Connecticut River. Lumber, shingles, bobbins, flour, corn meal, and cider seem to have been the chief products, and although one or two of these mills survive to the present day their influence has never gone much beyond the town line. No industry of special interest has ever sprung up in Lyme to distinguish it from its neighbors. Orford, for example, was a producer of soapstone from 1800 to 1835, which was widely used through this country for

FIG. 21—The old church at Lyme plain.

gravestones, box stoves, mantelpieces, and chimney connections. As late as 1870 we find the "manufactories" in Lyme numbered as 23, with a total number of but 53 "hands employed." Five of these were lumber mills, which employed a total of 20 hands; one was a gristmill with a single "hand"; one a tannery with two "hands"; and one a small starch factory. There was never a cotton or woolen mill in town. From scattered information one is led to think that the "manufactories" of Lyme in the seventies (when Manchester was forging ahead in this field) were cider mills, blacksmith and harnessmakers' shops, a stonecutter's establishment, a tin shop or two, and a milliner's shop.

In the mercantile business and trades these New Hampshire villages show odd division and combination of technique, especially

55

from 1860 to 1890, when specialization was rife yet decline in population put into the hands of a few of the more ambitious and prosperous survivors the diminishing business or trades of many individuals.

Chiefly on account of the absence of factories in Lyme and adjoining towns, there has been hardly any incoming of French Canadians or others of foreign birth. The old New England stock survives, almost unaccompanied. This makes the picture of the decline simpler and clearer than in most New Hampshire towns. In the southern part of the state, especially, foreign-born workers in mills after several years of careful saving of their earnings have purchased deserted farms and are occupying and developing them successfully.

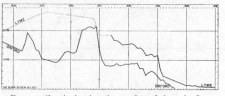

FIG. 22—Graph showing the number of sheep in Lyme and Orford townships from 1836 to 1910.

It is unfortunate that we cannot get exact information as to the extent of land actually under cultivation in the period of greatest occupation (1820–1840) and of the changes in choice of crops and uses of farm land in that early period. From Belknap and others we learn that Indian corn and wheat were regarded, at first, as the leading crops of the state, corn averaging over 40 bushels to the acre and wheat 20 to 50 bushels according to the character of the soil. The intervale lands of the Connecticut valley, such as those along the western side of Lyme, produced the richest crops. Winter rye was thought to be the best crop for newly cleared land. Barley, flax, oats, and peas were raised on land that had been several years under cultivation. Potatoes, averaging 200 to 300 bushels to the acre, were grown everywhere; and in several towns there were large starch mills. Pork, beef, mutton, butter, cheese, and poultry were produced in quantity.

The westward emigration of farmers was reflected in a westward movement of wheatfield and cornfield areas, and by 1845 or 1850 the stony hillsides of Grafton County had largely become sheep pastures. The passing of the era of homespun clothing and the coming in of improved machinery, with growth of mills in southern New England, in the 1830's, created a demand for wool which found ready response here. The number of sheep in the town of Lyme in 1836 was 9867[12] and had increased to 12,557 in 1848 and 13,176 in 1855.[13] Lyme, Hanover, Lebanon, and Walpole were the largest sheep-raising towns in New Hampshire for several decades, but neighboring townships on both sides of the Connecticut River were close competitors, and

[12] C. Benton and S. F. Barry: A Statistical View of the Number of Sheep in the Several Towns and Counties in Maine, New Hampshire, Vermont, Massachusetts, Rhode Island, Connecticut, New York, Pennsylvania, and Ohio . . . in 1836 . . . Cambridge, Mass., 1837.

[13] E. A. Charlton: New Hampshire As It Is, Claremont, N. H., 1855, p. 277.

the Vermont towns as a rule were slightly in the lead. Although the fortunes of the sheep farmer rose and fell irregularly during and after the Civil War, sheep raising continued to be the chief occupation in Lyme until 1890, with the total number, up to 1886, never falling much below 6000 (see Fig. 22). Pride was felt in raising pure Merino stock. Out of 74 "live stock breeders and dealers" in the "Classified Business Directory" in Child's Gazetteer[14] in 1886, 68 farms advertise sheep and only six stock farms specify cattle or swine in addition to sheep.

One credits the traditions and statistics of this vanished sheep industry when he explores the wilderness around Holt's Ledge and Smart's Mountain and finds not only in shrub-covered pasture but even in full-grown pine forest the high stone walls and enclosures and the rudely outlined foundations of sheep barns and sheds. Today there are hardly 150 sheep in the whole township, or scarcely more than one per cent of the old number. In spite of the fact that a recent Bulletin of the U. S. Department of Agriculture[15] has called attention to the practicability of reviving the sheep industry in the New England upland, no one in Lyme seems able or willing to try it. The killing of sheep by dogs, trouble from diseases, and the cost of renewing pasture fences—by sheep wire in place of field stone and rails— are the reasons usually given.

The Four Maps of Lyme: 1830, 1860, 1892, 1925

The earliest known map of Lyme township showing houses is that of Woodford in 1855.[16] This forms the basis for the plotting of houses on the first map of our series (Pl. IV); but there have been added to it about twenty house sites of earlier date revealed by field work in 1925. For want of better information it is assumed that all houses standing in 1855 were also standing as early as 1830 (when the population was at its maximum) and also that all cellar holes of date prior to 1855 mark sites of houses standing in 1830. While neither assumption can be strictly true, we have in them the only practical means of mapping the approximate condition of things in 1830. Further search over the forested tracts in the eastern part of the township will doubtless disclose a number of other cellar holes of this early period; for even the oldest of them are not badly blurred by time but are merely hidden by bushes and trees.

Although the rugged eastern half of the township even in 1830 was less fully occupied than the western half, nevertheless, roads ran

[14] *Op. cit.*, pp. 341–342.

[15] D. A. Spencer and others: The Sheep Industry, *Yearbook U. S. Dept. of Agric. for 1923*, pp. 229–310.

[16] Map of the town of Lyme, Grafton County; from actual survey by W. C. Eaton. Published by E. M. Woodford . . . Philadelphia, 1855. Scale, 100 rods to an inch.

57

out across it in all directions and climbed far up the slopes of Smart's
Mountain and the hills west and south of it. The "Quinttown road"
ran diagonally up the southwest spur of Smart's Mountain to the
1700-foot contour and thence northward two miles more beyond
"Hardscrabble," passing through a rocky saddle among the hills
and down into the township of Orford where, in a remote corner, was

FIG. 23—A handful of sheep where thousands used to graze.

the then flourishing village of Quinttown. Here were about fifteen
houses, a few sawmills, shops, a schoolhouse or two, and a store; and
there was a schoolhouse (gone before 1855) at the top of the long hill
on the mountain side, with 50 or 60 pupils. From 1820 or 1830 down
to 1878 limestone was quarried on the mountain side and burned for
plaster in a small limekiln on the farm half a mile north of this schoolhouse—a rare industry in New Hampshire.

From the old Dorchester road several branch roads, bordered as
a rule by stone walls, ran up to farms on both Smart's Mountain and
Gline's Hill, where now the cellars and orchards of the pre-1855 period
are found well above the 1500-foot contour and over a mile from the
main road. The exact upper limit of this early settlement can only
be guessed by means of stone walls, pastures cleared of field stone,
and occasional apple trees. A few of the locations shown on the map
are approximate.

The southeast corner of the township was traversed by the Grafton
Turnpike, chartered in 1804, over which a stage made regular trips
from Orford through Lyme Center to Canaan and Andover as late
as 1847. There were probably more houses on it in 1830 than we have
located. At least one road extended eastward from the turnpike into
the wooded wilderness south of Gline's Hill, where there was a small

settlement still referred to as Tinkhamtown. Two cellar holes have
been located here; and somewhere in the woods beyond them there
is a "lost" graveyard. It may be that a road once passed all the way
over the ridge east of Tinkhamtown into the township of Dorchester.

The rugged pair of hills west of the turnpike, called Bear Hill
and Holt's Ledge where cliffs of granite and schist are enveloped in

FIG. 24—A corner of the deserted cemetery on the road to Dorchester.

rocky slopes, had their farms also. A road ran up over the high saddle
between them. Its north and south ends are still marked by cellar
holes and walls; but the course across the saddle itself cannot be traced.

A crooked road with heavy grades swung around the south side of
the Bear Hill mass below the 1400-foot contour, on which there were
several farms. One of these houses was occupied until 1924, although
the road was among the first to fall into disuse.

The western half of the township, though not without uncultivated
tracts of highland, was more uniformly occupied. In this region the
northeast-southwest system of roads fitted more obediently the grain
of rock structure and topography. In the region of Plott Hill, for instance, were four parallel roads about a half mile apart. All were
well occupied, although two of them followed valleys, one lay along
a sidehill, and the fourth followed the crest line of the bleak ridge of
Plott Hill for nearly two miles at an altitude of over 1000 feet. A continuation of this Plott Hill road, a mile or two to the northeast along
the western slope of Acorn Hill, was in use in colonial times but was
probably abandoned before 1830 and is therefore not shown on the
map.

The second map of the series is based upon the one by Walling.[17]

[17] See footnote 2.

In most respects it agrees in detail with the earlier one by Woodford but is much more accurate as regards directions and distances. It appears that before 1860 at least twenty-eight houses had been abandoned—the number is probably much larger. Twenty-three of these are in the eastern half of the township at an average altitude of more than 1400 feet and all but one above 1100 feet. Of the 321 occupied

FIG. 25—Down the old Quinttown road toward Holt's Ledge.

houses in the town of Lyme in 1860 sixty (or approximately 20 per cent) were in the eastern half of the town. In this section at least six miles of road had been abandoned by 1860.

The Smart's Mountain-Gline's Hill gap had lost heavily in population, although two or three branch roads still served in 1860 and for five or ten years longer. One new house, indeed, had been added close to the Dorchester line on a low spur of Smart's Mountain; but three houses had been abandoned in that immediate vicinity. A noteworthy record of the outgoing tide from this neighborhood is found in the little graveyard beside the Dorchester road just west of the height of land, where 10 out of 14 of the family names that apear on the 35 headstones are not found among the families living in this district in 1860. They record deaths between 1810 and 1852. In those days of many children, the vanishing of a family name from a community means emigration. Here on the side of Smart's Mountain the tide was ebbing fast by 1860.

The condition of Lyme township in 1892 has been taken from the map in Hurd's Atlas.[18] By that time the Quinttown road had been abandoned, as had also the village at its north end in the next township. The entire northeastern quarter of the township, so largely occupied by Smart's Mountain, thus became a blank on the population map. Up the Dorchester road, east of Lyme Center, all branches

[18] See footnote 3.

of the road system had withered away on the slopes of Smart's Mountain and Gline's Hill; and along the main stem there were left occupied a bare half-dozen houses on a three-mile stretch, with one little schoolhouse and the old graveyard. Location on this old highway had lost its advantage; for by this time the adjoining township of Dorchester had become almost wholly deserted, and no one used this road except these inhabitants of Lyme themselves.

On the turnpike every house had been deserted by 1892, but the road, still kept up, served as a line of communication for a single family who lived on the hill road that ran from the turnpike toward Bear Hill. The rest of this road had been discontinued, two houses on it finding communication southward by steep downhill roads toward Toad Hollow, which was still a real neighborhood. Farther west, Plott Hill had been wholly deserted, although the road along its crest still shows on the 1892 map.

Eight miles of road were given up between 1860 and 1892. Forty-five houses were abandoned. Of these, 19 were in the eastern half of Lyme. In other words, out of 60 occupied houses in this eastern half in 1860, one third were deserted by 1892.

The loss both in houses and in miles of road during the final 30-year period (1892–1925) has been as heavy as during the preceding one. Fifty-nine more houses have become unoccupied. Of these, 22 were in the eastern half of the township; and there are only 24 left. More than 12 miles of road have been given up or at least allowed to become unsafe.

The Dorchester road is still kept in repair and is traveled over from May till November; but it is used in winter only for hauling out pulpwood and cordwood. Five houses on this road that were occupied in 1892 are gone or in ruins. The last occupied house on the road (which was built after 1860) is only halfway out from Lyme Center to the town line. Beyond it on the Dorchester road and its old tributaries are the sites of at least twenty-two former houses. The tide of humanity has drawn down to the 1100-foot contour, leaving the old graveyard in a silent wilderness.

The Quinttown road, long ago become impassable, makes a good trail for the Dartmouth Outing Club. It is nearly five miles from the last occupied house in Lyme to the first one in Orford. The old Grafton Turnpike is in an uncertain state of repair. At the time of our survey, in 1925, parts of it were scarcely passable. From time to time, however, a lumber company gets busy or money is appropriated by town or state to "bush out" the road, fill up the gullies, and mend the culverts; and despite the fact that there is no occupied house on it for several miles through Lyme, Hanover, and Canaan, it may still be saved as a traveled road instead of becoming permanently disused. Its branch, the "Old Tyler Road," is entirely abandoned, the last

61

house on it becoming vacated in 1925. The road over Plott Hill and the crossroad at its north end have been officially closed by the town. But it is in the Acorn Hill neighborhood that the most striking change has come. Here several families have moved away from as many houses during the last few years, and the little schoolhouse is closed. One family only remained in this neighborhood in 1925 on the most remote farm of all, three-quarters of a mile up Trout Brook, one of eight houses still occupied in the township above the 1100-foot contour out of 69 once occupied at that altitude. Not one of the eight houses stands at more than 1150 feet. The 1100-foot contour, therefor, marks a rather definite population strand line for 1925.

So the town is still moving downhill. When will it stop? Where will recovery of strength begin? What social and economic factors will bring it about? And if the tide of population sets in again here, as it has already begun to do in more favored parts of the state, will it rise uniformly across the contours, or will it no longer obey the simple influence of slopes and altitudes?

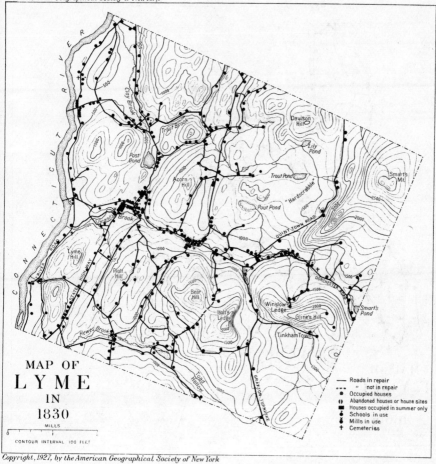

MAP OF
L Y M E
IN
1830

MILLS

CONTOUR INTERVAL 100 FEET

— Roads in repair
- - - " not in repair
● Occupied houses
◖ Abandoned houses or house sites
▰ Houses occupied in summer only
● Schools in use
● Mills in use
† Cemeteries

63

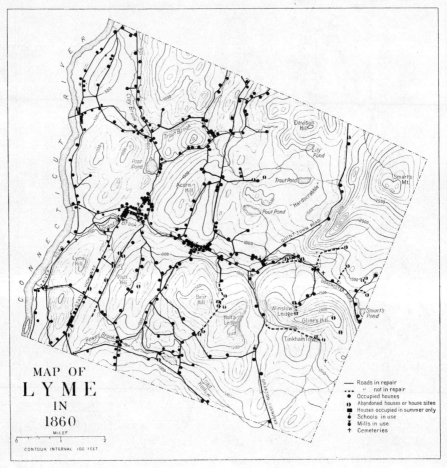

MAP OF
LYME
IN
1860

MILES

CONTOUR INTERVAL 100 FEET

Roads in repair
"   not in repair
● Occupied houses
◖ Abandoned houses or house sites
■ Houses occupied in summer only
● Schools in use
⚫ Mills in use
+ Cemeteries

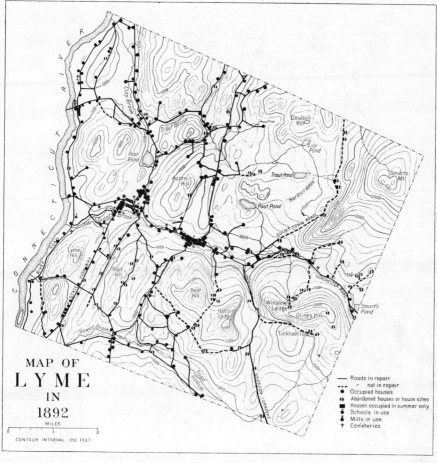

MAP OF
LYME
IN
1892

MILES
0   1   2

CONTOUR INTERVAL 100 FEET

——— Roads in repair
- - - -   "   not in repair
● Occupied houses
◖ Abandoned houses or house sites
■ Houses occupied in summer only
♦ Schools in use
♦ Mills in use
✝ Cemeteries

CONNECTICUT RIVER

Clay Brook
Trout Brook
Post Pond
Acorn Hill
Grant Brook
Lyme Hill
Pout Hill
Bear Hill
Holt's Ledge
Hewes Brook
Toad Hollow
Grafton Turnpike
Winslow's Ledge
Gline's Hill
Tinkham Town
Davison Hill
Lily Pond
Trout Pond
Hardscrabble
Pout Pond
Quint-Town Road
Dorchester Road
Smarts Mt.
Smart's Pond

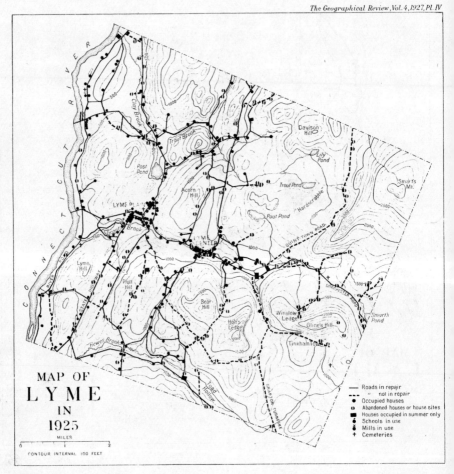

MAP OF
LYME
IN
1925

MILES

CONTOUR INTERVAL 100 FEET

Roads in repair
" not in repair
● Occupied houses
◑ Abandoned houses or house sites
■ Houses occupied in summer only
⬥ Schools in use
⬥ Mills in use
+ Cemeteries

THE GEOGRAPHICAL RELATION OF SOIL EROSION TO LAND PRODUCTIVITY

Hugh Hammond Bennett

U. S. Bureau of Chemistry and Soils

SOIL erosion is the greatest single menace confronting the physical side of land utilization in this country.[1] That we have had at our disposal tremendous areas of fine agricultural lands and have employed these for the production of enormous crops, and shall continue so to employ them for a long time to come, does not alter the situation or make it any less menacing, regardless of the soothing complacency found in the annual outturn of our expansive fields. The nation is not at the moment suffering from any land shortage, and we are not on the verge of starving as the result of wholesale wastage of soil productivity by unrestrained erosion.

Nevertheless, the problem is an exceedingly serious one and will surely become increasingly so under the prevailing inactive attitude of most farmers in relation toward it, that is to say, of doing little or nothing to check it and much to accentuate its evil effects. Already thousands of farmers have moved to town or to other farms because of the impoverishing effect of soil erosion, and a very large total area of land has been abandoned, in so far as cultivation is concerned. Little of the abandonment took place before the topsoil had been washed off or the fields riddled with gullies. The area thus abandoned is being increased every year and probably at a much faster rate than soil recuperation is taking place in the older abandoned·areas now covered or partly covered with vegetation. The writer ventures the opinion that between 40 and 50 per cent of the land now in tilled crops in this country has suffered in some degree from soil erosion and that about one-fourth of this has suffered seriously, that is to the extent either of materially reduced yields or of requiring markedly increased soil management efficiency to maintain the yields.

PLANT-FOOD WASTAGE: SOME PERTINENT ESTIMATES

With the information available, meager as it is, it is yet possible to make rough minimum estimates of erosional wastage. If we use as a basis of calculation 500 million tons of the 513 million tons of suspended matter annually transported to tidewater by the rivers of the United

---

[1] See also H. H. Bennett and W. R. Chapline: Soil Erosion a National Menace, *U. S. Dept. of Agric. Circular No. 33*, Washington, 1928.

States,[2] together with twice this amount of material removed from fields and pastures but stranded en route to the sea, it is found that at least 126 billion pounds of available and potential plant food, as well as the soil containing the plant food, are taken out of the fields and

FIG. 1—This former excellent farm land in Georgia (Greenville sandy loam type) has been permanently destroyed by gullying, as the result of a wash which had its beginning from the drip off the eaves of a barn. (Photograph by Division of Agricultural Engineering, Bureau of Public Roads.)

pastures of the nation every year. This figure is based upon the average chemical composition of 89 samples of surface soils collected throughout the country. That it is a minimum calculation is obvious to those familiar with field conditions. There is no doubt whatever that the amount of soil material annually stranded upon lower slopes, over

[2] As estimated by R. B. Dole and H. Stabler: Denudation, *U. S. Geol. Survey Water-Supply Paper 234*, Washington, 1909, pp. 78–93.

68

stream flood plains, and in reservoirs and stream channels is vastly greater than the amount that actually enters the oceans every year; probably it exceeds that going into the sea by more than a hundred times. Furthermore, the estimate given above does not include the

FIG. 2—This land should never have been plowed. The soil, originally Susquehanna fine sandy loam, washes excessively on steep slopes. Here the former subsoil is now the soil and is valueless.

270 million tons of dissolved matter annually lost to tidewater, much of which comes from the soil. Nor does it include the drag material, the coarser particles, swept along the bottoms of the rivers. Again, there is reason to believe the determinations of the amount of material carried in suspension are too small, since they are based upon measurements of the surface water, not deeper than two feet, in the case of the Mississippi River, which carries by far the greater part of the material going out to sea.

Even the plant food contained in this minimum of material exceeds the annual net loss of plant food in the crops removed by twenty-one times.[3]   Crops remove only the plant food, which can be restored; whereas erosion removes not only the plant food but the whole soil, which cannot be restored.

Since the greater part of the wastage is the work of sheet erosion, the bulk of the material comes from the surface soil, the most productive part of the land.   In terms of money value for the estimated amount of material removed it is impossible to reach any very definite conclusion, since a variety of pertinent complications, chiefly bad ones, follow in the wake of erosion.   When the mellow topsoil is gone, stiffer and less productive subsoil material generally takes its place, that is, where still more unfavorable gravel, sand, and loose rotten rock are not exposed; and this is more difficult to till, although needing more efficient tillage.   In dry times when it is most needed by crops it

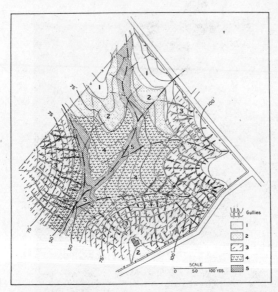

FIG. 3—Soil impairment by erosion, Granitic Piedmont, Orange County, Virginia.   1, only slightly eroded: good Cecil fine sandy loam, with eight or ten inches of soil; 2, washed until only two to five inches of soil is left: poor, eroded Cecil fine sandy loam; 3, all soil washed off down to clay subsoil; numerous gullies; useful for trees only; 4, both soil and subsoil largely washed off to rock: mainly useless land; 5, stream alluvium formed of local erosional débris: forest and meadow land.   (Surveyed by B. H. Hendrickson, Bureau of Chemistry and Soils, 1927.)

is less absorptive of moisture and less retentive of that which is absorbed; and the contained plant nutrients are not so readily available. This necessitates more liberal use of fertilizers, manure or soil-improving crops, and often lime.   The farmer must deal with all of these obstacles in order to maintain his acre yields, or else abandon the land to grass and trees or, as more frequently happens, to useless brush and weeds.

---

[3] Annual net loss of plant food for the United States by crops removed has been estimated at 2,900,000 tons (The Condition of Agriculture in the United States and Measures for Its Improvement: A Report by the Business Men's Commission on Agriculture, published jointly by the National Industrial Conference Board and the Chamber of Commerce of the United States, Washington, 1927, p. 106).

Calculating the value of the phosphorus, potash, and nitrogen contained in the material stripped from the fields by erosion, in the minimum estimate given above, on the basis of the cheapest commercial fertilizer that carries these nutrients, we arrive at a money valuation of approximately two billion dollars. For obvious reasons not all of this can be charged up as a direct tangible loss to the farmers of the nation; but there is evidence that about two hundred million dollars of it is a yearly tangible loss.

Probably not less than ten million acres of land formerly cultivated in this country have been permanently ruined by soil erosion, in so far as having value for cultivation, and an additional three million acres of good stream alluvium have been rendered valueless or have been severely impaired as a result of overwash of comparatively inert sand and gravel and increased swampiness due to choked stream channels. Half or more of the former productive bottom lands along the streams of the southern Piedmont have been made unfit for cultivation, and countless strips of alluvial soil through the Ozarks region have been buried with gravel on farms, where, in many instances, most of the arable land was that along the streams.

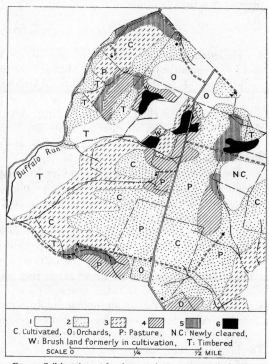

FIG. 4—Soil impairment by sheet erosion on comparatively smooth Appalachian Plateau, Hampshire County, West Virginia. Numbers have reference to amount of topsoil removed: 1, uneroded or only slightly eroded; 2, 20 to 30 per cent removed; 3, 30 to 40 per cent; 4, 40 to 50 per cent; 5, 50 to 75 per cent; 6, all topsoil removed. (Surveyed by B. H. Williams, Bureau of Chemistry and Soils, 1927.)

But this kind of land destruction and impairment represents but a small part of the damage done. The great wastage has been that which has effected partial or complete removal of the more productive surface soil by the less spectacular phase of erosion known as sheet erosion.

71

The damage that has been done and continues to be done by this process cannot be calculated. The worst aspect of the situation is that since the less absorptive subsoil layers are more erosive than was the more absorptive soil layer, now gone and going over immense areas, we really stand upon the threshold of unthinkable erosional wastage, if present practices continue.

LACK OF QUANTITATIVE DATA

The qualitative aspect of the soil erosion problem is obvious enough and has frequently been discussed,[4] but it is rather disheartening that at this stage of our development we have accumulated in this country what amounts to almost nothing in the way of the quantitative data necessary for its intelligent solution. Only three stations for studying the problem have thus far been established, and these only recently. They are located at Spur in western Texas, at Columbia, Mo., and in the Piedmont region near Raleigh, N. C.

The problem of soil erosion is complex, for the process is exceedingly variable in its effectiveness from place to place, on varying soil and slope, with varying vegetative cover, type of land usage, and character of precipitation. The average depths of surface denudation that have been computed from river discharges alone mean very little. They imply that the surface everywhere, on steep hillsides and flat prairies, on sand dunes and loam and clay and silt, is being planed down at an equal rate. The statement we so often read that the surface of the vast Mississippi Basin is being lowered by erosion at the almost insignificant rate of .0028 of an inch annually is not only too small as an average but, since erosion does not operate according to any fixed plan of averages, is meaningless and dangerous for its complacency. In this paper illustrations will be given of the process at work under varying conditions, these illustrations being largely taken from the writer's own field work.

SOME MEASUREMENTS IN THE FIELD

At Spur, Tex., 40 tons of soil material were removed from one acre of bare land, with a two per cent slope, by 27 inches of rain. From one acre, with nine per cent slope, in the Piedmont of North Carolina, 25 tons were removed by 36 inches of rainfall. On another soil of approximately four per cent slope in central Missouri, the Shelby loam,[5] 41 tons were lost per acre per year, with 36 inches of rain, on bare ground tilled four inches deep.

From grassland in North Carolina, the rate of erosion was 415 times

[4] For a recent statement see W. C. Lowdermilk and J. Russell Smith: Notes on the Problem of Field Erosion, *Geogr. Rev.*, Vol. 17, 1927, pp. 226–235.

[5] For description of the Shelby soils, and other soil types subsequently referred to, see H. H. Bennett: The Soils and Agriculture of the Southern States, New York, 1921.

FIG. 5

FIG. 6

FIG. 5—Effect of a single rain upon a gently sloping area of rich Iowa loam.

FIG. 6—Complete destruction of fine silt loam soil in the loessial region of Mississippi. The clay subsoil exposed in this view is unsuitable for the growth of anything.

73

slower than on bare ground of the same slope and soil; while at the Missouri station the rate of wash-off from sod land was 137 times slower than from bare ground plowed four inches deep. In the latter instance the rate of wearage for bare ground was seven inches in 24 years, and for blue-grass sod seven inches in 3547 years. Grass proves not only highly efficient in restraining soil erosion but also in conserving rain water. In Texas grassland held back 82 per cent of the rainfall, at least temporarily; whereas only 55 per cent was retained in cotton fields. In Missouri grass retained 88 per cent of the rains, and shallow-tilled, bare ground only 69 per cent; in North Carolina grass caused 98.5 per cent of the precipitation to remain on the land, whereas only 65 per cent of it remained on bare ground.

Such data are indicative of what has been taking place on the sloping areas of the Mississippi Basin since the breaking of the vast mat of sod that originally covered the prairies of that region. They are suggestive also of the powerful restraint exerted by forests upon the wash-off and run-off; for much of the land concerned was originally timbered, and trees, like grass, hold back both soil and water.

If grass sod in the Piedmont enables an important agricultural type of that region to hold back 51 per cent more of the rainfall than bare ground, and 33 per cent more than fields planted to cotton, what saving are we to expect from a well-forested area with a good ground cover of woods mold consisting essentially of peat, knowing that some forms of peat are capable of holding water in excess of a hundred times their own weight? That we do not have an abundance of measured data of this nature for our key soil types, proves the pressing necessity for research in this field.

FACTORS AFFECTING SOIL EROSION

Soil erosion[6] has been going on undoubtedly since the first rain that followed the development of the first film of soil. We are not especially concerned here about natural or normal erosion, since it is largely unpreventable[7] and, as a rule, does no great damage to the land. It is abnormal erosion that we are concerned with: that excessive washing of the soil which is due to removal or impairment of the vegetative cover and to physical disturbances of the ground, as a result of land clearing, grazing, fires, plowing, ditching, etc., most of which is the direct or indirect result of man's activities, chiefly his unwise methods of using the land.

---

[6] This paper is concerned with water erosion. Wind erosion functions in a manner quite similar to water erosion and does a vast amount of damage. It is a major phase of erosion, however, and will be treated in another paper.

[7] It should be noted however that there are some exceptions to this statement. It might be possible, for example, to find some shrub or vine or grass that would thrive on such wasting areas as the Bad Lands, bind the soil, and keep large quantities of silt out of the streams. And it is quite possible to check erosion along the sea coast in places.

Over large areas normal erosion proceeds at a rate that about equals the formation of soil from the rock and other parent materials. On the other hand, abnormal erosion, which we here refer to simply as *soil erosion*, usually exceeds the rate of soil formation on sloping areas, although varying in its progress with: (1) soil character, (2) character of vegetative cover, (3) degree of artificial ground modification, (4) degree of slope, and (5) climate. This order of arrangement has little to do with the relative importance of these most important erosional variants, except that soil character probably should head the list.

Climate is a very important erosional factor, as a matter of course. Hard beating rains of summer are much more destructive than the slowly-falling showers that characterize some regions. When the ground is frozen deeply or covered with a blanket of snow for long periods there can be no erosion until thawing starts the water downhill; and this, as a rule, will be a gradual process, less destructive than heavy rains. Probably the loosening effect of alternate freezing and thawing upon some soils gives a condition of porosity that makes them more resistant to erosion than similar soils of warmer latitudes. Spew frost, by lifting films of soil, effects considerable local downward movement of material on steep slopes of certain soils, when the small columns of supporting ice melt.

Most of these climatic effects are modified by soil types, usually very greatly. One of the most important points about the relation of climate to erosion is that there is erosion wherever there is enough rainfall for water to run downhill. There are some peculiar soils that absorb most of the rainfall, even clay types, no matter how heavy the precipitation; but even on these the open pore space is sometimes temporarily filled, and some of the rainfall does flow away and accomplish a small amount of surface wastage. The least erosion ever observed by the writer, the one place where there was no appreciable washing, was on a soil type that belongs to a class of highly erosive soils, that is wind-blown silt loam. In this instance, encountered on the slopes of the Tanana River below Fairbanks in northern Alaska, one and three-fourths degrees south of the Arctic Circle, the resistance to erosion is entirely climatic. The rainfall is exceedingly light, about 11.5 inches, and it falls as light showers. The soil is frozen eight or nine months, and the region has a sub-ice cap, that is, the ground is permanently congealed from depths of a few feet below the surface down to bed rock.

Indirectly, climate is closely related to soil erosion. Under certain climatic conditions, as those characterizing the humid tropics, highly percolative clays which are very nearly nonerosive,[8] have been

---

[8] H. H. Bennett: Some Comparisons of the Properties of Humid-Tropical and Humid-Temperate American Soils, *Soil Science*, Vol. 21, 1926, pp. 349–374; H. H. Bennett and R. V. Allison: The Soils of Cuba, Tropical Plant Research Foundation, Washington, 1928.

formed under forest cover. Again, in the dry regions soils have been formed which are tremendously susceptible to erosion because of peculiar structural conditions associated with high contents of the soluble bases.

Dole and Stabler's figures for river silt in suspension[9] reveal striking correlations between erosion, on the one hand, and soil and

Fig. 7—Soil "mining" in the loessial region. These corn rows running up and down the hillside have well-started gullies between them. (Photograph by W. R. Mattoon, U. S. Forest Service.)

climate, on the other. For example, the amount of material carried in suspension by the Missouri River near its confluence with the Mississippi is 1138 parts per million; whereas the average content for three rivers of the northeastern United States, the Kennebec, Housatonic, and Hudson, is only 8.3 parts per million. The Rio Grande at El Paso carries 14,140 parts per million. The Missouri flows through a region including much highly erosive silt soil (loessial soils); the Rio Grande traverses dry country where much of the soil upon desiccation breaks down into a fluffy structure favoring rapid removal by rainwash; whereas the group of northeastern streams receive their drainage from an area largely comprising absorptive glacial till soils that are but slightly inclined to wash. The Rio Grande carries 700 parts of dissolved matter per million; the Missouri, 294 parts, and the northeastern stream group only 77.5 parts.

[9] Paper cited in footnote 2.

VARIATIONS IN CLAY SOILS

Reference has already been made to the case of a two per cent slope of clay loam (Abilene) in subhumid western Texas, which showed an erosional loss of 40 tons of soil per acre with 27 inches of rainfall;

Fig. 8   Fig. 9

Fig. 8—A field in northeastern Kansas (about twelve miles from the Missouri River) that was riddled by erosion during a single rainy spell in the fall of 1927. Some 40 tons per acre of the richest topsoil was then lost.

Fig. 9—By a peculiar soil-scaling process upon drying, the face of this gully of deep silty clay in southwest Texas has cut through into the next gully abnormally quickly.

whereas sandy clay loam (Cecil) in the Piedmont of North Carolina showed a loss of only 25 tons per acre from a nine per cent slope, with a precipitation of 36 inches. Considering the fact that the carrying capacity of water increases enormously with the velocity, as does also the scouring capacity, the results obtained at the Piedmont station stand out as a remarkable example of the influence of soil upon the rate of erosion. Even so, the Piedmont soils suffer greatly from rain-wash on all unprotected slopes. But for the fact that a large proportion of the soils of this region contain much highly weathered clay of a peculiar porous character, functioning as erosion-resistant material, this part of the country doubtless would have been largely washed down to its bed rock long ago, as has happened in many rolling Piedmont areas of the plastic Iredell soils.

Clay land having powerful resistance to erosion is very extensive in the humid forested areas of northern California and in western Oregon and Washington, such as the Aiken clay and clay loam.[10] These lands are used on steep slopes for prunes and other fruits with very little evidence of washing, even where cultivation is carried up and down the slopes, rather than along the contours. These are tropic-like soils of low silica and high iron and alumina contents, much like those of eastern and middle Cuba.[11] As a result of recent studies within tropical regions of the western hemisphere it has been learned that certain extensive types of highly weathered clays, those having low ratios of silica to iron and alumina (a molecular ratio of less than two) are practically immune to erosion.[12]

The less weathered clays, whose products have not been highly oxidized or severely leached since the disintegration of the parent materials, show opposite properties, with respect to erosivity, to the tropic-like or highly-weathered clays. These types have relatively high contents of silica and low contents of iron and alumina (a molecular ratio greater than two).

Such impervious, plastic clays are characteristically exemplified in the extensive yellow clay soils of the Iredell series of the southern Piedmont, a derivative of basic igneous rocks; the very extensive Susquehanna soils, having mottled clay subsoils, derived from plastic clays of the Gulf Plain area, extending from west-central Georgia to central Texas; and the Lowell and Fairmont soils of the limestone areas of northern Alabama, central Tennessee, Kentucky, and southern Ohio and Indiana. In a single county of the Piedmont, 90,000 acres of land, formerly cultivated, productive soil, have been largely destroyed by gullies. This was mapped by the Soil Survey as Rough gullied land,[13] that is largely non-arable land, with a considerable part washed off to bed rock. The general appearance of the area indicates that since the survey was made, seventeen years ago, several additional thousands of acres have attained this all but desert condition. Centuries of soil building will be required to restore the land to cultivation.

In one county of the coastal plain region 70,000 acres of land, most

10 E. F. Torgerson, Charles Hartmann, Jr., E. J. Carpenter, and W. G. Harper: Soil Survey of Polk County, Oregon, *U. S. Dept. of Agric., Field Operations of the Bur. of Soils, 1922—Advance Sheets,* pp. 1681–1721.

11 H. H. Bennett: Some Geographic Aspects of Cuban Soils, *Geogr. Rev.,* Vol. 18, 1928, pp. 62–82; reference on p. 80.

12 Bennett and Allison, *op. cit.,* pp. 238–239; H. H. Bennett: Agriculture in Central America, *Annals Assn. of Amer. Geogrs.,* Vol.16, 1926, pp. 63–84; *loc. cit.:* Some Comparisons of the Properties of Humid-Tropical and Humid-Temperate American Soils.

13 M. E. Carr, F. S. Welsh, G. A. Crabb, R. T. Allen, and W. C. Byers: Soil Survey of Fairfield County, South Carolina, *U. S. Dept. of Agric., Field Operations of the Bur. of Soils, 1911 [13th Rept.]* pp. 479–511.

of which was cultivated at one time, have been mapped as Rough gullied land and Susquehanna clay, now having very little or no crop value as the result of erosion.[14] Of this, 33,000 acres were classed under the latter designation and described as follows:

"The Susquehanna clay occupies steep slopes, the crests of rounded hills, and the tops of ridges. Erosion has so gullied the greater part of the type that there is practically no level land within its boundaries. . . .

"*The rough character of this land, which prohibits tillage operations over much of it, is the result mainly of erosion which has taken place since the land was cleared for cultivation.* [The italics are the author's.] The Susquehanna clay was one of the first soil types farmed in the county. It was considered strong land and produced as much as a bale of cotton per acre without the use of fertilizers. There are today on this type many deserted but substantial farmhouses, abandonment of which was compelled by the ruining of the fields by erosion."

Of the 37,000 acres of Rough gullied land the report says:

"Rough gullied land includes areas which, as the result of erosion, are so steep and broken as to be unfit for agriculture. . . . Some areas are available for pasture, but a considerable total area is not even suitable for this use, as there are many deep gullies with steep or perpendicular sides on which no vegetation can find a footing. Providence and Trotman "Caves," to the west and north of Lumpkin, are examples of such areas."

Until recently it had generally been supposed that all soils of high clay content were necessarily heavy, stiff, and impervious and that the sandy soils were friable and pervious. Recent studies have shown that this depends upon the kind of clay present, that is where any considerable amount of particles of clay diameter is present in the material. The low and high erosivities exhibited by the two varieties of clays discussed above are due, respectively, as well as can be determined from the accumulated evidence, to high and low degrees of flocculation[15] of the soil particles. Perhaps it would be more appropriate to define the physical condition in the latter instance as being due to a comparatively high degree of particle dispersion. At any rate the particles of these plastic clays, such as the Susquehanna and Iredell of the United States and the Bluefields[16] of eastern Nicaragua, are not flocculated soils as the term is generally understood. They are dense clays without free pore space through which water can move freely under force of gravity, and they shrink and swell violently at the extremes of moisture content. On the other hand, the group of clays having opposite characteristics have an abundance of pore space, through which water moves downward freely. Some of these clays are

---

[14] D. D. Long, M. W. Beck, E. C. Hall, and W. W. Burdette: Soil Survey of Stewart County, Georgia, *U. S. Dept. of Agric., Field Operations of the Bur. of Soils, 1913 [15th Rept.]*, pp. 545–606.

[15] Lack of flocculation corresponds to what soil technologists commonly speak of as dispersed soil. In this state the particles stand alone as individuals. Thus unsupported they are more open to attack than the particles of flocculated soils, with their grains bound together in clusters.

[16] J. C. Treadwell, C. R. Hill, and H. H. Bennett: Possibilities for Para Rubber Production in Northern Tropical America, *U. S. Dept. of Commerce Trade Promotion Ser. No. 40*, 1926, pp. 142–143.

FIG. 10

FIG. 11

FIG. 12

FIG. 10—This dike, protecting the highly productive Missouri River bottom land, has caught eight feet of erosional débris from the uplands in ten years. The rate of deposition of a forty-acre field here was 1200 tons per acre per year.

FIG. 11—Wheat straw dumped in a depression caught 430 tons of rich soil material washed from the adjacent slopes during fall rains (northwestern Kansas).

FIG. 12—These gravel-coated clay balls, found in a southwest Texas stream bed, illustrate a curious form in which land material is being transported to the sea.

80

FIG. 13

FIG. 14

FIG. 15

FIG. 13—Excellent valley grazing land in the arid southwest being rapidly ruined by erosion which started in the bedding ground of cattle.

FIG. 14—Channel-trench erosion in the Trans-Pecos region, southwest of Valentine, Tex., 1927.

FIG. 15—This is a deep erosional gully in a formerly timbered area in northern California. The vegetative cover was largely annihilated by smelter fumes.

81

almost as friable as sand and take up the rainfall just as readily. They also exhibit almost negligible properties of shrinking or swelling with decrease or increase of the moisture content.

EROSION OF SILT SOILS IN THE MISSISSIPPI AND MISSOURI BASIN

The upland silt soils of the United States, including some of the most important agricultural lands of the nation, are all erosive types, some representing probably the most erosive of all soils to be found in the country. Those that are most susceptible to destructive washing, both by sheet and gully erosion, are found in the great areas of loessial soil bordering the Mississippi River on the east side from the vicinity of Baton Rouge, La., across western Mississippi and Tennessee and southwestern Kentucky and bordering also the Missouri from its confluence with the Mississippi to the boundary of South Dakota. This great area includes some of the very best upland corn soils we have, such as the Marshall silt loam; also good corn, grain, and apple soils, as the Knox silt loam; and, in the southern part, good cotton lands, as the Memphis and Granada silt loams.

That these lands wash severely is due to three principal characteristics: (1) Lack of flocculation of the silt particles, coupled possibly with incoherency resulting from a low content of binding clay; (2) the presence in the substrata of a soft silt layer; and (3) the generally rolling topography, particularly of the Memphis and Knox soils. The wastage is by a three-step process, i.e. the silty surface layer is gradually removed from unprotected slopes by sheet erosion; then gullies cut through the normal silty clay subsoil into the soft silt layer beneath; whereupon devastating dissection begins, the gullies deepening and spreading very rapidly. In some parts of the southern extension of the region the major part of the uplands of a number of counties has been ruined by erosion, and, as a consequence, farming has been largely driven into the stream bottoms. Unfortunately, many parts of the stream bottoms have been covered with comparatively inert sand assorted from flood waters, and the channels of numerous streams have been so choked with erosional débris that overflows are much more common than formerly.

While the damage has not been quite so serious there has been a considerable degree of gullying in the Missouri River belt of loessial soils and an enormous amount of sheet erosion. In the fall of 1927 the writer found from one to two feet of rich, mellow silt loam over clay in areas of virgin timber in northeastern Kansas, where over adjacent areas having the same slope and soil, cleared about 40 years ago, all of the soil had been washed off in numerous abandoned and tilled fields. In some of these a half a foot or more of the subsoil had been removed after the soil had been carried away. Indeed, bed rock was exposed in places, which originally was covered with four feet of soil material.

In some fields of the region having only moderate slope it was found that more than 40 tons of soil material per acre were removed from the Marshall and Knox silt loams as the result of a single rainy period that followed the seeding of the land to grain. The grain was mostly washed out, and the fields were riddled with miniature gullies (Fig. 8). Against a pile of wheat straw at the foot of two converging slopes 430 tons of soil material that had been washed down by the fall rains (1927) were lodged (Fig. 11).

Already in this region of exceptionally productive soils, gullied fields are being abandoned to pasture, and most of the sloping areas have been impoverished in some degree by soil wash, with many thousands of acres denuded of their productive topsoil. Apple trees are dying in a number of orchards as the result of erosion. Generally on the lower positions where some of the wash has temporarily stranded the apple trees and other crops are doing well, showing that the deterioration on the higher slopes is the result of soil removal. In one orchard the surface now stands five feet higher than the ground upon which the trees were planted.

On another farm in northeastern Kansas the operator had constructed an eight-foot dike to intercept outwash from the adjacent uplands, which was damaging his rich alluvial corn land in the Missouri River bottoms and covering his roadways. In ten years the land behind the dike had been filled in level with the dike over a 40-acre field (Fig. 10). In other words, deposition of erosional débris had taken place here at the rate of 1200 tons per acre per year.

This sort of thing is going on in many places in the bottoms of the Missouri and its tributaries. Nothing of any importance is being done in the region to slow down erosional wastage; whereas much is being done to accentuate it. Corn rows are often run up and down the slopes rather than along the contours, a practice that invariably speeds up the effects of rainwash. It is also a common practice to plow furrows down the slopes in springtime in order to drain water from between corn rows. Many of these relief furrows grow into gullies which, dividing, dissect the fields and eventually cause their abandonment to pasture or brush. Even then the washing continues for a considerable time.

An Erosion Type in the Central Coastal Plain

A number of other important types of farm land have suffered disastrously from dendritic gullying owing to the rapidity with which the incisions extend themselves when the coarser materials underlying the soils have been cut into. Some of these types, such as the valuable group of soils characterized by the Orangeburg and Greenville series of the central coastal plain region, are so susceptible to this kind of wastage that it is safe to make the statement that not one acre of them should be used for the clean-cultivated crops without protection with terraces, whenever the slope exceeds four or five per cent. It was principally on these types that 37,000 acres of former cultivated land were found by actual survey to have been destroyed in Stewart County, Georgia, in 1913, as already noted. Probably not less than half a million acres of these excellent cotton and corn soils have been permanently destroyed or temporarily made unsuitable for profitable cultivation by soil erosion.

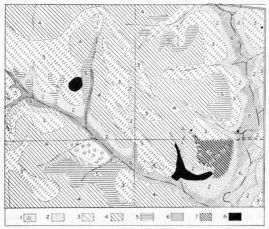

FIG. 16—Soil impairment by sheet erosion on Knox silt loam, Donipher County, Kansas. The area represented is 120 acres. 1, virgin timber: 12 to 24 inches of dark-brown mellow silt loam, over yellow silty clay loam, uneroded soil; 2, soil washed from higher slopes: 10 to 20 inches of brown silt loam over yellow silty clay loam of previously eroded areas; 3, cultivated fields: 4 to 10 inches of light-brown silt loam over yellow silty clay loam: 8 to 14 inches of topsoil washed off; 4, cultivated fields and orchards: 2 to 4 inches of yellowish-brown heavy silt loam to silty clay loam over yellow silty clay loam; 10 to 26 inches of soil washed off; 5, steeper cultivated slopes: light-brown, silty clay loam, i. e. exposed subsoil; 12 to 30 inches of soil washed off; 6, alluvium from slopes: 15 to 30 inches of brown to dark-brown silt loam over heavier silty material; 7, yellowish-brown silty clay loam, from which all the original soil has been washed off and from 4 to 6 inches or more of the subsoil; 8, non-arable land with abundance of limestone outcrops, most of the soil removed by erosion. (Surveyed by E. W. Knobel, Bureau of Chemistry and Soils, 1927.)

When it rains the material of the loose sandy beds beneath the subsoil clay readily washes out, with the result that huge chunks of the overlying soil and subsoil topple into the gullies. Gully growth by this process is rapid, extension being fastest by the heads, which follow up minor depressions in the surface, in many places having cut through formidable ridges, even those occupied by forests.

This *head-on extension* type of deep gully erosion can be controlled economically only by stopping the washes before they have cut down into the unstable substrata.

EROSION IN THE DRIER REGIONS

It would be reasonable to assume that in the dry regions of the West, where precipitation is often less than ten or twelve inches annu-

ally, soil erosion is far less active than in the humid regions. Such
is not the case, however, at least for numerous localities, where structural soil features and scantiness of vegetation contribute immensely
to the wastage.

In the Trans-Pecos region of Texas and in central New Mexico a
great deal of exceedingly destructive erosion is to be seen. Even over
smooth areas oc-
cupied by valley-
filling material,
representing the
accumulation of
centuries, the soil
has been bodily
swept away or cut
to pieces by a type
of erosion that has
been referred to as
channel-trench ero-
sion.[17]

The writer saw
last year (1927) lit-
erally hundreds of
places where for-
mer valuable graz-
ing areas had suf-
fered from various
phases of this type
of wastage, to de-
grees varying from
moderate impair-
ment of the land
to its absolute de-
struction. All of

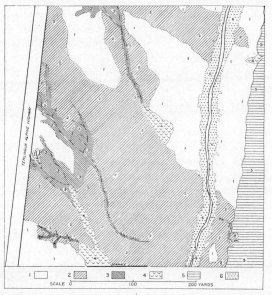

Fig. 17—Soil impairment by channel-trench and dry-climate-sheet
erosion, southwestern Brewster County, Texas. 1, uneroded, or only
slightly eroded: good Marfa clay loam; 2, half or more of topsoil
removed: Marfa clay loam; 3, all soil and much of subsoil removed:
severely dissected Marfa clay loam of low value; 4, accumulated erosional débris: silty clay loam, good soil; 5, upland: Brewster stony
loam; 6, stream gravel. (Surveyed by M. W. Beck, Bureau of Chemistry and Soils, and T. C. Reitch, Texas Agric. Exper. Station, 1927.)

the eroded areas studied in this region had their beginning in roadways,
cattle trails or bedding grounds, prairie-dog towns, or diversion ditches.
The washing, in other words, had its start in those situations where the
grass cover and ground equilibrium had been seriously disturbed.
Structural peculiarities of the soil and, in places, coarse-textured basal
material had contributed vastly to the rapidity of the erosion. As a
matter of fact, the tendency of many dry-region soils to crack and re-
crack on drying, thus to form a loose fine-fragmental or granular surface
layer, adds greatly to the erosional vulnerability of tremendous areas of
the lands. This applies not only to desert soils but to subhumid types.

---

[17] Kirk Bryan: Date of Channel Trenching (Arroyo Cutting) in the Arid Southwest, *Science*,
No. 1607, Vol. 62, 1925, pp. 338–348.

At Spur, Tex., for instance, on a two per cent slope 40 tons of soil were washed from one acre by 27 inches of rainfall, in a locality whose average annual precipitation amounts to 22.55, the minimum to 10.92 inches and the maximum to 35.61 inches. With heavy rains the chafflike soil is swept before rushing water as so much litter; then, with saturation, the emulsified mass flows rapidly down the slopes. Under the influence of this process enormous quantities of soil are swept into the streams and upon lower positions where it is not needed.

Another effect of dry-land soil structure is to assist erosion in a bi-active rôle. This is the common tendency of the heavier soils to split or crack vertically so as to develop a columnar structure. Washes begin in the fissures in some instances; and from the sides of gullies a splitting-off process, accompanying desiccation of the material, causes comparatively rapid wearage upon the exposed faces. This aids one gully to wear through to another much quicker than would happen in humid regions (Fig. 9).

In 1925 six square miles of the watershed of a stream near Redlands, Cal., were burned over; the following year 11 inches of rain falling upon the watershed in three days eroded the burned-over area and cut into the bed and stream banks of the valley, transporting and spreading débris over the lower valley floor, planted to oranges, to a distance of one and a half miles out from the point of debouchment of the valley from the highlands. The depth of this covering of loose, unfavorable gravel, sand, and silt ranged from a mere film to two feet through the groves. Where the depth ranged from six inches to a foot it proved necessary to dig the material away from the base of the trees. Where it exceeded a foot the orange trees began to die, and it was necessary to remove the detritus with the assistance of a steam shovel. It is said to have cost 60 cents a cubic yard to haul the material out of the grove, the average cost amounting to $1200 an acre. The expense of this operation was estimated to approximate the value of the land, and it is doubtful if the owners could afford to remove a second such deposit, even from the valuable orange groves.

A notable instance of destructive erosion following the removal of the vegetation from forest land by smelter fumes was observed last year in Shasta County, California, at Kennet. Here the vegetation was completely obliterated or very largely destroyed by fumes from a copper smelter over an area estimated as exceeding a hundred square miles. The original growth consisted of pine, live and deciduous oak, together with chaparral of manzanita, coffee berry, poison oak, etc., and the soil was a gravelly clay or clay loam. Partial rock decay had extended to depths of probably more than a hundred feet in places. On this hilly to mountainous area erosion has wrought unbelievable devastation. Deep, narrow gullies have riddled the affected area. Some of the trench incisions, with an estimated depth of 50 feet, wander about like glacier crevasses; others spread widely in dendritic fashion. The soil is completely gone, and with it every vestige of forest mold. It will be interesting to watch the rejuvenation of this devastated area, by encroaching vegetation, now that the smelter has moved; that is if rejuvenation takes place before the decomposed material has largely washed down to bed rock.

And finally it should be noted that though its greatest damage is taking place over certain large critical areas—the Piedmont, the upper

FIG. 18—Along this stream twenty feet of alluvial material was deposited in fifteen years, and the land was rendered practically valueless.

coastal plain, the loessial region, the region of shale soils in the Appalachians, the regions having rolling soils with plastic clay subsoils, the heavy lands of the dry Southwest, and the overgrazed sheep lands in parts of Utah and other western states—this must not be construed as meaning that erosional wastage is not going on elsewhere. As a matter of fact, land impairment is proceeding in many places where its activity has not been suspected by the average farmer, even on soils that seem nearly flat.

RELATION OF EROSIONAL SEDIMENTS TO FERTILITY

A word should be said regarding the reverse of the erosional process. It is commonly believed that the products of erosion largely go to improve the alluvial plains over which part of the material is deposited in times of flood. From this angle of viewing the situation it is sometimes contended that floods are of great value, serving as a powerful instrument for soil enrichment. There is a germ of truth

87

FIG. 19

FIG. 20

FIG. 19—The bottom of this stream, Oconalufty River, Swain County, North Carolina, was formerly covered by a rich strip of alluvial land, as represented by the small island area in the center. (Photograph by E. Block, U. S. Forest Service.)

FIG. 20—Deep gullies and abandoned hillside farm land in the Blue Ridge Mountain section. White pine is slowly and difficultly restocking the area. (Photograph by E. Block, U. S. Forest Service.)

FIG. 21

FIG. 22

FIG. 21—Erosional effects following overgrazing of sheep lands, Manti National Forest. (Photograph by U. S. Forest Service.)

FIG. 22—On this gullied slope in southern Ohio (Scioto County), locust trees have been planted to bring the wasted area to some degree of usefulness.

89

in the idea, particularly with respect to some types of flood plain. In a large measure, however, the conception is fallacious. In the first place, as already pointed out, a large proportion of the eroded material comes to rest temporarily upon lower slopes and flats where it is not needed and often does serious and permanent damage to the land and the crops growing on it.

Furthermore, much of the most productive part of the flood-plain deposits is left upon material of precisely the same origin and character, already having great depth and good productivity. There is, of course, some temporary enrichment of the alluvial soil of some areas by deposition of fine-grained material. Even in the Mississippi flood plain, some increase in the crop yields follow deposition of the finer particles, especially on the more sandy strips along the stream banks. Not much advantage from this source can be expected, however, in case of the highly productive "buckshot" land of this great alluvial plain, the Sharkey clay, which is a deep soil rich in available and potential plant nutrients, often containing three-tenths per cent of phosphoric acid and a good supply of organic matter. Some temporary refreshment is frequently observed, nevertheless, in the older fields, due to the fresh organic matter and nitrates in the deposits. But the increased yields are generally not astounding nor of very long duration.

On the other hand, comparatively infertile material of sand and gravel is frequently deposited over productive alluvial bottoms, causing much damage. Even the floods of the Mississippi lay down patches of almost inert sand, locally known as "sand blows," and injure other areas by deposition of loose sand near the banks and in the vicinity of levee crevasses. The Vermont flood of 1927 laid down over productive meadow lands blankets of coarse sand and gravel that were six feet deep in places. Even boulders weighing a ton were rolled out on some of the alluvial plains. Many thousands of acres of the best land in the state were thus severely damaged or entirely ruined.

In any appraisal of the effects of floods, it is necessary, of course, to weight first the damage done to farm improvements, live stock, and crops. And it is well always to remember that one acre of alluvial material in a stream bottom may stand for many acres of impaired or devastated fields and pastures, upstream, especially when there has been abnormally rapid deposition.

RELATION OF EROSION TO FLOODS

Inadequacy of measurements makes it entirely impossible to estimate the full relationship of soil erosion to floods. There is evidence, however, to indicate that erosion always tends to increase the volume of floods materially. There is abundant proof of this for the smaller streams, and it has not been proved that the same sort of thing does

FIG. 23

FIG. 24

FIG. 23—A properly terraced field in the Piedmont region. Many fields in this region have been saved by such terraces.

FIG. 24—This Piedmont hillside, formerly a waste of gullies and exposed clay subsoil, has been reclaimed by the use of hillside terraces. The man at left stands on a flat of accumulated material caught by the terrace embankment.

91

not take place in the larger streams, as the Missouri and Mississippi. We have entirely too little evidence relating to the rains that produced some of the earlier floods so often referred to by those who profess to believe that only conspiring rains and inadequate levee protection have anything to do with such disastrous floods as that along the Mississippi in 1927; and also there are too few precise data relating to these early floods themselves. It would not, however, in the least vitiate the argument of those who see a vital relationship between floods and denuded watersheds if some of the earlier explorers had looked upon floods in the Mississippi that very greatly exceeded the one of 1927, for there was then as now no natural law against overwhelming downpours. There is abundant evidence upon the pages of the world's history that every now and then all the probabilities have been rudely upset. This being true, they may be upset again. The important thing for mankind is not to permit improbable eventualities and unavoidable actualities (the rains) to constitute a negativating deterrent in the setting up of obstacles to those wasteful processes going on under more or less normal conditions.

The largely increased run-off and wash-off from unprotected slopes as compared with protected slopes cannot but add volume to the water of rising streams. Equilibria of current and load, balances of deposition and resuspension, eroding banks, eroding flood plains, etc., enter into the process, of course; but an increased volume of water in a stream is a definite enlargement that cannot be decreased except by part of the water getting away somewhere; and the place most of it must go is the sea, where it arrives as quickly as possible and in as large volume as possible, regardless of the methods of travel involved.

It is perfectly obvious that if a greater portion of water and of suspended and dissolved matter is withheld from the streams the flood hazards which occur at peak stages will be greatly relieved; and, furthermore, both the water and the soil are needed in the fields and pastures where they belong.

LOOKING AHEAD

As a nation we are doing comparatively little to abate the evil effects of this scourge of the land, soil erosion. Those who know from actual experience and observation anything of the process admit it is a serious land problem; but few have seemed to realize how exceedingly devastating it is in its wholesale operation. There is immediate need for a tremendous national awakening to action in bettering our land practices. Terracing and contour cultivation of sloping areas to check erosion has been carried on with excellent results for a long time in parts of the southeastern United States. Recently the method has crossed the Mississippi and is being extensively and increasingly employed in Texas and Oklahoma. But in the region north of the northern line of Oklahoma and Tennessee terraces are rarely employed to protect eroding slopes, or any other means for that matter. Most of the farmers have never seen an efficiently constructed terrace; many of them have never even heard of this embankment method of protecting sloping fields.

The terrace is a very practical implement for saving soil and also for conserving soil moisture in the drier regions. When terraces are properly built, including adjustment to soil and slope, they will pay their way many times over; and whatever they accomplish in holding soil in the fields, keeping it out of the streams, and storing moisture in the subsoil will be a by-product of the operation. In regard to this, however, as to other phases of the problem, investigational work has only begun. We do not yet know what is the best type of terrace for some of the most erosive soils; nor do we know at precisely what slope cultivation should cease on some of the more susceptible lands and the planting of trees or grass should begin. As yet only three types of soil, of the many involved, have had their erosivity measured.

VOTING HABITS IN THE UNITED STATES

A NOTE ON TWO MAPS

John K. Wright

THE approaching election invites attention to the geography of American politics. For certain regions it may be predicted with assurance that Hoover will receive a plurality; other regions will unquestionably be carried by Roosevelt; elsewhere the outcome will remain in doubt until the returns are tabulated. The accompanying maps give a clue to the distribution of habits of voting throughout the nation.

MAPS OF VOTING HABITS

Maps showing party voting habits may be constructed on the basis of the returns of successive elections. Figures 1 and 2 were compiled from the original drawings of a series of maps of Presidential elections recently published in Dr. C. O. Paullin's "Atlas of the Historical Geography of the United States."[1] By examining the sequence of "Atlas" maps it is possible to gain a general idea of party loyalties region by region, but only with the help of composite maps of the type reproduced herewith can we compare in any detail the habitual political behavior of different communities.

Figures 1 and 2 are composites for the Presidential elections of 1876–1928 inclusive. On Figure 1 are shown the areas carried by the Republicans and by the Democrats at every election during this period. These areas are the strongholds of party conservatism. Figure 1 also shows where minor parties have met with success.

Figure 2 contrasts Republican with Democratic successes county by county. Minor parties are disregarded. The number of times each county was carried by candidates of the two chief parties was counted. The percentage of Republican successes—and conversely, therefore, of Democratic successes—was calculated with reference to this total, and this percentage was then plotted for each county.

INTERPRETATION OF THE MAPS

In the interpretation of these maps the reader should bear certain facts in mind. Each symbol summarizes the voting habit of a fairly

---

[1] See the present number of the *Geographical Review*, p. 688; also J. K. Wright, "Sections and National Growth: An Atlas of the Historical Geography of the United States," in the July number of the *Review*, pp. 353–360.

long period—for most of Figure 2 fifty-two years, including fourteen elections. Habits change. A county may have voted Democratic at one or two elections during the early part of the period and Republican ever since. One might say, therefore, that its *present* habit is to vote Republican. Figure 2, however, represents the average habit of the period 1876–1928, and this average habit is by no means necessarily the habit of the present time. Hence the map should be used with caution as a basis for prophecy. For the regions west of the Mississippi recent elections have played a larger part in shaping the pattern than is the case farther east. Large tracts in the West were unsettled or unorganized for voting purposes at the time of some of the earlier elections. Moreover, Figure 2 does somewhat less than justice to the Democratic solidarity of South Carolina, Florida, Mississippi, and Louisiana. These states were still under "carpetbag" rule at the time of the election of 1876. The Republican pluralities then recorded in some of the counties are hardly representative of the political sympathies of the white population.

The strength of political parties depends mainly on the number of votes polled. More votes are polled where population is denser, but density of population is disregarded on both maps. The concentrated Democratic strength in some of the larger cities of the Northeast is lost sight of owing to the small size of the counties in which these cities lie. Yet the city vote has often placed otherwise predominantly Republican states—Massachusetts and New York, for example— in the Democratic column in the Electoral College.

Furthermore, neither map discloses the margins by which the successful parties have won in different regions. Votes polled by minority parties do not enter the picture.

The prevailing voting habits of any region spring from a complex interplay of geographical, economic, and social forces. The patterns on the maps express differences in history, wealth, occupations, traditions, and to some degree in the power of party leaders. To explain the details of these patterns at all adequately would require prolonged study of local history. Although no such explanation can be attempted here, a few salient points may be mentioned.

THE EASTERN AND THE WESTERN UNITED STATES

In the geography of party politics there is a pronounced difference between the eastern and western halves of the country. On the eastern portion of Figure 2 the presence of areas of definite and enduring party allegiance is plainly revealed by the sharp contrasts in the shades. The late Professor F. J. Turner wrote that "there are both interstate and intrastate party areas persisting in some cases for many decades or even generations and having clear relations to natural geographic

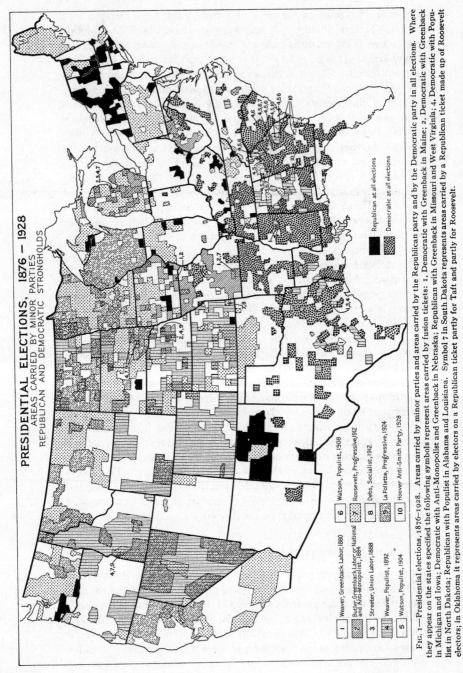

FIG. 1—Presidential elections, 1876–1928. Areas carried by minor parties and areas carried by the Republican party and by the Democratic party in all elections. Where they appear on the states specified the following symbols represent areas carried by fusion tickets: 1, Democratic with Greenback in Maine; 2, Democratic with Greenback in Missouri and West Virginia; 4, Democratic with Greenback in Michigan and Iowa; Democratic with Anti-Monopolist and Greenback in Nebraska; Republican with Greenback in Nebraska; 4, Democratic with Populist in North Dakota; Republican with Populist in Alabama and Louisiana. Symbol 7 in South Dakota represents areas carried by a Republican ticket made up of Roosevelt electors; in Oklahoma it represents areas carried by electors on a Republican ticket partly for Taft and partly for Roosevelt.

PRESIDENTIAL ELECTIONS, 1876 – 1928
AREAS CARRIED BY MINOR PARTIES
REPUBLICAN AND DEMOCRATIC STRONGHOLDS

1 Weaver, Greenback Labor, 1880
2 Butler, Greenback Labor or National and Anti-Monopolist, 1884
3 Streeter, Union Labor, 1888
4 Weaver, Populist, 1892
5 Watson, Populist, 1904
6 Watson, Populist, 1908
7 Roosevelt, Progressive, 1912
8 Debs, Socialist, 1912
9 La Follette, Progressive, 1924
10 Hoover Anti-Smith Party, 1928

Republican at all elections

Democratic at all elections

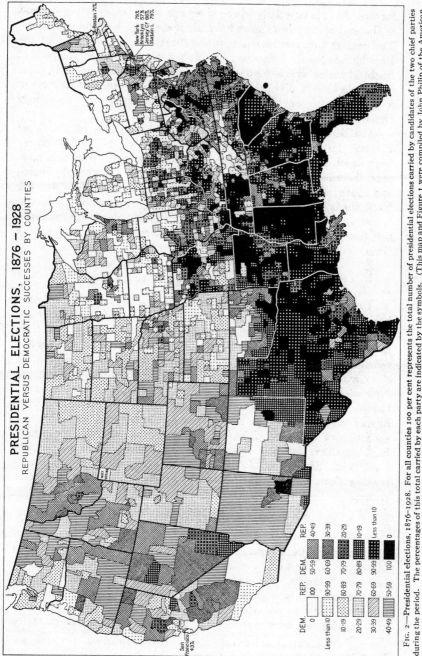
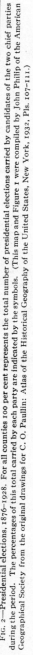

PRESIDENTIAL ELECTIONS, 1876 – 1928
REPUBLICAN VERSUS DEMOCRATIC SUCCESSES BY COUNTIES

Boston 71%

New York 79%
Brooklyn 57%
Jersey City 86%
Staten I. 79%

San Francisco 43%

DEM.	REP.		DEM.	REP.
0	100		50-59	40-49
Less than 10	90-99		60-69	30-39
10-19	80-89		70-79	20-29
20-29	70-79		80-89	10-19
30-39	60-69		90-99	Less than 10
40-49	50-59		100	0

Fig. 2.—Presidential elections, 1876–1928. For all counties 100 per cent represents the total number of presidential elections carried by candidates of the two chief parties during the period. The percentages of this total carried by each party are indicated by the symbols. (This map and Figure 1 were compiled by John Phillp of the American Geographical Society from the original drawings for C. O. Paullin: Atlas of the Historical Geography of the United States, New York, 1932, Pls. 107–111.)

97

factors."[2] It is especially in the older and more conservative sections
of the nation that these areas have become established and confirmed.
The outstanding contrast is between the Democratic South and the
Republican North.   Between the two lies an intermediate zone of
doubtful states where the outcome of elections is often decided. This
is a borderland of divided loyalty, a patchwork of small areas most of
which tend to be either persistently Republican or persistently
Democratic.

The three zones of the eastern United States end in the Great
Plains.   To the west neutral shades prevail on Figure 2.   Party
alignments are not so rigidly localized as in the east.   Here too, however, there is a suggestion of zones, but in this case the trend is north
and south: Republicanism along the Pacific coast; a belt where the
tendency is toward Democracy in the mining counties of California,
Nevada, Idaho, and western Montana; and a generally Republican
belt (though with notable exceptions) in eastern Montana, Wyoming,
Utah, Colorado, Arizona, and New Mexico.

SETTLEMENT AND PARTY AREAS

Party affiliations that originated on or near the eastern seaboard
have been carried across the continent on the tide of settlement.
Those sections of the Middle West settled before the Civil War from
the Federalist-Whig core of New England and New York have usually
remained Republican.   Hence the light shadings on the states fronting
the Great Lakes, and in the Dakotas, Minnesota, Iowa, Kansas, and
Nebraska, as well as in Oregon and Washington.   Republicanism in
the North "is strongest generally along the routes of capital, commerce, industrial energy, and density of population, with frequent
exception of the great cities, where class voting modifies the rule."[3]
Republicanism has also spread from the Middle West to southern
California.   Settlement of Northerners in Florida and parts of Texas
is also reflected in the lighter shading of some of the counties in these
states.

PARTY AREAS IN THE BORDER STATES

From the geographical point of view the intermediate zone between
North and South is perhaps the most interesting.   Here the relation
of politics to the history of settlement is everywhere evident.   Oklahoma, for example, was opened to settlers within the period covered
by the map.   Those who came in from the North brought Republicanism with them to the northern counties.   The southern and southeastern counties were settled from Texas and other southern states

    [2] F. J. Turner: Geographical Influences in American Political History, Bull. Amer. Geogr. Soc.
Vol. 46, 1914, pp. 591–595; reference on p. 591.
    [3] Ibid., p. 593.

and have remained Democratic. In the older states farther east, although the land was occupied by white colonists long before the opening of Oklahoma, the original party alignments still hold true to no less degree than in the newer state. Where the Southerners went, almost without exception, lasting promontories and islands of Democracy were formed.

The plantation system developed in those districts of the South where topography, fertile soil, and good drainage favored the cultivation of staple crops by slave labor. The Civil War and Reconstruction Period confirmed the Democratic loyalty of the old South and of the large landholders of Southern origin who had moved into the border states. The Democratic areas in Missouri, Tennessee, and Kentucky that appear so prominently on the map (Fig. 2) are for the most part areas of superior agricultural opportunity into which Southern planters had taken their slaves before the Civil War and where they had established a social and economic system like that left behind.

Professor Carl Sauer has discussed the party geography o Missouri, Tennessee, and Kansas.[4] His maps showing political areas are based on the vote for governors in 1915 and 1916 and correspond in all essentials with the facts brought out on Figure 2. Sauer shows that the Blue Grass Basin of Kentucky, its counterpart in Tennessee— the Nashville Basin—, and the alluvial lowlands along the Mississippi have long been areas of firm Democratic faith. These are also areas of relatively dense negro population. In Missouri the principal centers of the Democratic strength are the counties of the northeastern plain and of the Missouri Valley where it crosses the center of the state. This region was the first part of Missouri opened to farming on a large scale, and "the Missouri River counties, because of their settlement by slaveholders, still contain the highest percentages of negro population." Western and southwestern Missouri are also Democratic. They, too, were settled "at an early date via the Missouri Valley," although "a return movement of Southerners from Abolitionist Kansas" intensified their Southern character. Another Democratic nucleus lies in the rough country of the eastern Ozarks. "The amount of land that can be farmed here is small but the land is in general of good quality, consisting of limestone basins and alluvial bottoms. These limited tracts, near the Mississippi, were taken up . . . by settlers of Southern stock. The extreme roughness of the hills restricted the development of typical hill settlements, and the control rests therefore still with the old valley settlements."

---

[4] C. O. Sauer: Geography and the Gerrymander, *Amer. Polit. Sci. Rev.*, Vol. 12, 1918, pp. 403–426. This article illustrates by examples from the three border states the practice of gerrymandering— i.e. the arrangement of voting districts "so as to develop to maximum effectiveness the strength of the party in power and to render impotent the opposition groups." Professor Sauer shows that the gerrymander is "a violation of the geographic unity of regions" and indicates "the possibilities of equable representation by reorganizing electoral districts on a geographic basis." Gerrymandering of course does not affect the returns of the vote in Presidential elections as tabulated by counties.

99

Republicanism in the border states tends to be associated with the areas of less productive soils—the highlands or barrens cultivated by small farmers with little or no colored help. The mountains of western North Carolina and northern Georgia and the Cumberland Plateau of Kentucky and Tennessee have been almost undivided in their Republican sympathies. "The Republican character of the major part of the Ozarks [of southern Missouri] is analogous to the Republican nature of the hill districts of Kentucky and Tennessee, and the settlement was effected in large part by the same stock, reinforced later by small farmers from northern states." In the Republican area of west-central Tennessee "the land is generally poor in humus, and in places has been sadly damaged by soil erosion. . . . The scant agricultural attractions of the area have not resulted in the introduction of negro labor to any extent." On the other hand, Republicanism is not confined to the poorer lands. One of the best agricultural tracts in Tennessee, the Appalachian Valley, is staunchly Republican. This region was "occupied originally by small farmers, not slaveholders, who passed southward through this great structural valley, largely from the Scotch-Irish and German settlements of Pennsylvania and Virginia. Small grains, hay, and corn remained the principal crops, and the institution of slavery never became profitable or popular with these people. Thus does the story of political faith in the border states go back even today to the causes of an institution that has disappeared two generations since."

PARTY AREAS IN ILLINOIS

Illinois furnishes a particularly striking example of the adjustment of politics to natural features. "In Illinois a map of party grouping looks like a map of the original forest and prairie areas, with the glacial lobe extending from Lake Michigan clearly visible. In eastern Wisconsin and in the Illinois [and Missouri] counties adjacent to St. Louis, the German area emerges, in the former as a group of Democratic counties in a Republican region . . . and in the latter regularly as a group of . . . Republican counties in a Democratic area."[5]

These words of the late Professor Turner show clearly that party politics are often deeply rooted in the facts of geography. It is largely to Turner's inspiration that studies of this sort owe their origin.

---

[5] Turner, *op. cit.*, p. 593.

100

GARDENS OF THE MACKENZIE

W. D. Albright

THE two longest river systems of North America are counter-
parts. The Mississippi runs southward to a tropic sea; the
Mackenzie northward to arctic brine. From the source of
the Missouri to the Gulf of Mexico the former is 4220 miles long.
From the source of the Finlay down the Peace, Slave, and Mackenzie
rivers to Mackenzie Bay, on Beaufort Sea, the mileage is 2525. In
each case the trunk stream flows through a sedimentary lowland.
The drainage basin of the Mississippi comprises 1,244,000 square
miles; that of the Mackenzie about 682,000. The former has a latitu-
dinal range of 21 degrees, from near the 50th to the 29th parallel;
the latter crosses 16 degrees between the 53rd and 69th parallels.

It would surprise no one to find gardens throughout the length
of the more southerly system, but how far down the northern river
can fruits and flowers and vegetables be grown? Surely not to its
delta, where on July 12, 1789, the explorer of the Mackenzie found
frost at a depth of six to eight inches! And yet—but we must not
anticipate.

In 1930 the author was commissioned by Dr. E. S. Archibald,
Director of Experimental Farms, Dominion Department of Agriculture, to proceed down the Mackenzie River to its mouth, to visit
the several experimental substations conducted by the Roman Catholic Missions there, to report upon the advisability of extending experimental work in that field with a view to national stock-taking, as it
were, to inquire into the possibilities of interesting the natives in fur
farming, and to make a general agricultural reconnaissance of the
Mackenzie Basin.

From Beaverlodge in the Upper Peace country transport was by
rail 435 miles east-by-southeast to Edmonton; thence 305 miles north-

FIG. 1

FIG. 2

FIG. 1—Fitzgerald, within a few miles of the sixtieth parallel. View looking north. (Photograph by Royal Canadian Air Force.)
FIG. 2—Simpson, on an island below the confluence of the Liard and Mackenzie. View looking east. (Photograph by Royal Canadian Air

FIG. 3

FIG. 4

—Good Hope, on the Mackenzie, within twelve miles of the Arctic Circle.   (Photograph by Royal Canadian Air Force.)
—Aklavik, in the Mackenzie delta, over a thousand miles north of Edmonton. View looking east. (Photograph by Royal Canadian Air Force.

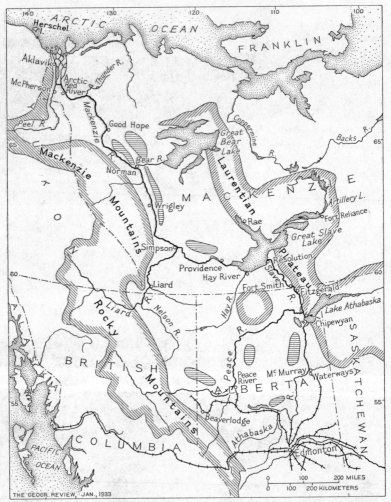

FIG. 5—The Mackenzie Basin showing main physiographical provinces after Charles Camsell and Wyatt Malcolm: The Mackenzie River Basin, *Canadian Geological Survey, Memoir 108*, 1919. On the west is the Cordilleran province; on the east, the Laurentian Plateau; between, the Great Central Plain with surface broken both in the south (Alberta Plateau) and the north (Mackenzie Lowlands) by uplands. Scale of map approximately 1 : 15,000,000.

by-northeast to Waterways, the depot of Fort McMurray, Alberta, on the Athabaska River; thence by seaplane of the Royal Canadian Air Force to Herschel Island, Yukon Territory, in Beaufort Sea. The return trip included a circuit of Great Slave Lake. The total rail mileage was 1480, the air mileage 4015, and the automobile mileage (in vicinity of the Slave River) 100.

Edmonton, capital of Alberta, is 314 miles north of the inter-

104

national boundary. A few decades ago only a depot of the fur trade, Edmonton today is a city of over seventy thousand and the center of one of the most flourishing agricultural regions of America. From points in Alberta and the "Peace River Block" of British Columbia lying wholly north of Edmonton, 21,545,836 bushels of wheat and 8,746,814 bush-

Fig. 6—The author's home at Beaverlodge in the Peace River district of Alberta, September 17, 1932.

els of coarse grains were loaded during the 1931 crop year, while 75,032 head of livestock were shipped during the calendar year.

The present agricultural settlement of the Peace, centered some 300 miles northwest of Edmonton, has already won four international championships in wheat, two in oats, and three in peas, besides four reserve championships and many first prizes. A volume might be written about the gardens of the Peace, but space is reserved for the valleys beyond.

AT THE GATEWAY TO THE NORTH

On a bend of the Athabaska River where it turns sharply northward on its last leg to the lake of the same name is the old trading post of Fort McMurray, 220 miles north of Edmonton. Two or three tributaries enter here, and the place seems to receive some extra precipitation. The river-flat site is backed by high wooded hills.

Here the Gordons, William and his sister Christina, have been established more or less permanently since the days of the Klondike rush. On July 2, 1930, their staked marrowfat peas averaged 36 inches in height; three weeks later the same peas averaged 5 feet. Potatoes stood thigh-high in dozens of luxuriant gardens. Cabbages, turnips, and all the usual range of hardy vegetables were incredibly rank. Strawberries were clustered on the vines in Hugh Macdonald's back yard.

Fig. 7—Peas in the garden of Angus Sutherland, McMurray, Alberta, July 23, 1930.

105

But the show place of McMurray is the flower garden of Cecil Potts. A spruce tree planted twelve years before, when it was 8 or 10 inches high, had attained a height of 21 feet. Birch grows well and is represented by fine specimens. A good lawn had been made from the native turf. The sweet peas were a sensation, while the range of other flowers ran from portulaca to a choice assortment of gladioli (see Fig. 8).

Fig. 8—Flower garden of Cecil Potts, McMurray, July 23, 1930

And yet they were complaining of a dry season at McMurray! All places appear to have their off seasons when visitors happen along. The weather improved after the author's departure. August brought copious rains, and Miss Gordon wrote that when frost caught her scarlet runner beans at the end of August they were 18 feet tall. According to reports the seasons of 1931 and 1932 proved equally favorable.

Prize-Winning Wheat from Athabaska

In 1778 Peter Pond is said to have arrived on the Lower Athabaska, presumably towards its delta, and there he planted the first garden in what is now the Province of Alberta. Alexander Mackenzie, finding it a few years later, pronounced it as fine a kitchen garden as he had ever seen in Canada. Nearly a hundred years later the Roman Catholic Mission at Fort Chipewyan was awarded a bronze medal for wheat at the Philadelphia Centennial. Chipewyan is on the north shore of Lake Athabaska, 357 miles north of Edmonton.

Itself established in 1847, the Mission still carries on. In a drained slough between polished rolls of glaciated rock a fine flower and vegetable garden flourished. The vegetables included celery, beans, and

106

tomatoes. At the end of September 700 sacks of potatoes were harvested from 70 planted. The vines were unhurt by frost and were cut to facilitate the removal of the tubers. As a rule there is some frost in the fore part of September.

The most beautiful garden in Chipewyan was that of Mr. and Mrs. Thomas Woodman. Vines, flowers, lawns, shrubbery, and birch trees embellished a fine home flanked by valley walls of granite. Wild

FIG. 9—One of William Gordon's potato fields, McMurray, July 24, 1930.

cucumber vines shaded the veranda, some on the east wing attaining a height of 24 feet. Intermingled were Japanese hops and tall nasturtiums. Among the flowers unfailing success is met with calendula, lavatera, sweet alyssum, zinnia, kochia, eschscholtzia, mignonette, cornflower, cosmos, petunia, clarkia, godetia, balsam, nasturtium, sweet pea, schizanthus, snapdragon, portulaca, stocks, verbena, African daisy, linum, everlasting, etc. The aster bed was a wonderful sight and was not spoiled with frost until October 16. Even such tender things as nasturtiums and cucumbers were unscathed until October 10. Vegetable successes in 1930 included cucumbers, tomatoes, marrows, and mushrooms.

Radiation of heat from the surrounding rock masses, plus lake influence, probably accounts for the warding off of autumn frost in a latitude 671 miles north of the United States.

On the east side of the Slave River, opposite the Wood Buffalo Park, Charles Hilker grows not only good vegetables, including celery and tomatoes, but in 1931 produced a plot of No. 1 hard wheat. In that year there had been but slight frosts to September 12. Sunflowers were then ripening, the largest being 10 inches across. He had red tomatoes, roses in bloom, and was still eating strawberries.

FIG. 10—Fort Smith, North West Territories.   (Photograph by Royal Canadian Air Force.)

At the end of July, 1932, despite a frost on June 21, he had corn in tassel. His flower garden of thirty varieties was a mass of color. Sunflowers volunteering from 1931 were in full bloom. His vegetables were good, and he had tomatoes the size of hens' eggs.

Later he reported that wheat (the early varieties Reward and Garnet) sown May 5 grew 3¼ to 3½ feet tall and, because of blackbirds, was cut August 8 on the green side, yielding at the rate of 31½ bushels an acre (1890 pounds) and showing no sign of frost injury. On August 14 Pickaninny sweet corn had perfect cobs 5½ inches long. Tomatoes and cucumbers ripened. The season had been characterized by light showers of insufficient volume.

THE FARTHEST-NORTH TOWN IN ALBERTA

At the head of the rapids on the Slave River is Fort Fitzgerald, within a few miles of the sixtieth parallel. As we circled over the town a strange sight met our eyes. A mile north, carved out of the poplar bush, was a well-appointed homestead resembling an experimental station. Here were neat plots of wheat and oats from seed supplied from Beaverlodge. On July 3 Steve Yanik's wheat was 23

FIG. 11—Hay River post at the entry of Hay River into Great Slave Lake. View looking northeast by east. (Photograph by Royal Canadian Air Force.)

to 28½ inches tall, oats 23 to 25½ inches. On July 19 the grain was headed, both wheat and oats standing 3 feet, 8 inches. The grain was cut on the green side on August 16 after wind and rain had lodged it badly. The oat straw then averaged 5 feet, 3 inches, the wheat, 5 feet. The wheat graded mostly No. 1 and No. 2 Northern at Edmonton; the oats, 1 C. W. and 2 C. W. (see Figs. 12 and 13).

The garden was equally remarkable. Roses bloomed the year of planting, wintered successfully with protection and bloomed again in 1931. Lilacs, Zumbra cherries, and pin cherries blossomed. Raspberries, gooseberries, strawberries, blackberries, black and red currants all ripened in 1931. Potatoes have been grown at Fitzgerald for forty years, and all the patches observed appeared promising. In 1931 Mr. Yanik reported 920 bushels from 3 acres. In 1932 he produced fine samples of grain.

BEYOND THE SIXTIETH PARALLEL

On a 120-foot bank along the majestic Slave, just below the rapids, is Fort Smith, N. W. T., 446 miles north of Edmonton. A generation

ago Warburton Pike pronounced it the most disreputable establishment he had seen in all the north. Today with its orderly, red-roofed,
white-walled buildings it is one of the prettiest towns one would wish
to view from the air. Once the southern beach of a much larger Great
Slave Lake than now exists, the site of Smith is a sandy soil supporting
a native forest growth almost exclusively of jack pine.

The long summer days give an amazing fillip to growth. In July,
1930, corn at Smith was far ranker than on the same date in the Peace.
New potatoes were being used on July 21. Two-inch tomatoes were
produced from seed sown in the open ground without protection.
Seed onions attained a diameter of nearly two inches. Verbena and
phlox filled the flower beds until covered with snow about October 9.

The most famous garden of Fort Smith is that of Mrs. L. Conibear,
who regularly succeeds with sweet-william, scarlet lychnis, Iceland
and California poppy, caragana, bush honeysuckle, Japanese sunflower, Siberian perennial lavatera, larkspur, ribbon grass, gypsophila,
pyrethrum, achillea, and columbine. She does not deny that gardening north of sixty has its disappointments. Spring is late, the summer
is usually short, and rainfall often scant. In 1930, however, there
was still blossom on potato vines until at least September 17, and
cellars were stocked with first-quality vegetables. The summer of
1931 proved droughty, but gardens were again fairly good, and a
letter dated September 11 reported no hard frost to that date. The
season of 1932 was droughty too, and growth was small, except where
watering was practiced.

Apple Culture on Great Slave Lake

At McMurray one feels he is getting north, but that is not the
north at all—only the gateway. At Fitzgerald and Smith he regards
each horticultural success as an amazing triumph over latitude, but
he is told that he should see Resolution; they have apple trees there.

Fort Resolution is on the south shore of Great Slave Lake 526 miles
almost due north of Edmonton. In front of the Roman Catholic
Mission are two seedling apple trees which have been bearing for
years. The fruit is small but is used for pickles and jam. Each tree
when seen was several inches in trunk diameter, was ten or twelve
feet tall, and had hundreds of apples. In 1930 the larger specimens
selected made 20 pounds of good jam, and in 1931 a wireless crop
report concluded "apples plentiful."

Field and garden crops were good. In 1930 the Mission harvested
775 sacks of potatoes from 70 planted. Cabbage attained an average
weight of 15 pounds a head. The early summer of 1931 was less
favorable, but from the end of June conditions were excellent except
for a hot, dry period in July.

110

An Old Garden at Hay River

At the entry of Hay River into Great Slave Lake is the old post of Hay River, where the Anglican Church Mission has long had a successful garden. The soil is eighteen inches of black-silt loam overlying sand. Four hundred bushels of potatoes were gathered in 1930 along with a considerable assortment of other vegetables. Tomatoes and celery were notable achievements. Three weeks' time produced fine radishes from a sowing made in hot July weather after a rain.

Half or three-quarters of a mile upstream is the police post, where gardening is ordinarily less successful than near the lake though never without some reward. In 1930 the first killing frost there was September 7, but the flowers planted close to the house were untouched until October 5. Celery has not succeeded; but tomatoes do well, though they have to be ripened indoors.

Hay River is 506 miles north of Edmonton. Spring growth is retarded by latitude and lake influence, though the latter compensates in the autumn. In 1930 ice had not cleared from the shore until June 9, when it was driven back by a south wind. In 1931 the season appears to have been less favorable owing to dry weather in June and July, with cloudy weather in half of August and in September.

Up to about the second week of July conditions were promising in 1932, but from then until about the end of August no rain fell at Hay River. The six weeks of drought coupled with intense heat were hard on vegetables. Cabbage at the Anglican Mission refused to develop during this period but did better subsequently. Cauliflower, strangely enough, produced large, firm heads, which were in constant use after the middle of August. Flowers did well with watering. Fodder corn planted May 26 was 3½ feet high by September 7. The cobs were small with partly developed kernels. Alfalfa, sweet clover, and grasses sown in the spring became from 20 inches to 2 feet in height. Early varieties of wheat (Garnet and Reward) grew about 3½ to 4 feet tall, maturing patchily. Some of the better-matured heads submitted were reasonably well filled. Banner oats were good, and barley was excellent. Sunflowers were not killed until near the end of September. In October Corporal Cook of the Mounted Police submitted excellent samples of grain and told of hyacinths, gladioli, and asters having done well.

Potatoes Double Their Height in a Week

Beyond the embouchure of Hay River the western arm of Slave Lake tapers down into the beginning of the Mackenzie. On its north bank a little below where it assumes river proportions is Providence. A Roman Catholic Mission was founded there in 1862. In 1867, when confederation was being accomplished, Sisters of Charity came

///

FIG. 13

FIG. 14

FIGS. 12 and 13—Wheat and oats on Steve Yanik's place at Fitzgerald. Figure 12 was taken July 3, 1930: the wheat was 23 to 28½ inches tall, oats 23 to 25½ inches. Figure 13 shows the same rows 16 days later: some of the wheat was 4 feet, 4 inches tall, the oats about 3 feet, 8 inches.

FIG. 14—John Goodall's potato field at Simpson, July 8.

from Montreal, and gardening has been conducted from about that date. Celery has done well at times and occasionally tomatoes. Corn was in silk on July 17. The Hudson's Bay Company manager had a good potato patch.

On an alluvial island below the confluence of the Liard with the Mackenzie is Simpson, 578 miles north of Edmonton. Cropping has been conducted there for many years. After leaving steelhead one heard reiterated "You should see Simpson." We saw it twice. The growth that occurred in ten days is contrasted pictorially (Figs. 15 and 16).

Domestic livestock was kept as far north as Simpson, and at the Oblate Mission the visitor dined on home-produced eggs, butter, milk, onions, and other local produce. More than 50 acres of land was under crop, and its yield is supplemented by wild hay. Father Robin explained that some gardening and farming efforts have been carried on since 1858 or 1859.

A typical potato plant selected for measurement doubled in height in a week. Potato tubers, carrots, and rutabagas grew very large. The Mission was threshing grain in August. In this and other gardens on the island more than a thousand sacks of potatoes were produced in 1930.

Rev. C. F. Clarke, the Anglican missionary, testified that in ten years he had never seen a failure of the potato crop. His own vines made practically the same growth as those at the Roman Catholic Mission, being 18 to 22 inches on July 17. The writer really could not see that one religion was better for potatoes than the other. One of Mr. Clarke's delphiniums stood 7 feet, 5 inches by July 17. White clover had wintered successfully. The caragana shrub was flourishing. For the second season in ten he ripened tomatoes in the open air. He had also achieved a success in producing winter eggs, using artificial light, heat, and cod-liver oil.

FIG. 16

FIG. 17

FIGS. 15 and 16—Potato field of the Oblate Mission, Simpson. Potatoes were planted May 20. One staked plant measured 10¾ inches on July 7 (Fig. 15); on July 14, 21½ inches; on July 17 (Fig. 16), about 24 inches.

FIG. 17—Potato garden of the Oblate Mission at Aklavik, July 11, 1930. Potatoes planted June 14 measured 3 to 6 inches. The ground was broken only four years ago.

. The best husbandman at Simpson is John W. Goodall, who had farmed for fourteen years at Athabaska Landing, going to Simpson in 1927 with the idea of catering to the local demand for truck. In 1930 his Netted Gem potatoes showed an increase ratio of 25 to 1. Squaw corn produced a mess of roasting ears. Tomatoes ripened in the house all fall. Marrows were raised from seed sown in the open. The first killing frost in 1930 fell on September 24–25.

In 1931 the season was dry, and grasshoppers, a hot-climate pest, multiplied. Yet, with the help of a little irrigation good gardens were again grown. Goodall's experience convinces him that anyone with a small plot of ground can produce more than his household can use of the choicest summer and winter vegetables.

Another garden seen in 1930 had onions growing from seed sown in 1929 and wintering outdoors; sunflower stalks, which afterwards became ten feet tall; and corn, which afforded several feeds of sweet corn on the cob.

Hoppers threatened gravely in 1932; wet weather, however, checked the pest in time, and a bountiful harvest was gathered. Mr. Clarke was using new potatoes eight weeks after the planting of cellar-sprouted sets. In the autumn eight thirty-foot rows yielded eight sacks. By actual weight two rows averaged over 700 bushels an acre. Goodall had 450 bushels an acre from unmanured land given no special cultivation. Despite a frost on September 3 he had garden corn and 40 varieties of flowers. Canary creeper was still blooming on the north side of his house on October 5, while pansy, antirrhinum, phlox, and stocks were still surviving the autumn winds. The settlement produced about 1200 sacks of potatoes in 1932 and is looking to supply the Great Bear Lake mining trade.

Washtubfuls of Tomatoes on the Liard

Unfavorable flying conditions precluded a coveted side trip up the Liard, but several upriver residents were met at Simpson, and astonishing were the experiences related. Their statements were afterwards checked as might be in official quarters.

Martin Gardner is a Norwegian who in 1923 went from a homestead in the Peace to trade on the Nelson, where he remained until 1932, when he headed for Great Bear Lake. In seven years he had never had potatoes frozen until September and sometimes not until October. In the summer of 1925 he stuck tomato seeds in the ground here and there and in the fall had two washtubfuls of ripe tomatoes. He extolled the climate of the Liard as superior to that of the Peace.

Rev. Father J. C. Lefebvre, who is in intimate touch with the Northern Oblate Missions, tells of very successful farming and gardening efforts upriver at Fort Liard and expresses the opinion that the whole region of the Liard is as favorable for cultivation as the Peace. John A. McDougal, until recently the chief government official resident in the Mackenzie District, was quite as complimentary in his opinion.

Almost certain it is that, unless checked by legislative control, settlement will soon be crossing from the Upper Peace to the head-waters of the Liard, pressing down that river, and probably meeting another vanguard working up from Simpson.

PETROLEUM AND POTATOES

We return to the Mackenzie. Wrigley is situated on the west bank of the river where it speeds through a trough hemmed by low mountain ranges. It is a ramshackle place with a magnificent situation. A fair garden was found at the Hudson's Bay Company post, and wild fruits were laden on July 9.

Where the Bear River pours its cold, clear current into the muddy Mackenzie, Fort Norman, the oil-well town, stands on two benches, one thirty or forty feet above the other. On both levels natural vegetation was rank. On July 15 a stem of grass measured 5 feet tall. Most of this growth had been made since the middle of June.

The Catholic Mission on the upper bench had a fine garden. One patch of potatoes had vines averaging 5½ to 6 inches, and during the next five days they grew an inch a day. At the end of September Father Houssais reported that the summer had been warm and dry. The first frost of two degrees came on August 28; another of two degrees on September 7; but the potato leaves were scarcely touched, being still green and unflattened when the crop was lifted on the twelfth. Some of the tubers were as large as a double fist. One of the turnips weighed 8½ pounds. Many of the carrots were more than a foot in length. Peas matured and began to shell towards the middle of August. The cabbages had enormous leaves but were not too well headed.

In 1931 results were again very favorable, although worms ate the cabbages. Despite a frost at the beginning of June, 1932, potatoes were better than the year before. Cabbages averaged 8 pounds. Peas and lettuce were enjoyed all summer. Norman is 787 miles farther north than Edmonton.

At Norman we met a Swede, Oscar Granath, who lived seventy miles downstream at Oscar Creek. In 1929 he was using potatoes 55 days after planting. Potato seed balls gathered from the 1929 crop produced small tubers. Subsequent reports were that Granath had a wonderful garden in 1930, much better than any at Norman. The following season, he admitted, was not so good, though his potatoes from seed continued to develop well.

115

Fig. 18—Norman at the junction of the Bear River and Mackenzie. View looking west. (Photograph by Royal Canadian Air Force.)

YIELDS AT GOOD HOPE

Just below the famous Ramparts of the Mackenzie and within twelve miles of the Arctic Circle, Fort Good Hope perches on an abrupt bench some sixty feet high, with a deep slough behind, affording air drainage in nearly all directions. For many years this point supplied the Lower Mackenzie with potatoes. The Roman Catholic Mission was established on its present site in 1862, and potatoes have been grown on the same land almost without fertilizer for about 66 years (Fig. 20).

On the evening of July 12 an impressive sight met the eye. Blossoming potato vines were 20 inches high and a picture of health.

FIG. 19—Arctic Red River, a short distance above the head of the Mackenzie delta. View looking north. (Photograph by Royal Canadian Air Force.)

It was all spade work at Good Hope, there being in 1930 no draft animals north of Simpson except dogs. A large amount of seed is required, but the acre yields are respectable. There were several patches, some not planted under the best of conditions. Also there was a killing frost on August 17, so that the Mission's average potato yield in 1930 was only 393 bushels an acre. They had not been artificially watered.

All the staple vegetables did well, while Reward and Garnet wheat plots seeded May 21 were harvested August 9, slightly on the green side for fear of rain. Two hundred and twenty-five cabbages reached a maximum weight of 12 pounds. Good Hope is 869 miles north of Edmonton.

North of the Circle

Some eighty miles north of the Arctic Circle is Thunder River, a small tributary entering the right bank of the trunk. "Clark's place" furnished on July 13 one of the horticultural surprises of an eye-opening voyage. One thousand two hundred and seventy-seven

Fig. 20—Potatoes and cabbages in the Oblate Mission garden at Good Hope, July 14, 1930. Ramparts of the Mackenzie in the distance.

miles north of the international boundary, carved out of the moss-bedded spruce forest, were two flourishing gardens. The owner had been out with his motor boat gathering blueberries with a picker. On hearing the planes he returned with two pailfuls of ripe berries, remarking that the country was covered with blueberries from end to end. There were also wild raspberries, strawberries, red and black currants, but no saskatoons. For the fourth successive season Clark was gardening successfully, raising potatoes to the size of goose or duck eggs. In 1930 his place was making a wonderful showing. The carrot tops on July 13 stood 6 to 9 inches tall; beets 7 to 9 inches; peas 12 to 24 inches and well podded; Swedes 8 to 15 inches; cabbages 6 to 8 inches; potatoes 7 to 10 inches; beans 6 to 9 inches and ready to blossom; oats and barley 30 inches tall and shooting. Lettuce was being thrown away by the armful. The beans had been covered one night for fear of frost.

In the adjacent thinly wooded muskeg a stick touched frost at 6 to 12 inches. In the garden cultivated for a few years the soil was thawed to a depth of 34 inches. Thunder River is 963 miles north of Edmonton.

The season finished strong. Frost on August 16 damaged only beans and potatoes, which latter nevertheless yielded 370 bushels an acre although grown from non-sprouted sets. The cabbages all headed well, and fifty weighed more than 8 pounds apiece. The little patch of grain ripened. Clark declared that a garden in that country was worth $500.00 a year to a man with a family.

The next summer was not so favorable. Frost got the beans and potatoes on July 26, but the other vegetables were again productive.

Fig. 21—Vegetable garden of William Clark at Thunder (Travier) River, 80 miles north of the Arctic Circle, July 13, 1930.

Barley from the previous season's crop was seeded May 22, headed July 19, and ripened August 14, growing 34 inches tall. Oats seeded May 22, headed July 23, and ripened August 18 when 46 inches high.

Mr. Clark was afraid to tell about the crop he raised in 1932! Everything except parsnip was immense. From 42 pounds of potatoes cut to one-eye sets he dug 985 pounds, a ratio of 1:23.5. Three sacks averaged half a pound to the tuber. Cabbage from seed sown in the open on May 16 ran from 6 to 14 pounds. Poppy, pansy, dianthus, and sunflower did well. Sweet clover grew 4 feet tall; oats and barley ripened. Splendid samples were forwarded by plane. One of two pumpkins ripened. No frost came till September 5 and then only a light one.

ICE-JAM IRRIGATION AT ARCTIC RED RIVER

With the sun still swinging an hour or so high the planes landed at the mouth of the Arctic Red River twenty-five minutes before midnight on July 10.

"Any gardens here?" was the unexpectant inquiry.

"Sure," answered D. McLeod, "come up and see mine." The garden sloped sharply down from his residence, which stood perhaps

40 feet above the water's edge. True enough, there was the universal patch of potatoes, clean and neat. They had been planted June 4 and were promising a yield. In a little corner at the foot stood a patch of grain planted May 17 and inundated directly afterwards by an ice-jam flood. The irrigation appeared to have done it no harm, for the wheat was 2 feet tall and in the shot blade. The barley measured 2 feet, 9 inches and was heading. Blue joint (*Calamagrostis*) and other grasses stood breast high. Fireweed was rank in full bloom. Wild currants, gooseberries, and raspberries grew luxuriantly. The currants were especially heavily laden. Yet on untilled land the frost had withdrawn but a foot or so, and water trickled in the midnight sun from the northward face of a cellar excavation being made in the frost-bound, peaty soil.

Arctic Red River is an important tributary of the lower Mackenzie. The confluence is 962 miles north of Edmonton.

RHUBARB PIE IN THE DELTA

At 1.30 a. m. of July 11 we landed at Aklavik, flying by mid-evening because it was cooler for the engines—there is really no midnight in early July. Mid-day heat was oppressive.

Aklavik is in the delta. It is about 60 miles from Mackenzie Bay and 1015 miles north of Edmonton. We pictured it as in the bleak tundra country. There, surely, would be no gardens, for was not one assured that the frost never drew out all summer to a greater depth than 6 or 8 inches?

The first surprise was the heat. At 1.30 a. m. we rode 2000 feet in the air with perfect comfort, bareheaded, and lightly clad. The next surprise was the forest, occupying the islands and bordering the river though not reaching far back from it in that latitude. Spruce trees 8 to 10 inches thick were plentiful, with odd specimens 70 or 80 feet tall and up to 18 inches in diameter, it was said.

And behold the ubiquitous potato! Planted June 14 the crop then stood 3 to 6 inches tall, later producing some tubers the size of hens' eggs. In a corner of the garden were rhubarb plants that had overwintered and made stalks big enough to use for pies.

In 1925 Father Trocellier had founded the Mission. The next year ground was broken for a garden. At first it was only 6 or 8 inches through moss to the frost. Radish, lettuce, and potatoes had been planted. The radish did well, but the lettuce was small. The potatoes grew only 6 or 8 inches tall the first year, but tubers the size of walnuts were produced and planted the next season. After that they yielded each year a little more than the seed. Double and single daisies came through one winter without care.

Rose haws, dewberries, and fruiting currants were observed.

120

Mooseberry and blueberry were said to occur, and gooseberries grew farther east. In autumn the author received seed of crowberries and moss cranberries.

In the unbroken forest frost had drawn to a depth of only 6 or 8 inches, as the explorer of the river had observed 141 years before. On land burned over on the first of June it had drawn 12 inches. In the garden the measuring stick pushed down 24 inches. It had been thus in the Yukon.

J. Parsons, the Hudson's Bay Company manager, said conditions at McPherson, over on the Peel River, were more favorable for gardening than at Aklavik. He had grown lettuce, spinach, radish, and turnip and could produce "tons of them." In 1914 he had seen it 90° F. in the shade at McPherson, at which point wild raspberries, blueberries, and yellowberries were found.

The summer of 1931 was a cold one with bad ice conditions in the sea. Potatoes had been killed August 11 by a frost following a snow storm. The rhubarb, however, grew well. October airmail messages from Aklavik reported success in 1932 with lettuce, carrots, and potatoes, and the author received plump, well ripened samples of barley and oats. Even wheat produced fair-sized kernels although not of milling grade.

No gardens were observed on Herschel Island, but the wild flowers on the hillside were abundant and in mass effects of the richest hues— red, purple, blue, white, and gold. Legumes were considerably in evidence. Grass grows, although not very tall.

Seeking Gardens on Great Bear and Slave Lakes

Inquiry in 1930 failed to reveal any gardening efforts around Great Bear Lake, but in 1931 Hugh S. Spence, of the Department of Mines, Ottawa, found vegetables growing on some raw sand and clay laid bare at Labine Point in the mineralized area east of the lake. Lettuce, radish, carrot, and beet had been planted June 14. The carrots and beets did nothing, but the radish grew and the lettuce cut two or three crops. Unverified newspaper allusions suggest that more ambitious attempts were made in 1932.

At the upper end of the north arm of Great Slave Lake is Fort Rae, 642 miles north of Edmonton, built on bare glacier-polished Laurentian rock. No gardens here surely! Yet as the plane circled over the settlement three very thrifty ones were espied. In depressions near the water the Oblate Mission had literally "made" gardens by carrying in rich soil found in crevices farther back. Representative potato plants found on July 17 measured 13, 14, and 21 inches in height, nearly covering the ground and coming into bloom. Here Father La Perriere has annually raised potatoes, cabbage, lettuce,

beets, carrots, turnips, and peas. After a very light frost the potatoes were lifted September 20, some of them averaging 14 ounces.

Domestic strawberries were one of the surprises. Some plants
were flourishing in cannisters on the balcony of a Ukrainian trader's
home. Others were growing in the Mission garden.

Unlike most of the river points, Fort Rae was blessed with a still
more favorable season in 1931. By the end of September Father La
Perriere wrote that only potato leaves had a touch of frost and the
crop was better than in 1930. There was "enough lettuce and spinach
to feed an army." Mice, however, had eaten the strawberries, root,
stem, and leaf, during the preceding winter, leaving wild ones untouched.

Lettuce and Radish for Musk-ox Rangers

No cultivated crops were growing at Reliance at the extreme
eastern end of Great Slave Lake, presumably because none had been
planted; but 40 miles east, at Artillery Lake out near the edge of
the musk-ox preserve (Thelon Game Sanctuary), a Swede had grown
lettuce, also radishes an inch in diameter. Oats and wheat headed
but failed to ripen.

The author did not visit the east end of Lake Athabaska, but his
traveling companions who did so in the companion plane reported
potato patches there too. He who would outrun the potato in the
North has a long chase.

In relating this tale of horticulture in the Mackenzie Basin one
realizes he is countering an instinctive discount of high latitude.
Truth is that the ecological influence of latitude is largely offset by
declining altitude, by long summer days, by the lowering frost plane
as the result of gardening itself, and, shall we add, by montane or
oceanic influence?

Three seasons have been reviewed in some detail, the first exceptionally favorable, the second one inclement at the more northerly
points. At the worst something is produced. At the best production
must be seen to be believed. Factors accounting for the phenomena
will be discussed in a future article.

GREAT CITIES OF 1930 IN THE UNITED STATES WITH A COMPARISON OF NEW YORK AND LONDON

Mark Jefferson

THE American public takes lively interest in the size of the city of New York. Is it larger than London? An odd sort of patriotic bias tinges the question. The answer is not easy to give. It is difficult to estimate the height of the atmosphere because it has no top—the air peters out. In the same way a great city thins out and comes to no definite limits.

Political New York is definite enough. It includes 299 square miles of territory within which in 1930 slept 4,736,883 inhabitants.[1] But the metropolitan district called by the census "New York-Northeastern New Jersey" covered 2514 square miles of territory and contained 10,901,424 persons. It includes nearly four times as much territory and twice as many persons as the metropolitan New York of the census of 1910. Each city is a New York, but which is New York? There are, in fact, as many New Yorks as you care to assign boundaries to. The boundary may be placed at various points with plausible reasons assigned for putting it at any of them.

It is the same with London. There is, for instance, a County of London with an area of 117 square miles and 4,396,821 persons. Then there is a Greater London, with 8,202,818 persons on 693 square miles; a municipal London, of the Lord Mayor, with one square mile of territory; and the London conurbation which "extends in several places beyond Greater London." No doubt if we pushed back the London boundaries to include 2514 square miles like "New York-Northeastern New Jersey," we should get many more than eight million inhabitants. Push it out to include the four Home Counties around the County of London, and we have over eleven millions. There are no natural limits to these great cities. But how then compare one with another in size?

DENSITY OF POPULATION IN A METROPOLIS

Before we can count the population of a great city we must define its boundaries. Political boundaries will not do if the place has active life and growth, because such boundaries have been adjusted to condi-

---

[1] On the consequences of census enumeration by residence or sleeping place see the writer's article "Distribution of the World's City Folks," *Geogr. Rev.*, Vol. 21, 1931, pp. 446–465; especially pp. 457–459.

123

tions of the past. It is a recognition of the inadequacy of legal boundaries of cities that impels censuses to lay out metropolitan districts. The United States census has been doing it since 1910. The method first used was to push back the political boundary ten miles in every direction and then readjust to the boundaries of the civil divisions that fell mostly within it, including every civil division that had more than 150 persons to the square mile. How the 1930 boundary has been made is described in the new bulletin on metropolitan districts (1932).[2] "In this census no such [ten mile] limit has been applied." All that is now insisted on is that every civil division included in the district have more than 150 persons to the square mile and that the total population of the continuous areas be more than 200,000. A density of 150 persons to the square mile means 40 families to a mile, 16 acres to a family. But that is farming density and not even intensive farming. Extensive farming is the customary occupation with densities from 125 to 250, more than 250 persons to the square mile becomes intensive farming or truck gardening. The writer's own conception of city densities begins at 10,000 to the square mile.[3] What such a density means is best seen by looking over the densities of the larger American cities (political boundaries) expressed to the nearest thousands: New York, 23; Chicago, 17; Boston, 18; St. Louis, 13; Detroit, 11; Cleveland, 13; Baltimore, 10; San Francisco, 15; Philadelphia, 15; Jersey City, 24.

The corresponding conception of the "Great City" is a closely built-up area—a continuous area of "brick-and-mortar" unity, to use Fawcett's phrase.[4] In this area there may be open parks for health and play but not open fields for agriculture. As an example of the way in which the boundaries of the metropolitan city may be worked out, the writer offers Detroit, with the local details of which he is familiar.

BOUNDARIES OF METROPOLITAN DETROIT

The upper map of figure 1 is the census interpretation, the lower is the writer's. Cross shading designates political Detroit, the single-lined parts designate the regions that should be also included. The most striking feature of this map is the way Detroit has expanded along its four great cement highways since 1910, when the whole city lay south of Highland Park and Hamtramck, which are now enclaves of two independent municipalities within the political city of Detroit. The city outlined by the dotted lines is a fairly continuous mass of

---

[2] Fifteenth Census of the United States: 1930: Metropolitan Districts, Population and Area. Prepared under the Supervision of Clarence E. Batschelet, *U. S. Dept. of Commerce, Bur. of the Census*, Washington, 1932. The bulletin contains an immense amount of valuable data and useful maps for the study of urban population.

[3] The Anthropography of Some Great Cities, *Bull. Amer. Geogr. Soc.*, Vol. 41, 1909, pp. 537–566.

[4] C. B. Fawcett: Distribution of the Urban Population in Great Britain, 1931, *Geogr. Journ.*, Vol. 79, 1932, pp. 100–116.

124

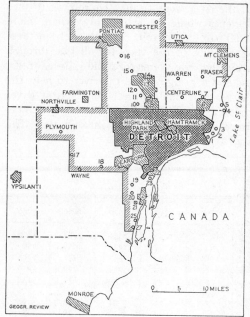

close-built houses along paved streets, policed and served by a variety of municipalities. True, country fields and farms lie in the angles between the tentacles, off the principal lines of travel; but the ground is level, and there is a close network of cement roads. Island urban communities lie out in the fields, but they are isolated and are not counted in our conurbation. All the urban outliers that touch Detroit and each other are included.

There have been included also, with less assurance, the seven Canadian settlements along the Detroit River. They amount to but

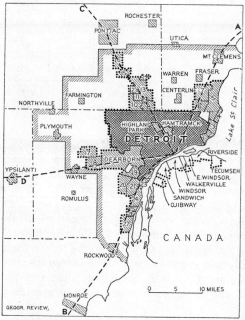

Fig. 1—The conception of Detroit as a "great city": above, according to the United States Census; below, according to the author. The cross-hatched area is the political city, extensions of this area which should also be included in the political city are shown by single ruling; the band of shading defines the metropolitan district; the heavy dotted lines of the lower figures, "anthropographic" Detroit, and the heavy broken lines, the four great motor roads out of the city.

The numbers have reference: 1, Grosse Pt. Park; 2, Grosse Pt.; 3, Grosse Pt. Farms; 4, Grosse Pt. Shores; 5, St. Clair Shores; 6, Halfway; 7, Roseville; 8, Ferndale; 9, Pleasant Ridge; 10, Oak Park; 11, Huntington Woods; 12, Berkley; 13, Royal Oak; 14, Clawson; 15, Birmingham; 16, Bloomfield Hills; 17, Garden City; 18, Inkster; 19, Melvindale; 20, Allen Park; 21, Lincoln Park; 22, River Rouge; 23, Ecorse; 24, Wyandotte; 25, Riverview; 26, Sibley; 27, Trenton.

Fig. 1

125

113,000 persons in all. If the river were vital to Detroit, as it once was, the Canadian settlements would be more truly urban, more important and more essential parts of Detroit. It is precisely in these years of diminishing long-way use of the lakes for all but through traffic in ores, coal, and grain that transverse road and railway traffic has demanded two tunnels and a bridge across the river to help the ferries handle increasing loads. For longway traffic the Detroit River is an artery of life, for crossway traffic an obstacle to be overcome. This Detroit of the writer's map has 1,989,000 inhabitants. The Detroit of the census has 2,105,000.

TABLE I—THE GROWTH OF NEW YORK

In Thousands

	1890	1900	1910	1920	1930
Manhattan	1441	1850	2332	2284	1867
Brooklyn	838	1167	1634	2018	2560
Bronx	89	201	431	732	1265
Queens	87	153	284	469	1079
Richmond	52	67	86	117	158
Yonkers	32	48	80	100	135
Mt. Vernon	11	21	31	43	61
New Rochelle	8	15	29	36	54
Jersey City, N. J.	163	214	268	298	317
Hoboken, N. J.	44	59	70	68	59
Bayonne, N. J.	19	33	56	77	89
Union City, N. J.	11	15	21	21	59
North Bergen, N. J.	....	9	16	23	41
West New York City, N. J. . .	....	5	13	30	37
Total	2795	3857	5351	6316	7781
Population New York	2207	3407	5067	6169	7781

BRICK-AND-MORTAR NEW YORK

The 1930 census gave the New York-Northeastern New Jersey metropolitan district a total of 10,901,424 persons. But from a quarter to a third of this number are rural or small-town folk. Evaluating New York as a metropolis of dwellers in a continuous region of high buildings, paved streets, police, sewers, lights, great wholesale houses, corporation headquarters, trust companies, publishing houses, hotels, museums, theaters, universities, and libraries, the writer finds 7,781,000 inhabitants really large-city dwellers. The composition of this unit is in the last column of Table I, which also illustrates the growth of the conurbation and its separate constituents in preceding decades.

The totals for the several constituents are not the same as the

126

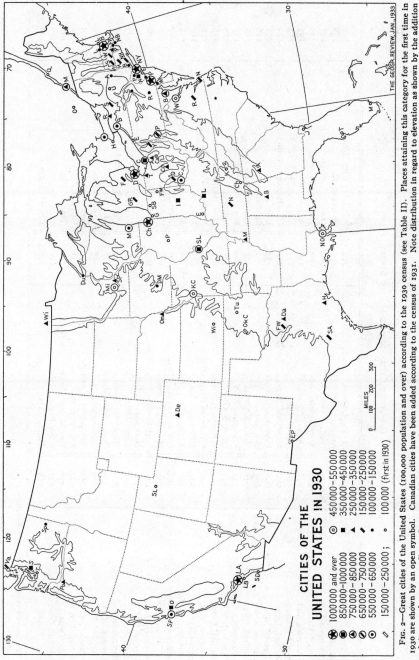

CITIES OF THE
UNITED STATES IN 1930

1000000 and over
850000-1000000
750000-850000
650000-750000
550000-650000
150000-250000 ;

450000-550000
350000-450000
250000-350000
150000-250000
100000-150000
100000 (first in 1930)

Fig. 2—Great cities of the United States (100,000 population and over) according to the 1930 census (see Table II). Places attaining this category for the first time in 1930 are shown by an open symbol. Canadian cities have been added according to the census of 1931. Note distribution in regard to elevation as shown by the addition of the 1000-foot contour line. Compare with the map of great cities in 1920 (*Geogr. Rev.*, Vol. 11, 1921, p. 439).

127

TABLE II—GREAT CITIES OF THE UNITED STATES, 1930

In Thousands

City	Pop.	City	Pop.	City	Pop.
New York,* N. Y.	7781	St. Paul, Minn.	272	Salt Lake City, Utah	140
Chicago, Ill.	3374	Atlanta, Ga.	270	Paterson, N. J.	138
Philadelphia,* Pa.	2083	Dallas, Tex.	260	Duluth,* Minn.	138
Detroit,* Mich.	1989	Birmingham, Ala.	260	Jacksonville, Fla.	130
Los Angeles, Cal.	1238	Omaha,* Neb.	256	Albany, N. Y.	127
Boston,* Mass.	1140	Akron, Ohio	255	Trenton, N. J.	123
Cleveland, Ohio	900	Memphis, Tenn.	253	Chattanooga, Tenn.	120
St. Louis,* Mo.	896	Providence, R. I.	253	Erie, Pa.	116
Baltimore, Md.	805	San Antonio, Tex.	232	Spokane, Wash.	116
Pittsburgh,* Pa.	738	Norfolk,* Va.	210	Fall River, Mass.	115
San Francisco, Cal.	634	Syracuse, N. Y.	209	Fort Wayne, Ind.	115
Buffalo,* N. Y.	597	Dayton, Ohio	201	Elizabeth, N. J.	115
Cincinnati,* Ohio	580	Worcester, Mass.	195	New Bedford, Mass.	113
Milwaukee, Wis.	578	Oklahoma City, Okla.	185	Reading, Pa.	111
Kansas City*	522	Richmond, Va.	183	Wichita, Kan.	111
Washington, D. C.	487	Youngstown, Ohio	170	Miami, Fla.	111
Minneapolis, Minn.	464	Grand Rapids, Mich.	169	Tacoma, Wash.	107
New Orleans, La.	459	Hartford, Conn.	164	Wilmington, Del.	107
Newark, N. J.	442	Fort Worth, Tex.	163	Knoxville, Tenn.	106
Oakland,* Cal.	421	New Haven, Conn.	163	Peoria, Ill.	105
Seattle, Wash.	366	Flint, Mich.	156	Canton, Ohio	105
Indianapolis, Ind.	364	Nashville, Tenn.	154	South Bend, Ind.	104
Rochester, N. Y.	328	Springfield, Mass.	150	El Paso, Tex.	102
Louisville,* Ky.	320	San Diego, Cal.	148	Lynn, Mass.	102
Portland, Ore.	302	Bridgeport, Conn.	147	Evansville, Ind.	102
Houston, Tex.	292	Scranton, Pa.	143	Utica, N. Y.	102
Toledo, Ohio	291	Des Moines, Iowa	142	Tampa, Fla.	101
Columbus, Ohio	291	Long Beach, Cal.	142	Gary, Ind.	100
Denver, Colo.	288	Tulsa, Okla.	141	Lowell, Mass.	100

*Indicates a composite city or conurbation.

population of the New York conurbation of the period because, while today the five boroughs and nine municipalities make a fairly continuous city around the harbor of New York, they did not do so forty years ago. They were then mostly discontinuous population nuclei.[5] Unlike the census bulletin the writer does not include Paterson and Newark in the New York conurbation. If at some time in the future the docks of Newark become a terminal for foreign commerce continuous and alternative with those of Manhattan and Jersey City, Newark will then have become geographically a part of the great city of New York.

New York and London

Professor Fawcett estimates that the London of brick-and-mortar unity in 1931 contained 9,150,000 inhabitants.[6] That is probably the best estimate that can be made at the present time for London. To the estimate I have made for New York, perhaps another five per cent—certainly not more—should be added for small fringing areas not taken into account and 160,000 for an additional year's growth, to bring it up to the English date 1931. That would give what is probably an outside total of 8,330,000 to be compared with the London of 9,150,000. London is still a considerably larger city than New York by night, as censuses count city population. In the daytime, with workers of many kinds added from outlying regions, New York may possibly be as large as London, but this is not known.

American Great Cities of 1930

Applying the criteria used for determining the conurbations of New York and Detroit the writer finds that there were in 1930 eighty-seven great cities—of more than 100,000 persons each—in the United States, thirteen more than in 1920.[7] The United States Census of 1930 listed ninety-six metropolitan districts. Six of the cities included should not, however, be counted as separate entities, being essentially parts of certain of the eighty-seven here listed; Jersey City and Yonkers of New York, Camden of Philadelphia, Cambridge and Somerville of Boston, and Kansas City, Kan., one with Kansas City, Mo. Several places listed in the census bulletin are not metropolitan at all. The city idea is inherent in the word metropolis itself. If places are not great cities they are not metropolitan. What could be less metropolitan than Atlantic City, Lancaster, Pa., Little Rock, Ark., Roanoke, Va., San Jose, Cal., and Wheeling, Charleston, and Huntington, W. Va.—all listed by the census?

---

[5] On the New York of 1900 see article cited in footnote 3.
[6] *Op. cit.*
[7] Mark Jefferson: Great Cities of the United States, 1920, *Geogr. Rev.*, Vol. 11, 1921, pp. 437–441.

The eighty-seven great cities are listed in Table II and are shown on the map, Figure 2, to which have been added the great cities of Canada (1931), seven in number.

For the first time in the history of the United States the decade 1920–1930 has seen great cities lose population. The four cities and

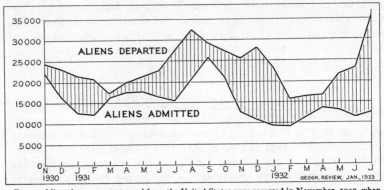

FIG. 3—Migration currents to and from the United States were reversed in November, 1930, when the number of aliens departing first exceeded the number admitted. The graph shows the population thus lost to the United States.

their losses (units) are Lowell, 12,525; New Bedford, 8620; Fall River, 5211, in Massachusetts; and Wilmington, 3571, in Delaware. That such a thing never happened before, that every city to attain hundred-thousand size in the 128 years since New York first reached it has continued increasing in size until the decade 1920–1930 is a remarkable record. Albany did fall back from 94,923 inhabitants in 1890 to 94,151 in 1900, but she had not then quite grown into a great city. Smaller places have fallen back in several cases.

In general a city attains hundred-thousand size by rendering services, and the vital momentum due to men who render those services keeps those cities growing. Natural resources may be exhausted, a temporary advantage may be lost; but the men who exploited resources and used their advantages may be counted on to look around for new tasks when old ones are worked out. The three Massachusetts cotton cities have seen some of their work shifted to the South. Manchester, N. H., shared the drop, 78,384 in 1920 and 76,834 in 1930; but other towns not especially concerned with cotton were affected in the same way.

A Turning Point in Population Growth

The fact is a turning point has been reached in growth of population in the United States. In the seventh decade of its history, 1850–1860, nearly 36 per cent was added to the population, but since that time the increment has been smaller in every decade except the last when

130

it was slightly greater. For 1910–1920 the increment was 14.9 per cent; for 1920–1930, 16.1 per cent.[8] The fifth doubling of the country's population was completed July 20, 1930, and took a little more than 41 years, almost twice as long as the first doubling, completed in 1812. The birth rate steadily falls, and immigration currents— also for the first time in our history—are reversed, as is graphically shown in Figure 3.

Our cities have received so much of our immigration of late years that they are sensitive to changes in the numbers. When unemployed men leave this country they go from cities, and news of city unemployment deters prospective immigrants who would mostly settle in cities.

TABLE III—GROWTH OF GREAT CITIES AND PROPORTION OF TOTAL POPULATION IN GREAT CITIES BY CENSUS DIVISIONS

NUMBER OF CITIES	CENSUS DIVISION	AVERAGE PERCENTAGE OF GROWTH				PERCENTAGE OF TOTAL POPULATION
		1890–1900	1900–1910	1910–1920	1920–1930	
11	New England	37	29	21	3	32.3
15	Mid-Atlantic	23	27	20	12	49.4
9	South Atlantic	50	69	91	52	15.0
6	East South-Central	32	63	37	56	13.0
8	West South-Central	51	355*	89	65	15.0
19	East North-Central	41	41	64	33	39.5
8	West North-Central	35	46	28	18	21.1
2	Mountain	22	66	24	16	11.6
9	Pacific	56	171	55	42	41.0

*But for Tulsa and Oklahoma City, boomed by oil, this figure would have been only 100.

COMPARATIVE GROWTH OF GREAT CITIES

Twenty-six cities of the Atlantic border increased only 8 per cent each in this decade, against 21 per cent in the decade before. The northeastern part of the country had the smallest city growth. In no other part of the United States did a great city fail to gain 10 per cent, with the one exception of St. Louis, which gained 7 per cent against 12 the decade before. The eastern cities that increased less than 10 per cent were Boston, Providence, Worcester, New Haven (only 118 persons more in 1930 than in 1920), Bridgeport, Lynn, Philadelphia, Scranton, Paterson, Newark, Trenton, Reading, Utica, Baltimore, Richmond, and Norfolk.

In the south and west, however, six cities more than doubled in size. Miami, Fla., 270 per cent—500 per cent the decade before—, Chattanooga, Houston, Oklahoma City, Los Angeles, and San Diego, in regions most remote from the old seat of industry in the northeast.

[8] For an exact ten-year period, however, these numbers are 15.5 and 15.7 respectively.

131

Table III sets forth the facts of growth of great cities and also in the last column presents the proportion of great-city dwellers. It will be noted that practically half the people of the Mid-Atlantic states live in great cities, more than a third in the Pacific and East North-Central divisions, nearly a third in New England, and only from a tenth to a fifth in the rest of the country.

Only the East South-Central cities increased faster than in the decade before. Percentage figures for 1910–1920 and 1920–1930 respectively are Louisville 9, 60; Birmingham 35, 45; Memphis 24, 56; Nashville 7, 30; and Chattanooga 29 and 107. Knoxville's rate, however, diminished from 119 to 36 per cent.

No city in New England grew as much in the twenties as in the teens of the century, and in the Mid-Atlantic region only New York (18, 23) and Pittsburgh (11, 13). In the South Atlantic division we have gains in Atlanta (30, 34) and Tampa (37, 94); in the West South-Central, in New Orleans (14, 19), Houston (75, 110), Oklahoma City (43, 103), and Fort Worth (45, 54). Four cities of the East

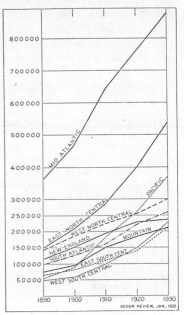

FIG. 4—Graphs of the population of the average city for each census division of the United States for 1890, 1900, 1910, 1920, and 1930.

North-Central also increased at an accelerated rate: Milwaukee (22, 26), Cincinnati (11, 13), South Bend (32, 46), and Peoria (13, 51); but Chicago could not quite keep up (28, 25). In the West North-Central region St. Paul (9, 16) and Wichita (39, 54) excelled their record, and in the Pacific states so did San Francisco (21, 25), San Diego (78, 100), and Spokane (0, 11)—in all, twenty-one of the eighty-seven cities of the country managed to better previous growth.

Such a comparison of rates of growth must not mislead us as to actual growths, which were greatest in the northeast, where the cities are so much larger. New York's 23 per cent growth consisted of 1,460,000 persons added in the decade; Oklahoma City's growth of 110 per cent only meant 154,000. The diagram of the *average city* of each region makes this clear. Thus 19 great cities of the East North-Central states in 1890 had a total of 2,771,000 inhabitants, or a mean city of 148 thousand, 210 thousand for 1900, 285 thousand for 1910, 398 thousand for 1920, and 526 thousand for 1930.

132

On these graphs actual growth is indicated by steepness of line, hesitancy of growth by convexity of the line upward. This hesitancy is most pronounced for New England. Concavity upward shows vigor of growth, best exemplified by the mean West South-Central city. The Pacific shows it strikingly except for the inflexion of 1910. New England, the Mid-Atlantic, and the Pacific districts all show a smaller proportion of great-city dwellers, which is a new condition with this decade. Ten years ago 34 per cent of the people of New England lived in their great cities, now only 32.3 per cent live in them. The percentage for the Mid-Atlantic has fallen from 50.2 to 49.9, for the Pacific from 41.4 to 41.0. In each case the number of city dwellers has increased, in the Mid-Atlantic by nearly two million, but not as fast as the population of the region grew. Actual exodus from great cities has been limited to the four cities named.

133

SNOW SURVEYING: ITS PRINCIPLES AND POSSIBILITIES*

J. E. Church
Nevada Agricultural Experiment Station

SNOW surveying is one of the newest sciences. Like most inevitable things, it has had several births though few survivals. It was born in Europe, evidently in the nineties, in the study of the density of snow. But no certain information has been gained regarding the character of the apparatus used except the facts that a portable snow-measuring instrument for use in forests was designed in Russia as early as 1901 and that Professor Angot, Director of the Bureau Central Météorologique de France, devised a cylindrical snow sampler with spring balance in 1908. It was born a second time in the eastern United States in the study of stream flow, when Mixer in 1901 began the cutting of snow cores in Vermont and Horton in 1905 invented a sampling tube with scales for the cutting and weighing of cores. From this pioneer effort were evolved the practice and instruments used later by the United States Weather Bureau. It was born a third time in 1904 on Mt. Rose in the Sierra Nevada. While the immediate origin lay in a dispute regarding the effect of forests and mountains on the conservation of snow, its applicability to problems of stream run-off was quickly recognized. Here was developed the Mt. Rose snow sampler capable of being driven by one person more than twenty feet into the normally deep snows of the Sierra Nevada.

These three origins—in Europe, in the eastern, and in the western

*This article, summing up a quarter century of studies, might be described as a biography of snow surveying. It represents an evolution in interests and viewpoint; some problems have been solved, others await solution; but the subject is here presented in its entirety for the first time. Other contributions by the writer about to be published are: Snow Surveying, Its Principles and Present Problems, *Journ. Agric. Research;* Snow Surveying in Relation to Forecasting Streamflow: Its Problems and Their Present Phases, *Nevada Agric. Exper. Sta. Monograph* (about 400 pp.).

Fig. 1—In the heart of the Central Sierra, Pyramid Peak (10,200 feet) from Lake Lucile. Panorama with view on facing page.

United States—were independent in purpose and method. The third origin was the most fortunate in its environment and continuity. Here, where high snow-covered mountains by their streams made life possible in the intervening deserts, was a human need to spur research— research that found an ideal center in the lately established Mt. Rose Weather Observatory.[1] Nature supplied the facts in variety; interest in winter mountaineering supplied observers. The Sierra became a great laboratory, and at its feet lay a testing ground of practical applications.

Some Practical Applications

In 1931 the residents of the Humboldt Basin[2] accepted with fortitude the report that there was but 51 per cent of normal snowfall at the source of their streams and that, owing to the nature of the stream bed and the lack of spring precipitation, only 10 per cent or even less of normal run-off would be available for crops. Only the earliest

[1] The Nevada Agricultural Experiment Station, under its director, Dr. Joseph Edward Stubbs, who was also president of the University of Nevada, financed the construction of the Observatory through the Adams fund for research and provided maintenance. Reference should also be made to Major Paul Norboe, chief assistant state engineer of California, whose interest stimulated application of the Nevada method.

[2] George W. Malone: Humboldt River Distribution and Different Features Affecting These Deliveries for the Years 1927 to 1931, Inclusive, Carson City, Nev., 1932.

FIG. 1 (contd.)—The scenery and sport offered by the mountains furnish an allurement to snow surveying. (Photograph by Frederick Herz.)

water rights along the thousand-mile stream could be satisfied, and many persons saw their lands dry up while water was passing their doors. This was the fourth dry season, each drier than its predecessor. In 1932 a normal quantity of water was forecast, and the residents of the basin with equal confidence set to work to buy seed and reëstablish their fields. Snow surveying saves buying seed when planting would be useless and lays the basis of confidence among the users of water. The forecaster has become the indispensable mentor of the state engineer vested with the task of acting as supreme arbiter of waters. Higher tribute to his function cannot be paid than was given to a water commissioner of Idaho after years of effort: "He brought peace to the Boise." Such peace far outweighs even the large dollar value conceded to the farming business.

In 1925 snow surveying gave the water commissioners of the Walker Basin courage to allot water not yet in the reservoirs and so saved the crops on the East Walker from ruin. For the residents of Lake Tahoe it has ended the dread of floods. It has warned power companies to lay in a supply of fuel for steam power or to make contracts with more fortunate districts far in advance of a shortage.

Snow surveying, like the air mail, has now reached maturity. It has become a division of state government in Nevada, California,

FIG. 2—Mt. Rose from the base (5535 feet). Precipitation experiment station, conducted in coöperation with the U. S. Weather Bureau, in the foreground.

Utah, and Oregon. It is practiced in Washington, Idaho, and Canada. It has become a state-wide coöperative system in New York. A Committee on the Hydrology of Snow has now been organized by the American Geophysical Union to bring all snow-surveying efforts together in common acquaintance.

Even now the field of the new science is broad and varied, comprehending, for example, snow surveying in the Alps for study of glacier growth, in Finland for mapping the depth of snow cover, in Greenland for study of the evolution of the inland ice, in southern Australia for power forecasting, in our own West for the regulation of the Boulder Dam in the Grand Canyon of the Colorado.

FIG. 3—Refuge hut and snow-survey station at Contact Pass (9000 feet). Hut of sand bags protected from erosion on windward side by wall of rocks.

FIG. 4—Mt. Rose Observatory, birthplace of Western snow surveying, at the summit (10,800 feet)

PRINCIPLES AND PHASES

In its origin snow surveying was a simple, practical thing. It was merely the attempt to determine the water content of a definite area of snow. Out of this have come its several phases.

Snow is an elusive substance when falling and is elastic and liable to erosion after it has come to rest. Only in sheltered places will the precipitation gauge give readings comparable to the water content of the actual snowfall; and even if the snow field is stable the snow stake will furnish a reliable index of the relative depth only after a sufficient interval has elapsed to permit the newly fallen snow to approach the density of that beneath. Gauge and snow stake both lack universality.

FIG. 5—Mt. Rose showing cornices forming in the lee of the crest and the checking of snow drift by the timber line.

FIG. 6   FIG. 7

FIG. 6—Mt. Rose snow sampler hanging in its balance. Compare with Figure 8.
FIG. 7—Evaporation pans. Left to right: tree pan; ice pan; snow pan. Below: core cutter for filling snow pan; false bottom to raise snow above melting water.

Neither is accurate under all conditions, nor are their standards interchangeable.

On the other hand, the snow sampler reduces the snow to the inelastic standard of water and by the simple expedient of cross sections makes possible the close determination of the water content of snow fields however irregular in depth or contour. Cold is no barrier to the work, for the colder the weather the easier and quicker is the sampling. Rising temperature creates a temporary hindrance only when discordance of temperature between snow sampler and frost-laden snow causes "stickiness." Wind, however, at least in its higher

FIG. 8—Deep driving: the snow is as deep as the sampler is tall.

FIG. 9—The value of hooded pans in preserving the continuity of measurements: on the left unprotected pan; on the right protected pan.

phases, must be avoided by seeking shelter from oscillation for sampler and scale during weighing. If to the snow sampler are added other auxiliary instruments, the complete evolution of snow in the field can be studied in its various details.

The original technique of snow surveying was worked out for the solution of local problems, and around it other problems gradually accumulated. In historical order they are: (1) the relation of mountains and forests to the conservation of snow; (2) the forecasting of run-off, including the rise of lakes, flow of streams, and occurrence of floods; (3) the evolution of the snow cover; and (4) the evolution of glaciers. The broader principles underlying the several phases of this pioneer work will be discussed in order.

The Conservation of Snow

Mountains and forests are a complex rather than separate units in the conservation of snow. By their elevation mountains create reservoirs of snow that melts slowly in response to the gradual advance of the season and descends gently to water the valleys. The mountaineer indeed cannot help meditating on the gentleness and deliberateness of this descent and its human significance.

The higher the mountains the longer the period of snow storage. The Sierra Nevada, extending from about latitude 35° to 41° N., or roughly 400 miles, rises highest in the warmer south with the result that the maximum flow of the tributary streams runs contrary to the latitude, ranging from April in the plateau region of northern California to June in the southern High Sierra. The mountain passes of the north are about 5000 feet high; those of the south 10,000 feet.

The mountain slopes themselves may aid in conserving snow. Irregularities of slope afford windbreaks to prevent drift to lower altitudes and to dome the snow into greater masses where it will be less subject to the effects of evaporation and to melting from beneath.

140

Melting from beneath, as shown by black bulb thermometer determinations, occurs when the depth of the snow is less than about 18 inches.

The extreme evaporation of snow on mountain crests is suggested

FIG. 10—The effect of a timber screen on the lip of a canyon in accumulating snow.

by measurements on the summit of Mt. Rose (10,800 feet). During a continuous period of 69 hours, April 18–20, 1911, on the exposed windward side of this peak, a total evaporation of 2.32 inches was recorded, or 24.21 inches monthly (water content). The average velocity of the wind was 30.6 miles an hour. However, during the latter part of the period, as the wind increased in intensity, erosion was observed. During the same period, on the semi-protected lee side of the crest where the average wind movement was 10.8 miles an hour, a total evaporation of only 0.687 inches was observed, 7.17 inches monthly, or less than one-third of that on the exposed windward side.[3]

Similar measurements were made on a snow dome behind a small timber screen at the base of the summit of Mt. Rose, at an elevation of 9000 feet. The experiment was made at night, on April 30, 1911. The temperature was below freezing, and the snow itself was frozen hard when placed in the pans. Yet under the wind movement that averaged slightly more than 31 miles an hour a loss of about .08 to .10 inches of water content occurred, or 1/120 of the snow on the ground. This extraordinary evaporation of 5.52 inches monthly demonstrates the need of dense timber screens on exposed slopes. In contrast is the relatively small evaporation in the forested areas of the Tahoe Basin.

[3] This disparity in rate of evaporation accords broadly with the results obtained by Burton E. Livingston: The Relation of Desert Plants to Soil Moisture and to Evaporation, *Carnegie Instn. Publ. No. 50*, Washington, 1906.

141

The efficiency of mountain forests as gatherers and retainers of snow is plainly evident from a comparison of measurements made on the rocky summit of Mt. Rose and in the timber-line forests at 47 stations in April, 1910. Depth of snow is given in inches, water

Fig. 11—The resistance to early melting offered by a snow dome.

content in parenthesis:

Unforested talus slope, 40.8 (18.4); distributed thus: cornice below observatory, 52.5 (25.1); wind-swept slope, 8.1 (2.6); protected slope, 78.1 (35.1)
Forested slope, 88.6 (41.1)

The superiority of the forested slope is even more evident in the following comparison made the same year:

	MARCH 1	APRIL 5	NET GAIN
Forested slope	88.1 (36.8)	88.6 (41.1)	0.5 (4.3)
Protected slope	81.3 (32.3)	78.1 (35.1)	3.2 (2.8)

The influence of scrub of varying heights is shown by measurements made April, 1910, at 52 stations:

Talus slope covered with low scrub, 32.4 (13.4)
Slightly steeper talus dotted with timber screens 10 to 20 feet high, 61.4 (26.5)

In a season of normal or heavy precipitation the snow on the first slope rises as high as the tips of the scrub, but no higher, for the slope is then exposed to the unobstructed sweep of the wind.

Area for area on mountains of gentler contour—and such mountains are the rule rather than the exception—the talus slopes are less efficient than forests as conservers of snow. It is true that some of the snow above timber line outlasts the snow in the forest below. This phenomenon is confined, however, to the deeper cornices of limited area. The use of timber screens instead of a forest cover evenly distributed would create drifts but little inferior in size and

142

lasting power to the cornices on the talus slopes. Furthermore, the number of such drifts can be multiplied by planting trees, while the cornices on the rocks not only cannot be increased in number but they place too large an area under contribution compared with the moisture conserved. Their only virtue is that the water supplied by them is released late.

Forests, even apart from mountains, retain in some measure a capacity to accumulate and shelter snow, providing their crowns are not too dense. Their capacity is proportionate to the strength of the wind that drives the snow over and through the forest canopy until it finds lodgment beneath. The remnant left in the trees ultimately finds its way to the ground with only moderate loss by evaporation. The interception losses of snow are light as compared with those of a similar quantity of rain.

An attempt has been made to obtain exact measurements of the evaporation of snow in tree crowns. A drip pan provided with a mezzanine story of wire screen to expose snow from both above and below after the manner of branches was hung in the trees, but the technique was never perfected. That the factor is small is suggested by the following comparison of the net gathering power of open and forested areas in Tahoe Basin:

	NET GATHERING POWER MARCH 11, 1910	NET RETENTION IN SPRING APRIL 20, 1910
Treeless meadow . . .	29.8 (11.7)	Gone April 10–13
Forest of pine and fir .	31.4 (12.1)	1.3 (0.6)
Fir forest	30.4 (11.0)	7.1 (2.7)

A further comparison of various types of forest at Blackwood Creek indicates that the dense forest with glades has a maximum gathering and retaining power:

	MARCH 13–14	APRIL 25
Open forest of pine and cedar	34.9 (13.5)	0.5 (0.2)
Very dense fir forest	31.0 (10.9)	2.1 (0.9)
Dense fir forest with glades	42.7 (16.5)	7.8 (3.2)

The index of protection capacity is confirmed in the figures (inches of water) for total evaporation, December to May, 1913–1914, at Tahoe City: Small fir glades, 1.492; large forest opening, 2.152; open meadow, 4.766; deforested southern slope, 5.865.

The ideal conservation forest is one honeycombed with glades whose extent is so related to the height of the trees that the sun cannot reach the surface of the snow. Such a forest will permit far more snow to reach the ground than will a forest of great and uniform density and yet will amply protect the snow from the effect of sun and wind.

The preceding statement, however, has entirely omitted consideration of the net run-off from the snow after passing through

143

FIG. 12   FIG. 13

FIG. 12—Protection against evaporation in a forest glade.
FIG. 13—An ideal forest glade for conserving snow. Lake Tahoe (6200 feet).

the soil and suffering diminution from transpiration losses due to vegetation; for only where ample catchment basins exist below or where the geological structure of the watershed affords underground storage can the regulation of the flow be subordinated to its quantity. Even then, other attending factors such as protection against erosion may intervene.[4]

The Forecasting of Run-off

Snow surveying had first taken the form of measurement of the cubic contents or acre feet of water in the snow for entire basins with estimate of losses suffered en route to the discharging streams. This

[4] See also by the writer: The Conservation of Snow: Its Dependence on Forests and Mountains, *Scientific American Suppl. No. 1914*, Vol. 74, 1912, Sept. 7, pp. 152–155; Recent Studies of Snow in the United States, *Quart. Journ. Royal Meteorol. Soc.*, Vol. 40, 1914, pp. 43–52; Das Verhältnis des Waldes und des Gebirges zur Erhaltung des Schnees, *Meteorol. Zeitschr.*, Vol. 30, 1913, pp. 1–10.

144

was accomplished by the use of numerous measurements at random or in fixed positions as the surveyors might elect. It was known as "the method of areas" and differed in no wise from the precipitation gauge except that it covered the area in greater detail.

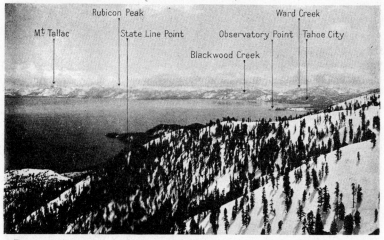

Fig. 14—A view over the northern end of Lake Tahoe showing stations of snow-survey courses.

The Percentage, or Nevada, Method

The percentage, or Nevada, method discards entirely the method of areas and merely seeks to determine the percentage the snow field at any fixed point bears to the average snow field at that point. To do this it was necessary only to maintain a series of measurements carefully taken in the same spot each year. These measurements, laid out at definite intervals from one fixed point to another, were named "snow courses." To avoid the effects of drifting, long courses with twenty-five to fifty samplings were employed, and the average was taken as indicating the snow cover.

Fortunately, the snow courses laid out for the study of the effect of mountains and forests on the conservation of snow were long and reliable. When these were turned to the study of stream flow, it was soon apparent that the relative snow cover (i.e. its seasonal percentage of normal) throughout a basin was the same wherever measured, providing neither drifting nor melting had occurred.

It was then merely necessary to maintain a single fixed course in each basin to determine the relative amount of snow in that basin. If averaged for a fair number of years the course would give a "normal" or "mean" water content by which to estimate the percentage relationship of coming seasons. This would be done simply by dividing the new snow cover by the mean snow cover. Variations of snow cover range from 30 per cent to 160 per cent of the normal and even more on occasion.

This percentage relationship was found to correspond closely with a similar percentage relationship of run-off in the stream fed

FIG. 15—Snow-survey course on Rubicon Peak (8100 feet).

by the snow field. Thus a 75 per cent snow cover of April 1 assured an approximately 75 per cent run-off during the months of April to July, inclusive, after which the streams rapidly become low and dependent almost entirely on the late summer rains.

The same relationship was found to exist also between the snow fields and the rise of Lake Tahoe when corrected for discharge, except that Lake Tahoe because of its proportionally large water area was more affected by the April-to-July rains upon its surface.

The percentage method avoids practically all the objections to the rainfall or area method and permits unified treatment of all basins irrespective of their size, elevation, physical character, forestation, and the nature of their drainage floor.

The only modification that has been made in the Sierra Nevada is the establishment of a series of outpost stations on each side of the range to detect and measure possible variation in the relative snow cover on both crest and foothills and, more lately, a series of altitude zones covering each watershed or basin to determine the relative loss that may have occurred in the snow cover at the lower elevations through premature melting.

Factors Affecting Forecast

The factors affecting the forecast are few. The basic preliminary requirement is the maintenance of fixed snow courses with fixed points of measurement. All courses should be long enough and numerous

146

enough to provide a reliable average. Accuracy of stream measurements is equally important. Unless based on a long period the normals for snow cover and stream flow should represent the same series of years. The chief distorting factor is the possible divergence from normal of the precipitation during run-off, for normal precipitation

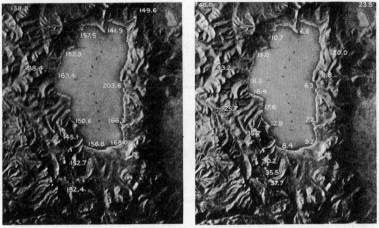

FIG. 16   FIG. 17

FIG. 16—Relief map of the Tahoe Basin showing the close uniformity of seasonal percentage of snow cover throughout the basin, 1917. Only at Glenbrook on the eastern shore does unusual distortion occur.

FIG. 17—Relief map of the Tahoe Basin showing increase in precipitation (inches of water content) due to elevation and decrease due to barrier ranges and distance from source of supply (see p. 553).

during run-off is essential in keeping the snow fields up to the percentage set by the snow survey. If precipitation is entirely lacking, the run-off will fall below the forecast to an amount depending upon the ratio of the water content of the normal snow cover to the normal precipitation during run-off. The ratio is smallest in the Sierra Nevada and gradually increases eastward to the Continental Divide where the summer rains nearly equal the winter precipitation representing the snow fields. East of the Continental Divide the precipitation during run-off is in the ascendancy (Table I).

The effectiveness of the snow cover as compared with the precipitation during run-off varies from 75:75 per cent in the rockbound, elevated South Yuba Basin of the Sierra Nevada to 35:15 per cent in the Boise Basin at Arrowrock Dam, Idaho. The figures represent the percentage of effectiveness of each medium upon the run-off. The explanation for the divergence in effectiveness between snow cover and precipitation during run-off is that the snow cover melts continuously and thus simulates a continuous downpour of rain, while the precipitation that falls during the run-off season often falls upon

147

dry soil and, like intermittent rains, is wasted in priming the soil.[5]

The above percentages apply only to river basins. In the case of large lakes, such as Tahoe, where much of the precipitation is caught without loss, the ratio of efficiency is nearly double that given above.

TABLE I—RATIO OF SUMMER (APR.–JULY) TO WINTER (NOV.–MAR.) PRECIPITATION
AND EFFECTIVENESS OF DEPARTURE IN SUMMER PRECIPITATION AND RUN-OFF

	PRECIPITATION (INCHES)		RATIO S/W %	PER CENT RUN-OFF FOR 100 PER CENT DEPARTURE, SUMMER PRECIPITATION
	SUMMER	WINTER		
Sierra Nevada Colfax, 1870–1923	6.89	37.52	18.2	16.2
Humboldt Basin Six stations, 1918–1930 . . .	3.83	6.31	60.7	22.7
Logan Basin Five stations	6.72	7.06	95.2	35.6
Continental Divide Durango, Telluride, and Leadville, Colo.	6.67	7.78	85.7	30 (approx.)
East of Continental Divide Denver	7.67	3.22	238.2	75–90
Calgary	8.52	2.99	284.9	75–90

It was the fortunate absence of a strong distorting factor of precipitation during run-off in the Sierra Nevada that made possible the discovery of the close relationship between the content of snow fields and run-off. It is, likewise, the absence of this factor that gives a high degree of accuracy to forecasting in the Sierra Nevada while farther east it is subjected to broad correction. Furthermore, west of the Continental Divide the precipitation during April-May is normally far heavier than during June-July and thus permits an early estimate of possible deficiency in precipitation during run-off and close revision of the original forecast.

This is one of the advantages of wet and dry seasons, which is lost east of the Continental Divide, where summer precipitation equals that of winter.

SUBNORMAL SNOW COVER

In the semiarid, mountainous West the amount of moisture required to prime the soil at the beginning of the run-off season is practically fixed irrespective of either previous precipitation or temperature. Only in meadowland or in broad alluvial valleys, like the

---

[5] A difference in effectiveness between continuous and intermittent rains of about 30 per cent has been found by Rice in Hawaii (Roger C. Rice: Relation between Rainfall and Run-off in Hillebrand Glen, Nuuanu Valley, Oahu, Hawaii, *Monthly Weather Rev.*, Vol. 45, 1917, pp. 178–181). A similar divergence has been found also by the author in sand-box studies.

148

Humboldt of Nevada, is water enough held over from one season to the next to replenish the soil water appreciably or permit surface freezing. The relative effectiveness of the soil-priming factor naturally depends upon the water content of the snow cover and the amount of saturation locally required to produce run-off. When the snow cover is normal the factor is negligible; but it becomes significant in forecast when its value is affected by either subnormal or excessive snow cover. Fortunately the factor can theoretically be fixed at the time the snow survey is made. Actually it has been detected only in the South Yuba Basin, where small area and a zoning system have made close measurements possible. Here a correction factor of −3 per cent in the run-off has been found applicable for a 60 per cent diminution of the normal snow cover (water content 44.12 inches). Strangely, in the Great Basin and the Wasatch, where the snow cover bears the approximate ratio of one-fourth and one-half respectively to that of the South Yuba, no trace of the soil-priming factor has yet been found. Here the factor may be eclipsed by porosity of the soil.

The problem of soil priming and that of the effect of obstructions in the stream bed are the chief problems awaiting solution in the forecasting of stream flow.

EVAPORATION, WIND, TEMPERATURE

In the order of probable effectiveness minor factors involved in the forecasting of run-off are evaporation, wind, and temperature. Monthly evaporation of snow on a watershed in the semiarid West is illustrated by the following series of measurements made in the Sierra Nevada from 1910–1911 to 1916–1917, inclusive.

ELEVATION 6,000 FEET

Typical fir forest	0.46 in.	Openings in forest	0.68 in.
Small fir glade	0.36 "	Semi-open forest	0.78 "
Pine and fir forest typical of		Small meadow	0.84 "
snow courses	0.52 "	Open meadow	1.26 "
Medium pine forest	0.59 "	Deforested south slope	1.17 "

ELEVATION 8,000 FEET		ELEVATION 9,000 FEET	
Semi-open forest	1.40 "	Timber line	5.52 "*

* A single measurement, undoubtedly much too large because of wind effect.

The averages are based upon evaporation from November through June, though the evaporation that affects the forecast of run-off is confined to the months of April-June.

On the basis of the extremes for any single month, as shown by measurements of evaporation in the open at 6000 feet elevation, the maximum monthly variation in evaporation to be expected from variation in the weather is about 1 inch, or 6 per cent of the normal snow cover at that elevation. Since the increase in evaporation with elevation will be offset by the increase in depth of the snow cover, this percentage may well be representative for the entire watershed.

Wind may drift the snow into sheltered positions or it may increase the rate of evaporation or accelerate melting. The maximum variation in the annual drifting of snow during deposition cannot be large, and its chief effect would be retardation of melting through increase of depth in the drifts.

Contrary to the usual belief, temperature changes within normal limits merely accelerate or retard the rate of run-off without noticeably changing the total amount. This is because dripping from the snow fields once started in the spring does not cease sufficiently to allow the soil to dry out and require a second priming: in other words, melting snow has the effect of continuous rain. Furthermore, the snow descends into the soil in the form of what may be called restrained rain rather than a deluge. This is especially true at the higher elevations where the depth of the snow gives it additional capillarity. Except in meadows and lowlands the soil beneath the snow fields is seldom frozen because of the tendency of the steep slopes to drain dry before the falling of the winter snow.

In four seasons of abnormal shrinkage in run-off the seasonal temperature during run-off was from 0.7° to 4.2° F. in excess of normal, suggesting that high temperatures are relatively ineffective in increasing the total flow. However, low temperatures of 3.3°, 3.1°, and 7.0° F. below normal persisting during March, April, and May of the current year in the Humboldt Basin are associated with a loss of 50 per cent of normal in the forecast of run-off. The loss may have occurred in the alluvial floor of the basin. It was evidently due to excessively low temperatures which caused repriming of the soil or reduced the rate of flow to absorptive proportions. Fortunately, such low temperatures after melting has begun are of rare occurrence. They have been recorded in the Humboldt Basin only four times in 38 years.

WIDE AREA FORECASTING

The possibility of forecasting for a wider area than the basin covered by the snow survey was first conceived in a comparison of snow and run-off near Salt Lake City in City Canyon Creek and Big Cottonwood Creek—14 miles apart. They were found to be so similar that for practical purposes the forecast for the one could be applied to the other. The maximum variation on the basis of seasonal percentage between the run-off of the two streams for the three years, 1913–1916, was only 4.3 per cent, and the maximum variation between the estimates of snow cover in the two basins was 7.1 per cent; but the maximum difference between the estimates and the actual run-off was as great as 16.7 per cent.

Comparison was then made of the snow cover along the axis of the Central Sierra Nevada including South Yuba, Tahoe, Carson, and Walker basins. The maximum divergence in percentage of normal is:

1915–16	1916–17	1917–18	1918–19	1919–20	1920–21	1921–22
9.8	5.1	11.0	12.8	13.0	14.0	24.7

Thus, unless greatly refined forecasts of run-off are necessary, snow surveys in one basin may be applied to the neighboring basin or basins or even to basins on opposite sides of the range. Hence key snow courses at wide intervals along the range may be used to indicate the snow cover lying between. The application of the average of two such courses to the basins lying between has been called "bridging." The method affords knowledge of the growth of the snow cover throughout the winter and furnishes inexpensive material for early preliminary forecasts before the detailed snow surveys and forecasts of April 1. The length of the "bridge" reaching over the rugged and broad Walker Basin is 60 miles.

QUADRANGLES FOR FORECASTING

The division of a mountain range into quadrangles for forecasting run-off depends on three factors: (1) date of maximum flow, (2) general harmony in seasonal percentage of run-off, and (3) presence of discordant streams.

On the basis of the first the Sierra Nevada, on account of its variation in elevation, should be divided into three quadrangles comprising (1) the Plateau and Low Sierra, (2) the Central Sierra, and (3) the High Sierra. On the basis of the second there would be three quadrangles divided as follows: (1) the Plateau, (2) the Northern Sierra, and (3) the Southern Sierra. The third factor would require the addition of a sub-quadrangle at each end of the range.

Since general harmony in seasonal percentage of stream flow is more consequential than date of maximum flow, the second set of quadrangles, subdivided to segregate the discordant streams, has been adopted as most feasible for forecasting. The length of the quadrangles along the axis of the range varies from 100 to 200 miles; their width, that of the range, is about 60 miles. To them has been added the Southern California quadrangle, where much of the precipitation is in the form of rain and quickly melting snow, which become a part of the underground water supply of that region.

In quadrangles so large more than one set of snow courses is necessary to assure estimates even within 20 per cent of accuracy. The present tendency is to make snow surveys and forecasts in each drainage basin with the quadrangle as a broad background for comparison. The quadrangles are shown in Figures 20 and 21.

ACCURACY OF FORECASTING

Accuracy within 10 per cent in the forecast is usually possible. Even in the case of a single group of snow courses at the crest of the Truckee River Basin in the Sierra Nevada the divergence between snow cover and run-off in twelve years out of seventeen was less than

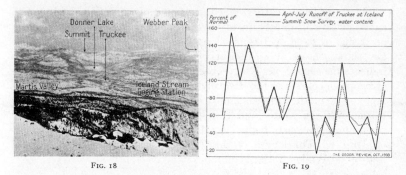

Donner Lake   Webber Peak
Summit | Truckee

Martis Valley   Iceland Stream Gaging Station

Percent of Normal
April-July Runoff of Truckee at Iceland
Summit Snow Survey, water content

THE GEOGR. REVIEW, OCT. 1933

FIG. 18   FIG. 19

FIG. 18—View of the Truckee Basin from Mt. Rose.
FIG. 19—Graph illustrating the harmony between snow cover of the crest of Truckee Basin, April 1, and run-off of Truckee River, above diversions, April to July.

10 per cent. This comparison was based wholly on original snow survey data of April 1 unmodified by later precipitation during run-off.

A broader comparison under difficult conditions indicates similar accuracy. Out of 63 forecasts for the Truckee, Tahoe, Carson, West Walker, South Yuba, and Mokelumne basins, covering 19 years, 41, or virtually two-thirds, were within 10 per cent, and all were within 31 per cent. Furthermore, 27, or nearly one-half, were within 5 per cent. However, this comparison was based upon the revised forecast of May 15.

Comparison of unpublished forecasts with actual run-off in the Sierra Nevada for 1932 made by the California Coöperative Snow Surveys shows that out of the total forecasts for 30 separate streams 12 were accurate within 5 per cent and 21, or two-thirds, within 10 per cent; of the remaining 9, 5 were within 15 per cent; 7 within 20 per cent; and all within 25 per cent.

This is a satisfying record in view of the fact that in all but three basins the basic period of snow surveys had not exceeded two years.

THE CALIFORNIA-NEVADA SYSTEM

Snow survey systems, with the percentage or Nevada method employed, have been planned to meet varying requirements in the West, and some are in active operation. These will be briefly described.

The California-Nevada system, which embraces the entire area of the Sierra Nevada Range, was originally designed for the dual purpose of securing flood control and storage for irrigation. California has now developed a Division of Water Resources with a Snow Supervisor to safeguard or forewarn irrigation, power, flood control, municipal water systems, hydraulic mining, navigation, and salinity control.

The Spokane and Columbia River Systems

The Spokane River system was developed for the Washington Water Power Company to permit maximum storage in Lake Coeur d'Alene, a lake which, in its susceptibility to flooding, is the antithesis of Tahoe.

The Columbia River system, to which the Spokane belongs, shares almost equally with the Colorado River system the western side of the Continental Divide from southern British Columbia to northern New Mexico, a distance of some 1300 miles. However, the Columbia lies in the storm track and drains a region of increasing precipitation toward its mouth, and its normal annual run-off at the Dalles (computed in 1922) is 151,710,000 acre feet, as compared with 17,449,000 acre feet in the Colorado at Yuma, or a ratio of 9 to 1.

The tremendous flow of the Columbia is furnished by three principal tributaries—the upper Columbia with the Kootenay (52,521,000 acre feet), the Clark Fork-Pend Oreille (19,180,000 acre feet), and the Snake (45,518,000 acre feet). The combined system covers with a more or less complete net the entire arid region of Idaho, Oregon, and Washington and thus guarantees to these states a permanent foundation for agricultural and power development. The chief problem especially downstream will be the lifting of water to the high lands, and its solution may be the power potential of the stream itself.

The three tributaries mentioned supply 77 per cent, or about 117,000,000 acre feet, of the total annual flow of the Columbia at the Dalles, and their individual basins are so large and their flow so abundant that at least two of them have become centers for a series of great reclamation projects. Of the other tributaries, the Spokane has long been the source of interstate power.

The problem of forecasting the summer, or April-July, run-off of the Columbia is virtually the problem of forecasting the run-off of its individual feeders, for the interests served are on the tributaries rather than on the main stream. However, the collective forecast for the feeders would represent the forecast for the main stream. This is shown by the record of 1913–1921, during which time the maximum annual variation between the collective run-off of the major feeders and the run-off of the main stream at the Dalles was within 7 per cent and the maximum variation for April-July within 11 per cent, although divergencies of 20 to 35 per cent frequently occur between the tribu-

153

taries themselves. Furthermore, on the basis of fragmentary records a similar closeness of agreement prevailed throughout the preceding decade.

However, forecasting for even the individual feeders is far more complex than in the Sierra Nevada. Precipitation during April-July

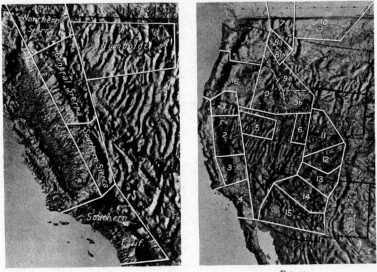

Fig. 20   Fig. 21

Fig. 20—Map of California and Nevada with quadrangles showing the longest feasible units for forecasting stream flow in the Sierra Nevada and Basin ranges.

Fig. 21—Map showing the proposed snow-surveying systems in the western United States and Canada. Sierra Nevada system: 1, Northern Sierra Quadrangle; 2, Central Sierra Quadrangle; 3, Southern Sierra Quadrangle; 4, Southern California Quadrangle; 5, Humboldt, Nev. Quadrangle; 6, Wasatch-Uinta Quadrangle. Columbia system: 7, Upper Columbia Quadrangle; 8, Clarks Fork-Pend Oreille-Spokane Quadrangle, (a) Clarks Fork-Pend Oreille Basin, (b) Spokane Basin; 9, Snake Quadrangle, (a) Salmon Basin, (b) Upper Snake Basin, (c) Lower Snake-Boise Basin. 10, Saskatchewan Quadrangle. Colorado system: 11, Green River Quadrangle; 12, Grand River Quadrangle; 13, San Juan Quadrangle; 14, Little Colorado Quadrangle; 15, Gila Quadrangle. 16, Oregon system.

grows relatively heavier with increase in distance from the Pacific Coast, and the snow cover on the upper Columbia watershed melts slowly during this period, thus catching and ultimately transmitting to the stream the bulk of the precipitation.

The lower Columbia drains the Cascade and Coast Ranges, which are here of low elevation and transmit the bulk of their snow immediately to the streams. For instance 57.0 per cent of the run-off of the Willamette is in December-March and 27.4 per cent in April-July. Furthermore, the precipitation on this watershed is relatively light during April-July and adds little to the summer flow in the lower stream. On the other hand, the Columbia above the Dalles flows only 16.8 per cent in December-March and 61.0 per cent during April-July.

154

Consequently the upper and lower Columbia are complementary to each other, and whatever late spring and summer rise occurs in the Columbia will be due to the snow on the Continental Divide. On the other hand, except for the influence of the chinook, the high water in winter should be due to heavy precipitation in the Cascade and Coast Ranges and should occur mainly in the lower Columbia and its immediate tributaries, for the bed of the upper Columbia is too capacious to be overflowed in its low water season except under abnormal conditions.

THE COLORADO RIVER SYSTEM

Unlike the Columbia the Colorado, with the negligible exception of the Gila, rises entirely in the highlands of the Continental Divide and receives practically no accretions toward its mouth. Thus the area of 225,000 square miles above Yuma is reduced for forecast purposes by about one-half, and the crest line of 760 miles is reduced to 330 miles. Furthermore, three tributaries, the Green (5,797,760 acre feet), the Grand or Upper Colorado (6,650,200 acre feet), and the San Juan (2,745,270 acre feet) furnish 87.1 per cent of the mean annual run-off at Yuma.

The purpose of a snow survey on this watershed will be the efficient control of the Boulder Dam to store the maximum water possible without flood strain on the structure. Unlike the Columbia the Colorado has far more irrigable land tributary to it than it can serve.

GREAT BASIN SYSTEMS

At the apex of the triangle formed by the Colorado, Columbia, and Sierra Nevada, lies a group of mountains that makes life in the Great Basin possible. On the east in Utah are the Uintah-Wasatch Ranges. Here water is abundant early in the season but relatively scarce in the late months of the summer. Hence the surveys are made particularly to determine the amount of high-level snow for forecasting late flow.

On the west in Nevada are the Ruby Range and the Charleston-Independence Ranges, which jointly create the Humboldt River, immortalized by Mark Twain as a rivulet so narrow that the covered-wagoners could run and jump across it for exercise and then drink it dry to cool off. He might have added that on occasion they could have sailed over the flooded valley its entire length of a thousand miles.

Although tributaries from these mountains furnish more than 90 per cent of the run-off in the main stream the alluvial soil and tight dams in the stream bed make forecasting both difficult and complex. The stream has well been termed the "last frontier" in the forecasting of stream flow.

155

THE SASKATCHEWAN SYSTEM

Forecasting has ventured east of the Continental Divide in the Bow River, seat of a large Canadian irrigation project. The establishment of a snow-survey system in the Saskatchewan Basin is perhaps more difficult than elsewhere in North America, for the Canadian Rockies in which the Saskatchewan and its tributaries rise are extremely precipitous and in their higher levels afford scant room for satisfactory snow-survey courses. The lower levels also may be subject to overloading by drift snow blown from the overhanging cliffs. Thus far no neighboring basin less rough topographically than the others has been found from which parallel forecasts could be made. Furthermore, the effectiveness of the April-July precipitation approaches 90 per cent of the winter snow cover, which latter thus represents the minimum rather than the probable run-off to be expected.

· FORECASTING FLOODS

The forecasting of floods involves the data of snow surveying in so far as they reveal the minimum menace of visible potential water. The maximum menace will depend on the march of temperature and the intensity and duration of subsequent rain and their possible effect on the premature melting of the snow. The density of the snow determines its power to hold the rain in suspension; depth determines its capacity.

Evolution of the Snow Cover

The evolution of the snow cover is of still larger interest. Its study involves a consideration of depth and density or water content, increase in quantity with elevation and decrease with distance from the sea, increase in density as the season advances, and the final melting.

One of the first needs is the establishment of a satisfactory water year. Because water from melting snow is far more effective than rain in creating water resources, the precipitation should be classified into rain and snow rather than into annual precipitation and departure as is done at present. The water year would thus be expressed in seasonal percentage of normal both for the snow cover and for the precipitation occurring during run-off wherever modification in the expected run-off due to departure from normal of the rain is closely observed, and for the late summer and autumn rainfall. Only in this way will the water bear an obvious relationship to the precipitation.

· TOPOGRAPHIC SNOW SURVEYS

A topographic snow survey would also be a happy substitute for rain-gauge measurements where such gauges are impotent because of

156

gales or depth of snow or where observers are infrequent. A topographic map of snowfall has been compiled by Brooks[6] for the region
embraced by the United States. Numerous data for the topographic
snow map are now provided by the various organizations conducting
snow surveys. Finland has actually made such a map in terms of
depth only.[7] The purpose was to determine the local difference in

TABLE II—DIMINUTION OF PRECIPITATION IN LEE OF BARRIER RANGES
(Precipitation in inches of water, November to March, or *snow cover, April 1)

RANGE	ELEVATION (FEET)	PRECIPITATION (INCHES)
1. COAST RANGE		
Mt. Hamilton	4,209	23.17
Newman	91	8.92
2. SIERRA NEVADA		
Main Chain		
Summit Station	7,017	40.6*
Tahoe City (west of Tahoe)	6,230	15.9*
Incline (east of Tahoe)	6,230	7.37*a
Eastern Spur		
Mt. Rose	9,000–10,800	29.15*
Reno	4,532	4.91
Marlette Lake	8,000	27.76*
Lewers Ranch	5,200	19.65
3. ROCKY MOUNTAINS		
Crest		
Climax	11,304	19.40
Leadville	10,248	6.31
Eastern Spur		
Pikes Peak	14,111	9.60
Colorado Springs	6,098	1.77

aApproximate.

accumulated water supplies in the form of snow before spring run-off
began. March 15 was selected as the date of maximum accumulation,
and straight traverse lines were employed except for slight deviations
to include various types of protective covering. The work was continued from 1923 to 1926.

In Czechoslovakia a monthly topographic map[8] of both precipitation and snow depths is compiled, and at least at some stations
graphs are kept of the seasonal cycle of the snow cover both in depth
and water content with parallel graphs of temperature fluctuation.

What such a topographic snow survey might be is roughly shown
by the following cross sections from the Pacific Coast to the Continental Divide, based partly on November-March precipitation and,

[6] Charles F. Brooks: The Snowfall of the United States, *Quart. Journ. Royal Meteorol. Soc.*, Vol. 39,
1913, pp. 81–86.
[7] W. W. Korhonen: Über die lokale Veränderlichkeit der Schneedecke, *Meteorol. Zeitschr.*, Vol. 49,
1932, pp. 72–76.
[8] Publ. l'Institut National de Recherches Hydrologique à Praha.

157

where available, upon April 1 surveys of the snow cover. They show graphically the diversity of precipitation and water supply between California and the Great Basin and specifically between the run-off

TABLE III—INCREASE IN PRECIPITATION WITH ELEVATION

(Precipitation in inches of water, November to March, or *snow cover, April 1)

RANGE	ELEVATION (FEET)	PRECIPITATION (INCHES)
1. SIERRA NEVADA		
Windward		
Sacramento	71	14.29
Lake Fordyce	6,500	43.3*
Summit Station	7,017	40.6*
Leeward		
Truckee	6,400	21.0*ₐ
Boca	5,531	17.34
Reno	4,532	4.91
2. RUBY RANGE		
Hylton	6,300	5.71
Harrison Pass	7,008	7.90*
Lamoille	6,100	7.49
Lamoille Canyon	7,400–7,600	12.70*
Thomas Canyon	9,000	21.83*
3. WASATCH RANGE		
Salt Lake City	4,292	8.78
Big Cottonwood Creek	6,880–8,530	13.79*
Brighton Basin	8,700–9,540	25.71*
4. CONTINENTAL DIVIDE		
Windward		
Lay	6,190	5.45
Rico	8,824	12.88
Climax (crest)	11,304	19.40
Leeward		
Leadville	10,248	6.31
Colorado Springs	6,098	1.77

* Approximate.

on the windward and leeward slopes of the Coast Range, the Sierra Nevada, the Wasatch, and the Continental Divide. The effect of barrier ranges in reducing precipitation is shown in both the Sierra Nevada and the Continental Divide not only by the sharp diminution of precipitation on the leeward side of all ranges but also by the diminution of precipitation even on the windward sides and crests of ranges parallel to but to leeward of others of similar or greater height (Table II and see Fig. 17).

INCREASE IN PRECIPITATION WITH ELEVATION

In general, precipitation in the Sierra Nevada has been believed by the writer to increase with elevation to the crest on the windward side, even in the case of the annual precipitation and particularly as

158

regards the precipitation of November-March representing the snow cover. An exception to this rule occurs in the Central Sierra Nevada (Table IV) and has recently been found elsewhere in this range. Further comparison, based on snow-cover data accumulated by the California Coöperative Snow Surveys, indicates that exceptions occur elsewhere in the Sierra even in the winter precipitation.

TABLE IV—SNOW COVER ON WINDWARD SIDE OF SIERRA NEVADA SHOWING
ELEVATION OF MAXIMUM WINTER PRECIPITATION

(Inches of water content)

BASIN	ELEVATION ABOVE SEA LEVEL IN FEET				
	6,000 —	7,000 —	8,000 —	9,000 —	10,000
Kern River	10.6	12.3	15.7	23.1	35.7	...
Stanislaus River	17.1	32.4	40.2	44.8	...	...
Kings River	27.5	27.9	39.3	38.4	44.4	42.8
Upper San Joaquin River	...	...	40.8	...	45.2	42.5
Mokelumne River . . .	...	36.8	48.1	48.8	...	...
Tuolumne River	17.1	36.0	51.4	38.7	40.6	39.0
American River	30.6	40.2	45.2	56.4	...	...
Yuba River	28.8	44.5	54.7	46.8	...	...
Feather River	25.2	32.0	32.4	50.7	...	...

Owing to the scarcity of normals, the comparison is confined to the past season of 1932; and, to eliminate local variations, the average water content of several stations grouped by altitude zones is employed. Since the problem belongs exclusively to the windward side of the mountains, only the basins on the western side of the Sierra are represented.

The Sierra Nevada offers an attractive opportunity for studying the variation in elevation of the zone of maximum precipitation both in summer and in winter.

REGION OF GREATEST SNOWFALL IN THE UNITED STATES[9]

On the basis of accumulated snow depth in 1915 the honor of being the region of greatest snowfall in the United States was almost equally divided between Blue Lakes and Summit Station at the crest of the Central Sierra. Later measurements have transferred the honor to Paradise Inn (5500 feet) on the flank of Mt. Rainier, which possesses a record of mean precipitation for November–March of 60.87 inches water. On the basis of November–March precipitation, Crater Lake, Oregon (7086 feet) also slightly exceeds Summit Station (7017 feet), the former having a mean of 36.78 inches (1931) as compared with 36.46 (1926) for the latter. Furthermore, the record at Crater Lake

[9] Andrew H. Palmer: The Region of Greatest Snowfall in the United States, *Monthly Weather Rev.*, Vol. 43, 1915, pp. 217–221.

is based upon a shorter and drier cycle of seasons. Obviously the closer the station is to the storm track the greater the precipitation should be.

The following list of crest snow survey stations along the Sierra Nevada with the normal water content of the snow cover at each, on April 1, shows a close competition for maximum snow cover.

BASINS	ELEVATION Feet	WATER CONTENT Inches
Upper San Joaquin-Owens at Mammoth Pass . .	9,500	46.7
Tuolumne-Mono at Dana Meadows	9,700	34.2
Tuolumne-Walker at Center Mountain	9,300	43.4
Stanislaus-Walker at Sonora Pass	8,800	29.0
Mokelumne-Carson at Blue Lakes	8,000	42.7
American-Tahoe at Lake Lucile	8,400	66.5
American-Tahoe at Rubicon Peak	8,100	50.0
American-Tahoe at Ward Creek	7,000	49.8
Yuba-Truckee at Summit Station	7,017	40.6
Yuba-Truckee at Webber Peak	8,000	46.8

A normal is lacking for Mt. Lassen (8400 feet). However, in 1932, a season slightly above normal, the water content of its snow cover at the point of measurement was 50.7 inches.

SNOW DEPTH ALONG ROUTES OF TRANSPORT

Thanks to the perfecting of the rotary snowplow the Donner Pass highway was kept open in 1932, a year of normal snow depth in the Central Sierra. Since the snow cover at this point is one of the deepest in the Sierra Nevada, success is promised on other routes where the highways possess roadbeds feasible for clearing.

The strenuous character of road clearing is shown by the following snow depths on April 1, when the snow had reached its maximum accumulation but owing to settling was less deep than earlier in the season.

STATION	DEPTH OF SNOW, APRIL 1	STATION	DEPTH OF SNOW, APRIL 1
Tioga Pass (9,900)	6.7 ft.	Carson Pass (8,600)	9.0 ft.
Sonora Pass (8,800)	6.2 ft.	Donner Pass (7,017)	7.5 ft.

However, success in normal years may not assure success in supernormal years, for depths of fifteen feet or more are possible though rare.[10]

INTERNAL CHANGES IN THE SNOW COVER

The internal changes in the snow cover from origin to final disappearance comprise a semi-microscopic world that few have entered.

---

[10] The confusion in stating depths by accumulated snowfall rather than by depth of snow on the ground is exemplified in successful snow removal at Crater Lake with a reported official snowfall record of 59 feet, 11 inches, an apparently stupendous depth. As shown above, Crater Lake precipitation is only slightly greater than that at Summit on the Victory Highway over the Central Sierra.

It ranges from the feathery crystals of the light snowflake to the ice granules into which the snow cover is ultimately resolved.

The chief factors causing the internal change in the snow that is called density are wind, pressure, and temperature. The wind grinds and packs the snow crystals into a solid bed. Wind-laid snow attains

FIG. 22—Transport conditions across the Sierra Nevada in midwinter. Descending from the Donner summit eastwards.

nearly its final density at the time of deposition. This is particularly true where the wind has a wide sweep and acts like a giant arrastre, slowly grinding the snow to fineness. Temperature acts more slowly but inexorably. It creates the coarse granules. Pressure is less obvious in its effects.

The composite effect of all three factors is shown in the following table, based on many measurements and computed to afford an approximate estimate of the water content of the snow under various conditions of depth, elevation, and season. In the original table, types of topography and protective covering were given and division was also made into relative depths. Consequently in the summary, which alone appears, the extremes in density are wide.

Exposure to Wind

That the effect of elevation is in reality due to wind is shown by the difference in density of two fields of snow situated at practically the same elevation but differently exposed, one being a cornice on the lee side of a mountain top, the other lying in a spruce forest. In this

TABLE V—INCREASE IN DENSITY OF SNOW WITH ELEVATION, DEPTH, AND SEASON

ELEVATION (FT.)	DEC.-JAN.		FEB.-MAR.	
	DEPTH (FT.)	DENSITY (%)	DEPTH (FT.)	DENSITY (%)
5,000– 7,000	10–160	20.8–27.1	10–120	34.8–37.5
7,000– 9,000	no measure		10–240	33.3–44.2
9,000–10,800	10–200	21.3–34.1	10–240	30.6–46.8
Average		21.1–30.6		32.9–42.8

ELEVATION (FT.)	APRIL-MAY		JUNE–JULY	
	DEPTH (FT.)	DENSITY (%)	DEPTH (FT.)	DENSITY (%)
5,000– 7,000	10–120	40.7–44.9	10–160	48.0–53.8
7,000– 9,000	10–240	40.5–52.7	10–240	49 3–58.7
9,000–10,800	10–240	35.7–50.6	10–200	47.4–59.2
Average		39.0–49.4		48.2–57.2

comparison temperature was relatively ineffective, for the heavier density occurred in the colder exposure (Table VI).

In the case of the cornice, the high initial density could gain little increase even from the effects of melting. In the snow protected by the spruce forest the increase in density is due mainly to the weight of accumulating snow.

RIPE AND OVERRIPE SNOW

When snow has attained its maximum capillarity it is "ripe," and when this point has been exceeded and it begins to lose its water content it is "overripe." The density of ripeness and overripeness varies with the initial density of the snow. This in turn is dependent on the character of the snow crystal.

Apparently snow crystals do not consolidate under melting as closely as under wind or compression but rather tend to become coarsely granular. Some increase in compactness results from melting, but

TABLE VI—EFFECT OF WIND ON DENSITY

CORNICE ON MT. ROSE (10,800 FT.)			SPRUCE FOREST, FLAGSTAFF, ARIZ. (10,500 FT.)		
1911	DEPTH OF SNOW (IN.)	DENSITY (%)	1917	DEPTH OF SNOW (IN.)	DENSITY (%)
Feb. 20	115.5	44.2*	Mar. 7	24.0	16.3
May 2	100.6	49.7	May 1	44.0	29.8
June 8–9	71.8	47.7	May 30	39.0	34.9
Maximum Increase		5.5			18.6

*Seven days after storm.

this is followed by a slight diminution in density as the water begins to drain from the snow.

In all types of snow the difference between ripeness and over-ripeness does not exceed about 10 per cent, whatever the density of ripeness may be. Consequently the snow that is protected from the

TABLE VII—DENSITY OF RIPENESS AND OVERRIPENESS OF SNOW WITH DEPTH AND EXPOSURE TO WIND, CENTRAL SIERRA NEVADA

LOCALITY, ELEVATION, AND EXPOSURE	YEAR AND PRECIPITATION	DEPTH OF SNOW (INCHES)	DENSITY (PER CENT)	
			RIPE	OVERRIPE
Tahoe City, 6,230 feet, forested, wind light	1911–1912 light	31.4	30.1	35.4
	1913–1914 heavy	68.8	34.6	38.6
	1915–1916 heavy	57.1	36.2	42.2
Marlette Lake, 8,000 feet, semi-forested, wind strong	. . . .	81.3	44.4	49.6
Summit Station, 7,017 feet, semi-forested, wind strong	1915–1916 heavy	133.5	48.4	51.6
Mt. Rose, 9,000–10,700 feet, wind-swept	1909–1910 normal	50.7	47.2	53.1
	1910–1911 heavy	94.8	47.4	56.5
	1912–1913 light	38.0	38.2	46.4
	1915–1916 heavy	73.9	47.2	53.4

wind and so is initially light will rarely attain the density or capillarity of its wind-blown neighbor. Herein lies the greater value of high mountain snow. The divergence between various types of snow is shown in Table VII.

TENDENCY OF SNOW COVER TO BECOME HOMOGENEOUS

A final trait to be noted is the tendency of ripening snow to become homogeneous, a development doubtless accelerated by water permeating the mass. This is not a wholly ideal trait, for when the entire depth has attained ripeness the capillarity reserve of the snow cover has ceased to exist and all further water from melting passes directly into the soil.

Solid pack snow lacks the spongy or suspensive character of snow of lighter density and even under normal temperature may lose some of its water prematurely. This is particularly true in March, when winter is passing into spring and nature is delicately balanced. At this crisis an overlay of newly fallen snow with its abundant capillarity

TABLE VIII—TENDENCY OF SNOW TO BECOME HOMOGENEOUS, SUMMIT STATION
(7,017 FEET), 1917

(Depth of snow in inches, density in per cent)

A—*In Timbered Flat*

STRATUM NUMBERED FROM SURFACE DOWN	APR. 1		APR. 23		MAY 6		MAY 20		JUNE 3	
	IN.	PER CENT	IN.	PER CENT	IN.	PER CENT	IN.	PER CENT	IN.	PER CENT
1	6.5	24.6	4.3	41.9	...	...	...	...	...	...
2	7.0	38.6	6.9	40.6	...	...	...	...	...	...
3	12.3	40.7	7.5	50.7	...	...	...	...	...	...
4	10.6	46.2	11.0	49.1	3.8	52.6	...	...	...	...
5	27.8	46.8	24.7	51.8	25.0	52.8	(1.8	22.2)[a]	...	...
6	59.9	48.1	54.9	49.0	56.0	50.2	59.6	52.2	29.6	53.0
Total snow cover	124.1	45.1	109.3	48.9	84.8	51.1	61.4	51.3	29.6	53.0

B—*On Wind-swept Hilltop* (*Continuous with Preceding*)

MAY 6		MAY 20		JUNE 3		STRATUM NUMBERED FROM SURFACE DOWN
IN.	PER CENT	IN.	PER CENT	IN.	PER CENT	
...	...	...	...	...	...	1
...	...	...	...	...	...	2
...	...	...	...	...	...	3
29.3	57.7	(8.5	43.5)[b]	...	...	4
						5
56.8	57.4	53.9	59.6	17.4	57.5	6
86.1	57.5	62.4	57.4	17.4	57.5	Total snow cover

[a] New snow.   [b] Partly new snow.

is needed to insulate the old snow against melting. For instance during March, 1923, under virtually normal conditions of temperature and depth of snow the snow cover in the Central Sierra of 4.1 to 8.5 per cent superdensity lost from 7.4 to 23.4 per cent of normal of its water content, though melting normally does not begin until April 1.

The above cross section series of snow-cover strata at Summit Station in 1917 gives a picture of this evolution in detail (Table VIII).

Evolution of Glaciers

SWISS ALPS

Snow surveying became associated with glacier study through the Zurich Glacier Commission, to whom a Mt. Rose snow sampler was delivered just before the World War. Dr. A. de Quervain, who with

164

Dr. Paul L. Mercanton led the Swiss Expedition to Greenland in 1912–1913 to study the inland ice, saw the necessity of measuring the alimentation of glaciers at their source.[11] In Greenland his estimates were largely theoretical. On learning of the ability of the Mt. Rose snow sampler to penetrate at least 20 feet in depth he ordered a sampler for Switzerland. To facilitate packing up the steep slopes of the Alps it was built in three-foot sections. Later a special toothed cutter was designed for penetrating the thin layers of ice encountered.

It had long been agreed that glaciers were dependent on climatic changes for their evolution, but it had also been noticed that individual differences in rates and times of advance and retreat were prevalent even between neighboring glaciers and, furthermore, that the movement of the tongue of the glacier did not immediately correspond with the accumulation or subsequent movement of material above.[12] A division of the glacier was therefore made into the accumulator or névé and the dissipator or tongue, each with its own mechanism.

It was plain that precipitation and melting were the two great factors balanced against each other. Joined to the former was condensation and to the latter erosion and evaporation, regarding the effectiveness of each of which there was some doubt.[13] Furthermore, precipitation and melting did not work in parallel cycles.

A first attempt to measure the accumulated snow by "buoys" or snow stakes failed because they were persistently wrecked. It was next attempted to catch the annual precipitation at the head of the glacier in a saline tank known as a Mougin Totalizator. The possibility of both erosion and overloading of the contents made the record uncertain. But, worse still, the annual precipitation does not represent the residue of snow available in the autumn for glacier growth, since erosion, evaporation, and melting each take their toll.

An annual snow survey made in the accumulator of the glacier just before the new winter accumulation began seemed the only feasible method of obtaining the exact increment that went into the annual building of the glacier. However, the task is not simple. The data at best are fragmentary and must be set into a larger mosaic. Such a mosaic, remarkable for its many omissions, is a table or clinical chart of the Klariden Glacier for the years from 1914–1915 to 1920–1921, inclusive, compiled by the writer[14] from annual reports by the Zurich Glacier Commission.

[11] Alfred de Quervain and Paul Louis Mercanton: Résultats scientifiques de l'expédition suisse au Groenland 1912–1913, *Meddelelser om Grønland*, Vol. 69, 1925, pp. 55–271.

[12] P. L. Mercanton: Les variations des glaciers actuels, *Rev. Gén. des Sci.*, Vol. 28, 1917, pp. 631–636.

[13] R. Billwiller: Aqueous Exchange Between the Névé and the Atmosphere, *Monthly Weather Rev.*, Vol. 45, 1917, pp. 601–602. (Abstract from *Archives Sci. Phys. et Nat.*, Geneva, 1917, Nov. 15, Vol. 44, pp. 358–359.)

[14] J. E. Church: Present Methods of Glacier Study in the Swiss Alps, *Monthly Weather Rev.*, Vol. 52, 1924, pp. 264–266.

165

The Ice of Greenland

Snow surveying followed de Quervain to Greenland, but it did not reach the apex of the inland ice. That consummation is still devoutly to be wished.

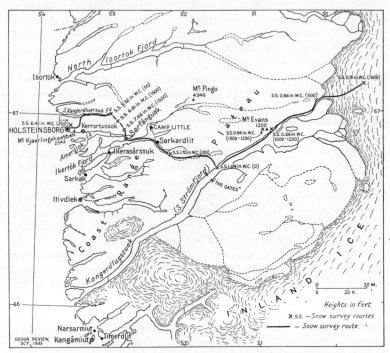

Fig. 23—Map showing the snow-survey route in western Greenland from Holsteinsborg to the inland ice on the Second Greenland Expedition of the University of Michigan, 1927–1928 (compare the report of the first expedition by W. H. Hobbs, *Geogr. Rev.*, Vol. 17, 1927, pp. 1–35). On the snow-survey courses depth is given in inches of water content: the altitude of stations is indicated in feet.

As a part of the winter program of the University of Michigan Greenland Expedition the writer and Helge Bangsted in 1928 conducted a snow survey from an elevation of 1500 feet above sea level on the western edge of the inland ice to Holsteinsborg, a distance of 115 miles in an air line.

The results confirm the effect of barrier ranges in diminishing the precipitation from the coast inland and emphasize the tremendous power of föhn winds to dissipate the snow cover and even to make ripple marks in the solid ice. This is a land of shrinking ice. While the pressure from inland ice caused movement of the ice front even in the winter, the snow residue within sight was too thin to counterbalance even a fraction of the summer melting. No soil marks showed in the crevasses as indices of earlier annual growth.

166

Continuous measurements of the evaporation of both snow and ice were made for considerable periods in both winter and spring on this cross section of Greenland and await tabulation and analysis. The snow survey results are represented in the map, Figure 23.

The larger problem of precipitation, evaporation, and melting in

FIG. 24—On the inland ice of Greenland. Ripple marks in both snow and ice showing evaporation effects. Depth of snow shown by pit in left foreground; a sealed ice crack on right.

inland Greenland still lies ahead. Here naturally at higher and less wind-swept elevations must be sought the snow residue that sustains the inland ice. Here also lies the continuous snow. Snow scud and transport occur on a titanic scale, but snow pigment and snow survey courses of unusual length should aid in identifying the new season's snow cover from the preceding one. It is a task worthy of snow lovers.

THE FUTURE

Snow surveying had a spiritual birth in love of winter nature, and its springs have been maintained also by the interests of pure science and human service. The present need of the "science" of snow surveying, as it is generously designated, is detail. Development, however, as has been suggested, is actively under way In five states snow surveying has become a large or state-wide coöperative effort. The users of water are seeking efficiency through unified practice, centralized direction, and detailed information. A Western Interstate Conference on Snow Surveying with annual meetings has been organized. A mailing list of organizations and persons interested in snow surveying is under way, and a report is nearing completion on collegiate courses in hydrology, particularly of snow. An annotated bibliography of snow and ice has been begun.

All this has been fostered and directed by the Committee on the Hydrology of Snow recently organized by the American Geophysical Union of the National Research Council.

But snow survey projects are seeking coöperation beyond their national boundaries. That in Australia has been referred to; another is in Newfoundland on a watershed as yet partly unexplored; several are in Canada, in consequence of which Canadian representatives have already been appointed to the American Committee. An inquiry has come from the Russian Caucasus. A Mt. Rose snow sampler has been purchased by Norway.

International coöperation seems propitious, and recommendation has been made by the Division of Hydrology of the American Geophysical Union to its international body that an International Commission on the Hydrology of Snow and Ice be established with functions similar to those of the International Commission on Glaciers. Thus the broad field of snow and ice would be covered in all its scientific aspects and geographical distribution.

168

OUR EXPANDING AND CONTRACTING "DESERT"

Isaiah Bowman

THERE is an assumption running through our present discussion of submarginal western lands that we have definitely and permanently destroyed large parts of them. It remains to be seen whether this is true. In the history of the West, up to 1915 at least, a severe drought was always accepted as a prophecy of doom, while a succession of good years led to the belief that a few shade trees or the breaking of new land had performed miracles of permanent reclamation. Popular thought about the permanence of agriculture in our semiarid lands swings from one extreme to the other. It would be possible to quote from scores of books and periodicals published thirty years ago to the effect that dry farming—it should properly be called water-conservation farming—was the key to the indefinite extension of permanent agriculture. When we learn that the Mier country of South Africa, with a rainfall of 6 inches a year, produces wheat and that the local advance of the grain belt in Russian Inner Asia temporarily passes the 10-inch annual rainfall line, the claims of the dry-farming enthusiasts do not seem so highly colored. However, good years and quite special techniques of planting and cultivating upon small areas give a deceptive quality to man's "conquest" of aridity. When we deal with large areas of dry land in which are to be anchored whole blocks of population that must take gambler's chances on the rain—and periodically seek public relief—we talk less of conquest and more of compromise with nature.

At the moment we are in a phase of depression that has reversed the enthusiasm of thirty years ago. The dust storms of April last and of November, 1933,[1] pointed dramatically to an alarming situation in the drought-stricken West. When the public learned that the dust was topsoil blown off the land in a region of generally precarious agriculture, it began to see that something was happening with such intensity and on a scale so vast as to affect the welfare of all of us. Current newspaper articles, responsive to the popular imagination, have spread the belief that the climate of the West has changed profoundly and that from now on we may expect the severe conditions of the present to remain or to recur with dangerous frequency. Popular belief in the permanent destruction of large tracts of submarginal agricultural land is strengthened by the reports of a steadily lowering water table and an increasing degree of inaccessibility of the ground water to surface plants, trees, and pumps. It is for these reasons that the idea of a "shelter belt" of trees north and south across the dry

---

[1] See note "Recent Dust Storms" elsewhere in this number of the *Geographical Review*.

43

plains had a wide popular appeal. Since shady forests are now found in the heavier rainfall belts, the layman concludes that we have only to increase the extent of tree-covered land in the plains country and we shall have improved the climate. It is the purpose of this paper to examine certain climatic ideas now current, some of them rooted in experience and scientific truth, others fundamentally unsound.

Fig. 1—Ranch at edge of Malheur Valley, Ore., with alfalfa on irrigated alluvium and grazing on the sage-covered hills of the background. On the northern edge of the desertic country of Figure 14.

The Retreat of the Glaciers

A striking fact bearing upon the climate of the United States has been disclosed by the Committee on Glaciers of the American Geophysical Union.[2] It has been found that the glaciers of the United States have been in retreat for a number of years past. The only exceptions are the glaciers of the Sierra Nevada of California, advancing since 1932 because of increased snowfall in 1931–1932. The retreat appears to have been continuous and steady since a time before 1850. If the retreat continues, the time is not distant when most of the glaciers of our western ranges will have disappeared as they are believed to have done a few centuries ago. During the past fifty or sixty years probably hundreds of small cirque glaciers of the Sierra Nevada have disappeared. Of this number is the first "living glacier" (under Merced Peak) to be discovered by John Muir, in 1871.[3]

Although we have few glaciers in the United States, it happens that some of them have a critical relation to the towns and farms that depend upon glacier-fed mountain streams. The city of Tacoma depends upon the Nisqually River for its hydroelectric power. The river depends in substantial degree upon the discharge of the Nisqually Glacier. In the seventy-five years from 1857 to 1933 this

[2] F. E. Matthes, Chairman, *Trans. Amer. Geophys. Union, Fourteenth Ann. Meeting, April 27, 28, 29, 1933*, pp. 345–350.

[3] *Ibid., Thirteenth Ann. Meeting, April 28 and 29, 1932*. pp. 282–287; reference on p. 284.

170

glacier retreated 3136 feet; since 1918 the retreat has been 926 feet,[4] and there has been a general shrinkage in volume as well as in length. Part of the retreat has been caused by the diminished rainfall since 1905; part of it is probably the result of increased ablation with a greater number of hours of sunshine, often in correlation with diminished rainfall. The streamflow of the past seventy-five years repre-

FIG. 2—Strand lines on border of Crump Lake six miles north of Adel on the east side of Warner Valley, Ore. A physical record of a fluctuating lake level. The highest lines are 200 feet above the present surface of the lake.

sented not merely the current precipitation but also rain and snow stored as ice. This stored precipitation was thought of in much the way that a stationary savings account in a bank is regarded. Measurements show that in response to natural causes that account has been in fact steadily drawn upon for some decades. We can do nothing about it, since the advance or retreat of glaciers is beyond our ability to stay. It is obvious, however, that if the process goes on long enough the time will come when the water and power requirements of the city cannot be met from this source alone.

Is there any indication that the West was once as dry as now and that it afterward became more moist? Is this a temporary drought or a sign of an indefinitely prolonged dry period that has set in? Should we look upon our western water supply as permanently diminished and still diminishing? Can we infer from past records of rainfall fluctuation that the present process of drying up will be halted or that a reversal will take place and we shall have more rain in the next few decades? If we are facing more severe conditions than ever before, does this call for extensive new measures, dislocation of population, and permanent abandonment of large areas once covered with grass and locally occupied by farmers? What measures can be taken to prevent or offset the continued bad effects of drought?

[4] Report of the Committee on Glaciers, 1933–34, F. E. Matthes, Chairman, *ibid., Fifteenth Ann. Meeting, April 26, 27, 28, and June 20, 21, 1934,* Part 2, pp. 279–285; reference on p. 280.

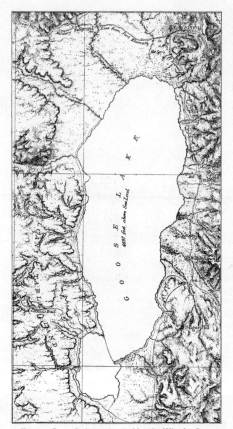

FIG. 3—Goose Lake as mapped by the Wheeler Survey of 1877–1878 (see footnote 6). Reproduced on half scale, i.e., 1 inch to 8 miles. The 42nd parallel crossing the northern end of the lake is the boundary between Oregon and California.

At most western stations rainfall records have not been kept for a long enough period of time to warrant making confident prophecy. The arid and semiarid western parts of the United States have relatively fewer rainfall stations than the rest of the country, and not many go back even so far as 80 years. There are those who claim that the great extension of settlement in the West in the past 80 years has taken place in a period of heavier rainfall and that the normal condition is more desertic than during the time that population has advanced beyond the 100th meridian. To those so minded the earlier maps showing "Great American Desert" written across the plains of western Kansas, Nebraska, and Texas represent the more nearly permanent condition. In their view we are now in process of returning to the desertic conditions that once prevailed.

Science means inquiry: facts plus logic. It means, furthermore, an open-mindedness toward the facts. If we approach the problem in this spirit it is hard to be positive about the great question of the degree of future aridity in the West. The main conclusion is that we ought to continue gathering records. We cannot speed up the seasons, so the process of record gathering cannot be speeded up! But we can increase the number of meteorological stations, and we can do a very great deal more in the way of analyzing records already in hand.

THE EVIDENCE OF THE LAKE BASINS

During the dry summers of 1930 and 1932 I traveled through the eleven arid and semiarid western states in the course of a study of

land settlement.[5]   This provided
an opportunity to examine the
floors of many basin lakes that were
exposed to view for the first time
since settlement began 75 or 80
years ago.   Several of these lakes
unexpectedly revealed most interesting records.   Goose Lake, lying
partly in Oregon and partly in California (Fig. 3), had always been
said by the old settlers to have
been in a contracted state when
the forty-niners and other early mi-
grants crossed the region. They had
driven their wagons over the dry
and exposed floor of the southern
part of Goose Lake. There has been
much dispute in the years since
then concerning the place of crossing, for the lake floor had been
covered with water continuously
since the first settlements were
made. It was also remembered and
recorded in some of the early news-
papers that the forty-niners said
that the climate of their day was
much severer than anything known
since then. This was put down to
desire to give a heroic touch to
their story.

But in 1915 the lake border
began to recede, more rapidly
about 1920. At last the floor was
almost, though never completely,
dry. Then was revealed for the

Fig. 4

Fig. 5

Fig. 4—The basin of Goose Lake, nearly
dry in 1930.
Fig. 5—Wagon tracks of the forty-niners
across the floor of Goose Lake basin, revealed
for the first time in the recent drought period.
(Photograph from V. M. Tanner, Yellowstone
Cut-Off Association.)

first time the wheel tracks of the wagons upon the road of the
forty-niners on the floor of Goose Lake! In other words, after the
lake basin had filled, following a drought period that included 1849,
the floor was not again exposed to extensive view until the 1920's. As
far as this basin is concerned, there seems not to have been so severe
a drought between 1849 and 1920 as that which followed 1920. The
Wheeler Survey of 1877–1878[6] shows Lassen's Trail crossing the floor

    [5] Isaiah Bowman: Jordan Country, *Geogr. Rev.*, Vol. 21, 1931, pp. 22–55; *idem:* The Pioneer
Fringe, *Amer. Geogr. Soc. Special Publ. No. 13*, 1931.
    [6] United States Geographical Surveys West of the One Hundredth Meridian, Topographical
Atlas, Sheet No. 38 B.

173

of Goose Lake near the southern end, and wagon tracks have been described on the peninsula on the west side of the lake as shown on the Wheeler maps (Fig. 3).

In order to check the historical record there were assembled from localities in the general region of Goose Lake several scores of cross sections of trees showing annual rings of growth,[7] and these have been analyzed by assistants of Dr. A. E. Douglass of Tucson. Figure 6

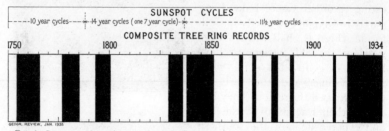

FIG. 6—Sunspot cycles and tree growth. In the upper part of the diagram are shown the dates of change in the lengths of successive sunspot cycles. The lower diagram is a composite representation of tree records in central Oregon and northeastern California. The shaded bands represent periods in which tree-rings are prevailingly thin, indicating lighter rainfall and a lower water table. Alternating blank spaces represent periods of thicker tree-rings, greater rainfall, and higher water table.

is a generalized diagram based on the analysis. It will be seen from the tree-ring records that a drought period set in about 1918 and that it was so general and severe as to affect immediately the thickness of the rings of growth of all the trees in that vicinity. These trees grew not on the basin floors but on the slopes and under conditions that made them peculiarly sensitive to changes of rainfall and ground-water supply. The result shows us exactly what happened in these cases. Diminished rainfall resulted in diminished ground-water supply, in the very great shrinkage of the lake, and in starved trees that put on thin rings of growth.

If we go back in the tree-ring record to a time before the establishment of meteorological stations, we find that at no time after 1852 has there been such general agreement among the tree rings concerning diminished rainfall except for periods of two or three years' duration. When we turn back to 1851 we find that we are approaching the end of a dry period that lasted from 1829 to 1852, rising to a climax about 1840. Between 1795 and 1800 there was a similar general starvation of the trees, and again between 1727 and 1737. For earlier dates the record is not so clear. We do not know why. The absence of thin rings between 1805 and 1829 seems to indicate a distinct and exceptionally moist period when, we may suppose,

---

[7] Some of these tree-ring records were gathered by me in 1930 and 1932, others by Dr. Ernst Antevs in 1931 as part of an investigation of Great Basin lakes sponsored jointly by the Carnegie Institution of Washington and the American Geographical Society. The latter group will be described by him in detail in articles on Great Basin tree rings and rainfall fluctuations to be published in the near future.

174

seedlings in considerable numbers were able to make a start and when the natural grass cover once more crept forward.

A second lake record may be noted. Northwest of Goose Lake is Tule Lake, which has a long history of repeated changes in area. In 1846 Lost River, its principal feeder, discharged at a point that was later submerged as the lake expanded. Applegate,[8] who participated in the emigration of 1843, was in the Tule region in 1846. Writing about his experiences in 1877, he then describes the lake as having been rising for many years and gives something more than 9 feet as the total amount of the rise. By referring the dates 1846 and 1877 to the diagram of tree rings (Fig. 6) we see that the earlier date falls in the period of protracted drought and the later one in a time of at least normal rainfall. Applegate's report on the changing levels of Tule Lake is therefore in complete harmony with the tree-ring record. In 1884 Tule Lake had an area of 150 square miles, but by 1924 the lake had shrunk to about half that area. Since 1905 the state as a whole has had a declining amount of rainfall. That successive periods of contraction and expansion mark the history of the lake may be seen from the position and extent of its earlier sediments, some of which lie below the lavas of the region and others above, the latter having been deposited presumably in late Pleistocene or in Recent time.[9]

If there is one clear conclusion that comes out of the evidence of such records it is that mankind in occupying marginal areas of the world should extend and intensify record keeping—of rainfall, ground water, streamflow, glacial discharge, snow cover, tree rings. It was not until about 1896 that the Division of Hydrography of the U. S. Geological Survey began systematically to gauge the western streams. It was not until the present century that most communities in the West began to see the importance of keeping a record of changes in the ground-water level. The vastness of the underground water supply seemed to indicate that they could go on pumping it out forever in undiminished amount. Now we see that over a large part of the Great Plains we have been drawing on savings just as we have done with the retreating glaciers. We know that in some instances either we have definitely used up a part of our inheritance of ground water or our present agricultural practices have steadily lowered the supply by alarming amounts.[10] Irrigation, for example, spreads upon the

[8] Lindsay Applegate: Notes and Reminiscences of Laying Out and Establishing the Old Emigrant Road into Southern Oregon in the Year 1846, *Quarterly Oregon Hist. Soc.*, Vol. 22, 1921, pp. 12–45, especially p. 24.

[9] M. A. Peacock: The Modoc Lava Field, Northern California, *Geogr. Rev.*, Vol. 21, 1931, pp. 259–275; reference on p. 273.

[10] O. E. Meinzer: Water-supply Conditions in the Drought-stricken Regions, *Public Works*, Vol. 65, 1934, pp. 19–20. See other instances in southern California in H. F. Raup: Land Use and Water Supply Problems in Southern California: The Case of the Perris Valley, *Geogr. Rev.*, Vol. 22, 1932, pp. 270–278.

fields water that will be evaporated in large part—thus permitting less of it than formerly to sink into the soil to replenish the ground water.

When the water table is lowered it is necessary to deepen wells everywhere. The deeper the well the more expensive it is to raise the water to the surface—expensive in human energy if the pump is operated by hand, expensive in machinery and gasoline if it is operated by either wind or motor. In many places in the West wells are so deep and the cost of gasoline for motor-driven pumps so high that a gallon of water costs as much as a gallon of gasoline! Merely deepening wells and pursuing the retreating ground water is not enough. In some cases the ground-water layer has actually been pumped dry.

THE RAINFALL CURVE

There is no such thing as a regular cyclic change in the rainfall of the United States. There is a "wave-like" progression of the rainfall curve for any one station, but there is no "apparent conformity to any law of succession."[11] That is to say, the change from dry to wet or wet to dry is comparatively uniform in progress, but the time intervals are decidedly irregular (Fig. 7). This is not the only difficulty. The *regions* of the United States vary in phase: that is, when one region is enjoying an increase of rainfall another may be suffering a decrease. If the intervals of greater rainfall are taken as 40, 60, or 80 years in length, and the periods of protracted drought 5 to 12 years in length, we may ask: "For what are we now planning and building— for the more limited period of drought or for the longer period of greater rainfall?" We do not depopulate the Lower Alluvial Valley of the Mississippi because there are occasional floods. We know that the floods will destroy some farm land, carry away houses, drown some of the livestock, and drive out people temporarily. But we also know that these burdens can be borne either by the local inhabitants or by the larger communities of which they are a part because the floods come only at intervals. In the period in which there are no floods tne crops that are raised restore the livestock and the farm buildings and reassure the people. In the meantime, there are built an increasing number of protective levees and extended drainage and water-impounding works. In spite of the earthquake hazard of California, which all recognize and which all know will mean death and property destruction for some persons at a future time, the state continues to grow in population. The hazards are accepted as a necessary part of life in that region, though measures are constantly applied to the minimizing of risk.

---

[11] J. B. Kincer: Precipitation Trends, *Bull. Amer. Meteorol. Soc.*, Vol. 15, 1934, pp. 191–193; reference on p. 191.

176

Applied to the submarginal lands of the West, this means that we have to balance longer periods of fairly good years against shorter periods of bad years. The records are not abundant and reliable enough for us to say at the present time how far we should go in drawing population off the land or in building dams and contriving other storage schemes in areas of deficient water supply. We do know this, that the beneficial effects of dam building, tree planting, and the

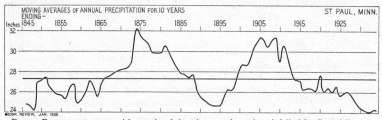

Fig. 7—From 1905 to 1934, with occasional short interruptions, the rainfall of St. Paul, Minn., has been declining. Past records show that equally prolonged dry periods have been followed by periods of more than normal rainfall. The surface of the ground water rises and falls (with lag) in sympathy with rainfall variability. The heavy horizontal line indicates mean annual rainfall, 27.3 inches. (Diagram supplied by the U. S. Weather Bureau.)

like encourage us to believe that we are on the right track when we extend these beneficent operations in places or within areas *where scientific studies indicate the greatest possibilities of success and where the population can profitably remain if the risk be reduced.*

How Far Can Science Go?

It is sometimes assumed that the answer to the question of so-called permanent settlement in areas of risk is to be found in economic conditions alone or in physical conditions alone. Only the amateur can think this way. Physical conditions and economic and social conditions dovetail. All economic opportunities rest in the last analysis on the land and its wealth in the form of agricultural soil fertility, minerals, grass and forest growth, and water supply.

The climatic facts alone are not going to decide which parts of the West will be permanently inhabited. Those submarginal areas that have lowest reliability of rainfall *and* that have the poorest soil and the roughest surface and lie farthest from transportation lines should be abandoned first of all. The word "abandoned" is used only in a relative sense. Such areas may have land suitable for grazing if not for grain. Access to transportation lines is not so important in the livestock industry, since, for reasonable distances, the product can be walked to market or to a railway. Motor transport and roads have improved so greatly that livestock is often transported a hundred or two hundred miles from ranch to market.[12] In 1932, when wheat was sell-

---

[12] Bowman, The Pioneer Fringe, p. 70.

ing at 24 cents a bushel at Dawson Creek in the Peace River District of British Columbia, the limit of haulage was set by the price. There were beautiful fields of wheat 80 or 90 miles from the railway, but it cost twice as much to haul the product to the railway as the farmer could get for the crop when he delivered it to the elevator! It was better to grow grain on poorer land nearer the railway. Thirty miles was considered about the limit for haulage for much of the wheat country in the High Plains in 1930; yet some farmers were hauling wheat 60 miles to the railway and making a small profit by selling at 60 cents a bushel.

It cannot be assumed that because we do not need all of our agricultural land at the present time we shall not need it in the future. Today there is only one acre of first-class land per inhabitant of the United States, and only one additional acre of second-class land; marginal, submarginal, and doubtful land amounts to five acres per person and desert or otherwise useless land, six acres. The federal government has embarked upon a scheme for the purchase of submarginal land. Anyone who has examined at first hand some of the precarious homesteads in the semiarid and arid West will agree that it is better to buy out a family and subsidize it for a fresh start than to supply it with food four years out of five as a measure of charity. When whole counties are in distress and require state or national help for a period of years it is time that at least experimental efforts be made to improve the lot of the settler. Rural slums are as definite a menace as city slums.

It can safely be said that some of the land that will be purchased under any present national scheme will some day be resold to settlers because of increasing rainfall over a period long enough to hearten the bolder spirits and lead again to a forward push of settlement. It can be predicted with complete assurance that members of Congress will rise thirty, forty, or fifty years from now and declaim against the shortsightedness of the legislatures and leaders of 1934–1935 who talked as if the whole West were becoming a desert once more, the grasslands permanently destroyed, the ground-water level permanently lowered, and the land faced with permanent disaster.

Nature has an answer to the prophets of disaster whose gestures are too wide. "The forces of life" have a curious way of ridiculing our prophecies. When we think that everything is improving steadily, we are disillusioned by disaster. After years of hardship, when we see permanent ruin about us, Nature picks up again and surprises us with her beneficence. There is in preparation a so-called "Atlas of Calamities." An essay should accompany it entitled "Calamities That Never Happened." Nature's time schedule seems to be made up only a little way ahead.

We speak of climatic changes as cyclic in character. If the cycles

178

FIG. 8

FIG. 9

FIG. 10

FIG. 8—Looking east between the South Platte and the North Platte over typical countryside in western Nebraska. Marginal agriculture on locally favorable tracts.

FIG. 9—Original sod cover of flat-topped High Plains of western Kansas, 80 miles north of Garden City.

FIG. 10—Tree-lined drainage courses of the plains country of northwestern Kansas near Atwood. No trees grow upon the broad, flat, naturally grass-covered interfluves.

179

were regular in the past, we could predict them by the simple process
of carrying the pattern of our curves forward. Unfortunately, this
is not the case. The sunspot cycles themselves have changed in length.
Up to 1645 they occurred in 11-year periods; from 1645 to 1715 they
"faded out";[13] between 1748 and 1788 there were four complete
sunspot cycles of almost 10 years each; between 1788 and 1837, three
complete cycles of 14 years each and one cycle of 7 years. What caused
the change? No one knows. Will they change in phase again and go
down to 7 or up to 14? No one knows. All that we do know is that
natural changes in climatic conditions seem inevitable and that they
are irregular whatever their cause. Changes in solar radiation cannot
be the whole cause of climatic changes or the forces involved must
have curiously variable effects, in view of the lack of correspondence
in cycle phase when we compare rainfall figures or tree rings from
different regions. Record keeping and analysis may reveal a clue to
the apparently complex causes of climatic change. The power of
forecast may one day be ours. As yet it eludes us.

The physical geography and climatology of a region are of first
importance because they show where economic effort of a given type
should be concentrated. The less extreme climatic conditions of
former years in the West will in all probability come again. The
grass cover may be permanently destroyed in some places. Where
are the places? Science is attempting to find out. Science is investi-
gating the local climatology of the region, the little climatic regions.
Some will appear as permanently too risky for agriculture; others will
show that only a moderate degree of risk is involved in their agricultural occupation. There is also the question of secular or long-range
changes in climate. Is the earth as a whole becoming hotter and
drier or colder and more moist? The Ice Age ended 25,000 years ago
and began perhaps a million or several million years ago. The longest
rainfall record in the United States is 121 years (New Bedford,
Conn.) or 196 years if a discontinuous record is taken (Charleston,
S. C.). It is uninformed boldness, not science, that ventures long-
range prediction upon this short record, however valuable the existing
records may prove to be for short-range prediction. One can safely
predict for our dry West a rainfall heavier than that of the present.
One can also be sure that this will come in a very few years; and even
that its return is near, if our weather records mean anything at all.

CLIMATIC VARIATIONS

A graphic expression of the variability of climate is given in the
series of maps elsewhere in this issue of the *Geographical Review*.[14]

[13] A. E. Douglass: Climatic Cycles and Tree-Growth, *Carnegie Instn. Publ. No. 289*, Vol. 2, 1928,
p. 133.
[14] H. M. Kendall: Notes on Climatic Boundaries in the Eastern United States, pp. 117 to 124.

180

FIG. 11

FIG. 12

FIG. 13

FIG. 11—Abandoned ranch buildings near Horse Lake, northeastern California, in a region of marginal agriculture.

FIG. 12—Forested mountain border on left (Sierra Nevada foothills), irrigation in right background, desert to right of photograph. Looking north between Reno and Carson City, Nevada.

FIG. 13—Light soil, locally windblown, in country west of Pasco, Washington, north of the Columbia River. Green and purple sage and greasewood. Submarginal agriculture on local tracts interspersed with grazing lands.

181

They emphasize the conception of a climatic boundary as the mean position of a transition belt rather than as a rigidly placed line. All our climatic belts expand and contract. In individual years a third of the United States may be "desert." It was once the fashion to laugh at the extension of the phrase "Great American Desert" upon our maps across the High Plains of western Kansas and the Panhandle of Texas (Fig. 14). The past few years suggest that in Long's day (1819–20)[15] and in Frémont's day (1842–44)[16] it may not have been so foolish. Coming out of the timbered Mississippi Valley, Long saw nineteen-twentieths of the surface in the Osage-Missouri region covered with prairie.[17] The sea of grass farther west—timberless, vast—naturally inspired extravagant terms in contrast. There were actually drier times in Frémont's day, if the record of the tree rings and the Great Basin lakes means anything. Now another long dry period has come—not only for the Great Basin, including eastern Oregon and Washington, but also for the central plains (Fig. 6). But wet or dry, the grass cover of plains and prairies east of the Rockies is now broken by the plow to an extent never before known since the white man discovered the prairies. This entails permanent injury to topsoil and a permanently lower water table unless we reseed the land where the damage is serious and change our type of land use at least locally.

The areas with which we are here concerned are so large and the bad effects of sod destruction so widespread that no local, county, or state measures will suffice. Coöperative measures are required, such as irrigation and reclamation measures of conventional type. Although we cannot change the climate of the future, we can protect ourselves from its economically worst effects. There will be for some time to come a rather constant shifting of agricultural settlement and land use due to the play of economic forces. Farmers deplore 20-cent wheat as much as a 10-inch rainfall where 20 inches of rain are customary. A severe drop in the market price of grain may be as serious as a drought. The marginal farmer is not self-contained to the degree that the early settlers were. He needs expensive machinery, his land is taxed more heavily than was that of the pioneers, and he and his family have a standard of living to maintain. We are not yet able to draw a line upon the map confidently and say that, given a set of economic postulates (including a given standard of living and a given market price for product), that line represents the limit of *permanent* agriculture. Back of the answer are population pressure, future living standards, world market conditions, and other unknowns as well as climatic variability.

---

[15] R. G. Thwaites, edit.: Early Western Travels, 1748–1846, Vol. 17, Cleveland, 1905, p. 191.

[16] J. C. Frémont: Report of the Exploring Expedition to the Rocky Mountains in the Year 1842, and to Oregon and North California in the Years 1843–'44, Washington, 1845.

[17] Thwaites, *op. cit.*, p. 123.

Not being certain that the water table will rise again by any given amount, or the glaciers advance to their former positions, or the rains become as heavy as at one time in the past, or the soil become as fixed as it was when the sod cover was unbroken, we are bound to take preventive measures. It is senseless to let floodwaters drain away to the sea if we need them for irrigation and power development. This is not only a matter of present kilowatts but also a matter of ground water and wells in the long future and over a vast area, a matter of soil erosion and population potential.

THE CLIMATIC MAP OF THE UNITED STATES

There are so many ways of describing rainfall that the selection of a method or a combination of methods in analyzing rainfall records is a matter of first importance if we have specific agricultural objectives in view. Annual and seasonal rainfall, intensity of rainfall, length of growing season, soil absorption, ground cover, evaporation rate—all are in constantly varying relation and intensity. The *effectiveness* of rainfall is determined only by rigorous experimentation in type areas, and the results have only local application. This is a matter of the greatest importance. It is possible to divide the United States into rainfall provinces according to averages extending back to the beginnings of the records, whether these beginnings are remote or recent. This gives us the usual generalized so-called "normal rainfall" map. From it we see that the eastern half of the country is in general moist, the western in general dry, and that in the southwestern section is territory that may be described as desert.

Generalizations of this type are of very little value except in a first elementary approach. As a working basis for analyzing agricultural or grazing activities, or as a means of understanding exceptional drought conditions, such a map is almost without value. The kind of map that we require for practical purposes is one showing in detail what happens to rainfall on its way to roots and ground water and how often it happens. The catastrophic years must be shown as well as the normal years.

Figure 14 shows a complex series of lines in the middle part of the United States. It is the significance and relationship of these lines that give the map broad diagnostic value. It is drawn to show how far away from a simple generalized map of the United States we must go to arrive at a realistic knowledge of the agricultural effectiveness of rainfall, locality by locality. East of the Mississippi the problem of rainfall is rarely a critical one. The only exception is the territory comprising Illinois, Indiana, and the parts of Ohio and Kentucky enclosed by the broken line that forms a loop south of the Great Lakes region. In that section there are occasional extensions of drought

183

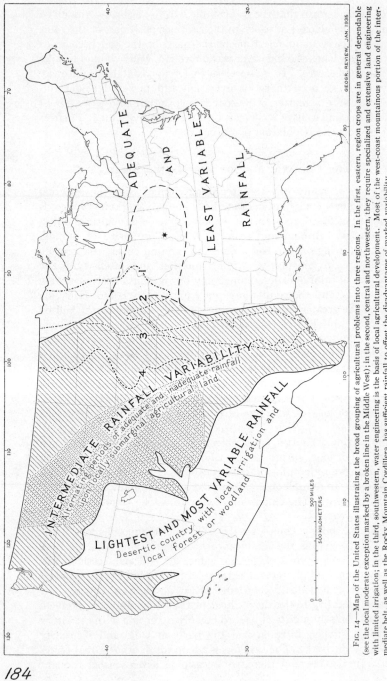

ADEQUATE AND LEAST VARIABLE RAINFALL

INTERMEDIATE RAINFALL VARIABILITY
Alternating periods of adequate and inadequate rainfall
upon locally submarginal agricultural land

LIGHTEST AND MOST VARIABLE RAINFALL
Desertic country with local irrigation and
local forest or woodland

500 MILES

500 KILOMETERS

FIG. 14—Map of the United States illustrating the broad grouping of agricultural problems into three regions. In the first, eastern, region crops are in general dependable (see the local moderate exception marked by a broken line in the Middle West); in the second, central and northwestern, they require specialized and extensive land engineering with limited irrigation; in the third, southwestern, water engineering is the basis of local agricultural development. Most of the west-coast mountainous portion of the intermediate belt, as well as the Rocky Mountain Cordillera, has sufficient rainfall to offset the disadvantages of marked variability.

This broad division illustrates a current political condition. To the Congressional bloc comprised of representatives of western mineral, reclamation, and public-land states are now added representatives of Great Plains states where rainfall deficiency creates widespread and intense agricultural problems that result in appeals for federal aid. The center of population (indicated by a star) of the United States, which has traveled westward continuously (see C. O. Paullin: Atlas of the Historical Geography of the United States, New York, 1932) is now only 150 miles east of the easternmost limit of "dry" years!

184

conditions that mark out a special climatic subprovince unlike any-thing elsewhere east of the Mississippi. Between the Mississippi River and the Rocky Mountains there is a broad belt of country that suffers from increasing risk of crop failure. The drought of the immediate past has afflicted it more severely, the area affected has been larger, and the drought has lasted longer than in any earlier period since meteorological stations were established west of the Mississippi. In addition, extremely high temperatures accompanied the drought, and the combination was especially destructive.

From east to west in Figure 14 are four north-south lines that represent four different ways of expressing the change from more favorable to less favorable conditions westward from the central axis of the Mississippi Valley. A moment's study of each will show why the climatic and agricultural crises have conjointly reached so sharp a climax in the states of the Great Plains.

Line 1 represents the limit of the so-called dry years as described by Russell.[18] East of that line in the period 1901 to 1920 there were no so-called dry years.[19] In both 1910 and 1913 there was widespread drought, but the 1910 drought was more intense. Thus it is not merely the extent of the drought that gives it its human importance. A sharp desert year may have more effect on crops, tree seedlings, and soil erosion than half a dozen normally moist years. Likewise, a single exceptionally wet year may start a grass cover that will sur-vive less favorable years. The tree-ring records seem to show that in many forested areas in the West the seedlings got started in a period of greater rainfall, the subsequent forest surviving periods of drought in which seedlings could not get started.

Between Line 1 and the Rockies the territory may be thought of as divided into an eastern portion and a western portion. The eastern has had dry years in the period 1901 to 1920 not more, and generally less, than half the time. The western has had dry years in some sec-tions half the time and in other sections all the time.

Line 2 on the map indicates a division between an eastern section and a western section of the country that takes into account per-centage departures from annual rainfall, relief, latitude, the incidence of summer thundershowers, duration of frozen ground, snowfall, and other factors. West of Line 2 there is an increase in rain variability and, almost up to the Rockies, a decrease in the annual rainfall.

Line 3 represents the division between the so-called humid East and the arid West on still another basis, that developed by Thornthwaite.[20]

[18] R. J. Russell: Dry Climates of the United States: II, Frequency of Dry and Desert Years 1901–20, *Univ. of California Publs. in Geogr.*, Vol. 5, No. 5, 1932, pp. 245–274.

[19] For those with a technical knowledge of climatology it may be noted that a dry year is defined by Russell according to Köppen's classification with slight changes that recognize nine types of effective precipitation regime.

[20] C. W. Thornthwaite: The Climates of North America According to a New Classification, *Geogr. Rev.*, Vol. 21, 1931, pp. 633–655, especially Plate 3 and the method employed on p. 643.

This is based upon the precipitation effectiveness, as related to temperature, for a period of years and therefore lies farther west than Lines 1 and 2.

Line 4 represents a division between territory having no desert years (east) and that having an occasional desert year (west). Between Line 4 and the Rockies we may expect to find in any given

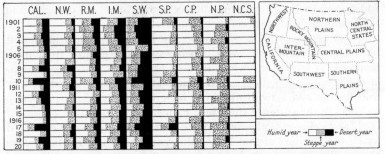

Fig. 15—Diagram, after Russell (see footnote 18), showing the prevalence of desert, steppe, and humid years in the western United States (see key map) in the period 1901–1920. The classification is based on the records of 569 stations and the limiting values are defined thus: "at the mean annual temperature of 55° F. places receiving between 9.5 and 14.0 inches are classed as Steppe . . . those receiving less than 9.5 inches as Desert. . . . At 70° F., Desert areas may receive as much as 13 inches of precipitation." (R. J. Russell: Climates of California, *Univ. of California Publs. in Geogr.*, Vol. 2, No. 4, 1926, p. 76.)

subregion a number of years out of the 20 involved in this study that have experienced desert conditions.

Taking the whole crosshatched area between Line 2 and the Pacific on the west or the Rio Grande on the south, we have a broad stretch of country in which the so-called submarginal lands are found. Given unfavorable soil conditions, these submarginal lands may lie as far east as Line 2. In the main, however, they lie west of Line 3; and most of them lie west of Line 4. We may omit consideration of the southwestern part of the United States that is left blank, because, except locally, the plains portion of this territory is desertic or steppelike and agriculture depends on local irrigation. It is the crosshatched area that contains the local territories in which dry farming has been practiced to offset the hazard not only of regular dryness but of recurrent exceptional dryness. In the southwestern section, the problem of land occupation is a problem in water engineering rather than dry farming and extensive cultivation. Mountains, lakes, lava flows, etc., excluded, the crosshatched area represents territory in which the risk of drought is great enough to enforce special modes of tillage. The eastern margin is an exception. There drought affects the amount of the crop but is not severe enough to require special modes of tillage except at long intervals.

Beginning in 1905 noteworthy changes took place in the rainfall regime of this territory, and these changes illustrate one of the great problems of agricultural meteorology—to know through more extended rainfall observations and deeper analysis what lies back of the strange contrast between the rainfall trends of adjoining sections of the country. In 1930–1931–1932 southeastern Colorado and the extreme western part of Kansas enjoyed exceptionally heavy rainfall. An examination of the records of the weather stations shows that these favorable conditions were shared by a wide extent of country reaching from western Kansas and Nebraska westward and northwestward to include all of Colorado, Wyoming, Idaho, and the western part of Montana. East of that territory there has been on the whole a decline in the rainfall of the shaded area from 1905 to 1934. In the same period the states of Oregon and Washington and a part of northern California also showed a decline broken only by single years of substantially greater rainfall at moderately long intervals. Between these two great areas of declining rainfall and lying astride the Rocky Mountain Cordillera is a broad area (stippled on Fig. 14) with increasing rainfall since 1905 as contrasted with the preceding period of twenty-five or thirty years of smaller rainfall. The state of Oklahoma has also had an increasing amount of rainfall since 1905.

The moral of this brief examination of critical climatological lines upon the map of the United States seems to be rather plain. First, we have no one mode of analyzing rainfall that will give us a result having immediate application to all forms of agriculture in all latitudes north and south across the United States. We are not able to tell the position and extent of belts of heavier rainfall in the future or whether they will disappear altogether for a time. Finally, we do not know whether we are in an ascending or a descending phase of a long-range change in climate. The extreme severity of the drought of the past two years in the Great Plains region cannot be taken to indicate that conditions are worse than they may have been a hundred or two hundred years ago before record-keeping began.

We must continue to employ different forms of expression for representing different aspects of the climate if we are to relate it to agricultural realities region by region. By the same token, the analysis of rainfall records, region by region, must continue at an accelerated pace, in still more variable forms, and for longer periods. Only thus can we expect to obtain a more accurate expression for the degree of risk involved in living in any part of the semiarid region that contains submarginal land upon which, through the technique of dry farming and because of the temporarily high price of grain, settlement became overextended.

187

CORN YIELD AND CLIMATE IN THE CORN BELT

John Kerr Rose

University of Chicago

THE correlation of variations in corn yield with fluctuations of climatic factors is more than an academic problem. Many of the human activities prominent in the Corn Belt, rural or urban, are directly or indirectly related to corn. Beginning with the preparation of the seedbed in spring and extending intermittently through the harvesttime of late autumn, the larger part of the Corn Belt farmer's time and activities is applied to corn. Wintertime activities include the feeding of animals with corn. Corn Belt villages exist mainly to serve the corngrower. The cities buy, process, and sell the products of the cornland and serve the corn farmer in many other ways. The average yearly value of the corn crop of the United States is roughly one twenty-fifth the total value of all plant products grown in the world suitable for human or animal food.

In recent years corn has occupied yearly about 100,000,000 acres[1] of land in the United States—roughly five times the total area of Indiana. Of these 100,000,000 acres, more than 60 per cent[2] lie in the ten states of which parts are included in the geographical division known as the Corn Belt. On an average, about 19 per cent[3] of the area of Iowa is planted to corn. In the heart of the Corn Belt, however, as much as 40 to 50 per cent of the area is in corn yearly. Here no other crop so dominates the landscape. Corn is king.

Perhaps no other thing about the corn crop is so interlocked with the weal and woe of the Corn Belt inhabitants as the yearly variation in yield. The corn crop of the United States fluctuates from about one and a half to about three billion bushels.[4] The yield per unit area fluctuates notably from year to year. For the state of Indiana, some years give an average per-acre yield more than twice as large as some other years. Iowa, commonly considered a relatively stable state climatically, in some years has an average per-acre yield 300 per cent greater than in others.

No other factor affecting the yield of corn from year to year in a given area fluctuates as does weather, or the longer phase of weather, climate. Soil fertility is more or less constant, as is the care given the crop. Varieties are changed slowly. Reed[5] has found that in Iowa

---

[1] *Yearbook of Agric., 1932*, U. S. Dept. of Agriculture, Washington, 1932, p. 608.

[2] W. A. Mattice: Weather and Corn Yields, *Monthly Weather Rev.*, Vol. 59, 1931, pp. 105–112; reference on p. 105.

[3] *Ibid.*, p. 106, Fig. 1.

[4] *Yearbook of Agric., 1932*, loc. cit.

[5] C. D. Reed: Weather and Corn Maturity in Iowa, *Monthly Weather Rev.*, Vol. 55, 1927, pp. 485–488.

the yield has increased slowly over a long period of years, owing, perhaps, in the main to better varieties and improved tillage but possibly also to changes in climate. Insect pests are a variable affecting the crop; insect damage, however, correlates fairly well with drought conditions. Thus climatic factors would seem to be the most potent and hence the most worthy of investigation among those causing fluctuations in the yield of this major crop. The tropical or subtropical origin of corn and the wide variety of climatic conditions even within the Corn Belt suggest that there may well be interesting and peculiar responses to the climate under which corn is now so largely grown.

EARLIER INVESTIGATIONS

It is not surprising that so important a problem early received attention from scientists. Wren,[6] writing in 1901, summarized the existing knowledge and theories concerning corn yield as related to climate. The earlier investigations dealt with temperature more than with any other factor and made no use of mathematical correlation.

Since that time a number of studies, mostly utilizing mathematical correlation, have been published on the various phases of the relation between corn yield and climate. Smith[7] in 1904 pointed out with the aid of graphs the correlation of corn yield with rainfall for June, July, and August, especially for July. In 1914[8] by means of simple correlation he studied the relation of yield to temperature and rainfall. He found that July was the most important calendar month and precipitation the most important factor. Wallace[9] in 1920 agreed with Smith that July rain was an important factor but not in all parts of the Corn Belt. He concluded that it was easy to predict corn yield from weather in the south half of the Corn Belt but difficult in the north half. Kincer and Mattice[10] in 1928 found several weather factors, mainly for weekly periods, which gave relatively high correlation coefficients. Mattice[11] in 1931 grouped states according to the climatic factors giving the highest correlation coefficients and thereby arrived at a threefold division of the states of the Corn Belt. In that study, too, early-season and late-season factors were first shown to be of considerable importance. Hodges,[12] in an examination of the effect of rainfall and temperature on corn yields in three type-of-farming areas in Kansas, found considerable variation within that state. In 1932 the present writer[13] showed by means of climographs that in Indiana high temperatures are bad for corn yield and that, other factors being equal, a short season between killing frosts gives a higher corn yield than a long frostless season. Huntington[14] in 1933 used the climograph method to show that climate all through the year, and not merely in the growing season, shows a considerable

[6] H. B. Wren: Climate and Corn, *Monthly Weather Rev.*, Vol. 29, 1901, pp. 8–14.

[7] J. W. Smith: Relation of Precipitation to Yield of Corn, *Yearbook U. S. Dept. of Agric. for 1903*, Washington, 1904, pp. 215–224.

[8] *Idem:* The Effect of Weather upon the Yield of Corn, *Monthly Weather Rev.*, Vol. 42, 1914, pp. 78–93.

[9] H. A. Wallace: Mathematical Inquiry into the Effect of Weather on Corn Yield in the Eight Corn Belt States, *Monthly Weather Rev.*, Vol. 48, 1920, pp. 439–446.

[10] J. B. Kincer and W. A. Mattice: Statistical Correlations of Weather Influence on Crop Yields, *Monthly Weather Rev.*, Vol. 56, 1928, pp. 53–57.

[11] *Op. cit.*

[12] J. A. Hodges: The Effect of Rainfall and Temperature on Corn Yields in Kansas, *Journ. of Farm Economics*, Vol. 13, 1931, pp. 305–318.

[13] J. K. Rose: Climate and Corn Yield in Indiana, 1887–1930, *Proc. Indiana Acad. of Sci.*, Vol. 41, 1931, Indianapolis, 1932, pp. 317–321.

[14] Ellsworth Huntington, F. E. Williams, and Samuel Van Valkenburg: Economic and Social Geography, New York and London, 1933, Chapter 4.

measure of correlation with corn yields.   A still later study by Robb[15] finds fairly high simple correlation coefficients between yield and rainfall for July and August in northeastern Kansas.

PURPOSES AND TECHNIQUE OF THIS STUDY

In the present study of the problem the whole Corn Belt has been dealt with on the basis of numerous selected county units.   The correlation coefficients calculated for these samples provide a basis for the determination of transitions from areas in which yield is influenced by one factor or set of factors to those in which it is influenced by others. As a result, more detailed and probably more reliable information regarding the correlation of corn yield with climatic factors within, and just beyond the margins of, the Corn Belt is available.   Such information, besides being an addition to geographical knowledge, may contribute toward better crop-yield forecasting by government and private agencies.   It is not too much, perhaps, to expect that, if the present trends toward planned agricultural economy continue, some information so gained may be found useful in modifying or changing present agricultural practices.

A second purpose of this study is to illustrate the possibilities of what may well be called "statistical method in geography."   Field methods serve mostly for the collection of data.   The problem of analyzing these data is complicated by the fact that the geographer commonly works with many variables, independent and dependent. Hence the methods of correlation analysis[16] would seem especially promising tools for geographical investigation.

Several of the writers mentioned above made use of statistical correlation.   It is significant, however, that these investigators used state averages for data if they wished to cover a large area or else confined their work to one or two small areas. Such areal units were not suitable for the present investigation, in which it was especially desired to discover such variation as exists from area to area.   Fifty-five counties, the smallest units for which yield data were available, were studied.   Such a number of counties, well distributed over the Corn Belt and just beyond its margins, covered the area fairly closely and also permitted closer spacing in a few areas for which greater detail was desired.   These sample counties were not chosen at random.   They were selected with a view to covering the Corn Belt as well as possible, and each county was supposed to have fairly uniform soils, topography, etc. Partly for this reason, small counties were preferred to larger ones.   In each county there was at least one weather station, fairly representative of conditions in the county. In the selection of the samples, office work, conferences, reconnaissance, and traverses in the field were supplemented by firsthand knowledge of parts of the Corn Belt.

Inasmuch as it was planned to consider the areal distribution pattern of the coefficients for the Corn Belt as a whole, it seemed best to have data for the several

[15] A. D. Robb: The Critical Period of Corn in Northeastern Kansas, *Monthly Weather Rev.*, Vol. 62, 1934, pp. 286–289.

[16] For a simple exposition see Mordecai Ezekiel: Methods of Correlation Analysis, New York, 1930. Chapters 3, 4, and 5 are especially recommended to those not familiar with simple concepts of correlation.

190

states as comparable in period as practicable. In connection with this question, correlations of yield with several climatic factors were run for a number of Iowa counties for three widely different periods. The results obtained showed that, although the coefficients varied somewhat in value with change in the length of period, they did not change greatly in significance: those of little significance remained so, and the significant ones remained significant. Even so, it was necessary to use a shorter period of years in some states, notably Ohio and Minnesota, than was desired.

TABLE I—LENGTH OF LONGEST PERIOD STUDIED

STATE	PERIOD*	STATE	PERIOD*	STATE	PERIOD*
Illinois	22	Michigan	19	Ohio	9
Indiana	22	Minnesota . . .	12	South Dakota . .	*16
Iowa	24	Missouri	19	Wisconsin	16
Kansas	24	Nebraska	24		

*In years. All periods end with 1932.

In all, more than 2000 simple correlation coefficients were calculated and then mapped and the isopleths drawn.[17] In numerous cases the relationship was linear; hence linear correlation was employed throughout. Slow upward trends in the yield data of many of the counties were not eliminated, partly because they were slight and partly because such trends are supposedly due, to some extent, to the effects of complicated and incomplete climatic cycles.

Multiple correlations involving in most cases seven independent climatic factors besides the dependent factor of yield were calculated for 29 counties. The resulting multiple correlation coefficients are shown on Figure 12. The climatic factors included in the multiple correlations commonly varied from one part of the Corn Belt to another. Factors to be included were selected on the basis of the simple correlation coefficients obtained. The results obtained in the multiple problems were calculated for neighboring samples and so as to cover the months May through August.

Two tests of the significance of the coefficients are the numerical value of the coefficient and the question whether or not the coefficient fits into the areal distribution pattern. In this study, if the coefficient is as high as ±.40 or higher, it is of considerable significance, statistically speaking, being three or more times the probable error. Even so, if it stands isolated in the areal distribution pattern of coefficients, its significance is to be seriously questioned.

In this investigation simple correlation coefficients of corn yields with 35 climatic factors or aspects of factors were determined for each of the 55 counties studied.[18]

CORN YIELD AND TEMPERATURE

An important part of this study has been devoted to correlating variations in corn yield with variations in temperature. Some twenty-

---

[17] It is suggested that isopleths applied to correlation coefficients be called *isocorrelates.*

[18] The 35 climatic factors and aspects of factors were: for May, June, July, and August: precipitation, mean temperature; for June, July, and August: accumulated degrees above 90° F., days having temperatures 90° F. or above, accumulated degrees below 60° F., nights having temperatures 60° F. or lower, clear days, partly cloudy days, cloudy days, rainy days (0.1 inch or more); length of the growing season measured in days between killing frosts; number of days before June 1 that the last killing frost in spring occurred; July rainfall weighted so as to eliminate the effect of local thundershowers upon a single station in any one year. Other factors and those mentioned for other months were also investigated to some extent.

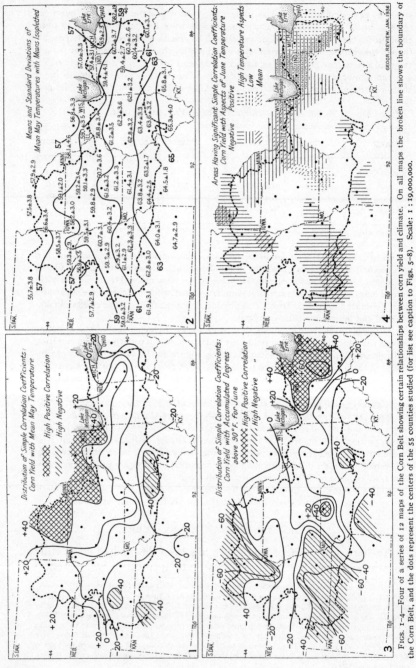

FIGS. 1-4—Four of a series of 12 maps of the Corn Belt showing certain relationships between corn yield and climate. On all maps the broken line shows the boundary of the Corn Belt, and the dots represent the centers of the 55 counties studied (for list see caption to Figs. 5-8). Scale: 1 : 19,000,000.

one maps were drawn up to show the distribution of correlation coefficients between corn·yield and various aspects of temperature during the spring and summer months. In general it was found that over large parts of the Corn Belt temperatures correlate more significantly with corn yield than has previously been believed.

Figures 1 and 2 show a sample pair of maps for mean monthly temperature. The areal distribution pattern of coefficients between corn yield and mean May temperature shows the Corn Belt practically halved by the line of zero correlation. It seems from this that variations in mean May temperature have little effect on corn yields throughout the middle zone of the Corn Belt. It may be said that to the north, roughly, the higher the mean May temperature in any year, the better the corn crop; whereas to the south poorer-than-average yields occur after May temperatures above average. It is seen, however, that in these regions only a few of the coefficients are high enough to be called significant. Thus in only a few relatively small areas would a knowledge of the mean May temperature be of much help as an aid in predicting the yield of corn.

Wallace, using state averages, found very low coefficients between corn yield and mean May temperature. Figure 1 helps to explain why that might be the case: such states as Illinois and Iowa are partly negative and partly positive in regard to this factor. Thus positive and negative areas would tend to cancel each other when included in state averages.

The areal distribution of the coefficients (Fig. 1) corresponds fairly well with the distribution pattern of mean May temperature (Fig. 2). Areas in which higher-than-average mean May temperatures are followed by lower-than-average corn yields have May temperatures of above 61° F.; areas of significant positive correlation have temperatures of 59° F. or lower. Comparison of the pattern of correlation coefficients with other supposedly related distributions sometimes gives positive and sometimes negative results. There seems to be a correspondence between the areal distribution pattern of coefficients and the date of corn planting. For areas in which corn is, on the average, planted before May 1 the correlation coefficients are negative; i.e., the warmer the month of May in such areas, the poorer the yield of corn. The yield in areas in which planting commonly is done after May 1 correlates positively with mean May temperature. There seems to be little correspondence between the distribution pattern of coefficients and such factors as soil and altitude.

One temperature factor that yielded surprisingly widespread significant coefficients is accumulated degrees above 90° F. For all three summer months this factor gave significant results. Figure 3 shows the large areas of significant correlation coefficients between corn yield and accumulated degrees above 90° F. for June. Some of the coefficients are more than seven times the standard error. It is notable that in the southwestern and northwestern parts of the Corn Belt high temperatures in June are bad for corn, whereas in the northeast much warm weather in June seems to be followed by good yields. However, in the area of positive significance there are usually less than ten accumulated degrees above 90° F. Areas having more than 30 accumulated degrees above 90° F. show for the most part relatively high negative coefficients. For this factor correspondence with soil, altitude, yield pattern, and date of planting seems to be lacking.

From an examination of Figure 4 it is plain that June temperature, in one or more of the aspects investigated, has correlated significantly with corn yield in certain parts of the Corn Belt, notably the northeastern, northwestern, and southwestern. On the other hand, it is evident that no coefficient as high as ±.40 has been found for large parts of the region.

June temperatures are significant,[19] highly significant, or even critical in the northeastern part of the Corn Belt. The coefficients are mostly lower than ±.60, but there is no disagreement among aspects; that is to say, high-temperature factors (accumulated degrees above 90° F. and the number of days 90° F. or higher) and mean temperature give positive coefficients, and low-temperature factors (accumulated degrees below 60° F. and the number of nights 60° F. or lower) give negative coefficients. Presumably the corn crop of the relatively humid northeastern part of the Corn Belt commonly needs more heat than it receives during early stages of its growth.

June temperatures are also significant or highly significant in the northwestern and southwestern parts of the Corn Belt. In June, corn is nearing the reproductive stage in the southwest but is considerably less advanced in the northwest. Nevertheless, June heat in both of these subhumid regions of blackerth or chestnuterth soils is too great to favor corn yields. The area of low correlation separating the two regions seems to differ from them in natural factors only in that much of it has deep loess soil.

From the summary map of the correlations of corn yield with aspects of July temperature (Fig. 5) it is seen that the correlations are not to be considered as critical in any part of the Corn Belt. Nevertheless, variations in July temperatures do accompany variations in corn yields in a highly significant manner on the northwest and southwest margins of the Corn Belt and in a significant manner along the whole of the south and east margins. Thus it would seem that July temperatures are somewhat too high for corn along the humid part of

---

[19] If, of the aspects (high, low, etc.) of a certain factor (June temperature, etc.) investigated for any particular sample, a maximum or near-maximum number gives coefficients above ±.40, that factor is said to be *critical*. If only one of the aspects investigated gives ±.40 or higher, the factor is said to be *significant*. A condition approximately intermediate between significant and critical is spoken of as *highly significant*.

the south margin and decidedly too high on the southwest and north-west margins, where moisture is not plentiful. As for low temperatures, except in an eastern area, July temperatures can scarcely be said to fall so low as to affect adversely the yield of corn.

The summary map of correlations of corn yield with three aspects of August temperature (Fig. 6) indicates that August temperatures are to be considered as critical in much of the western part of the Corn Belt. There is no disagreement among the aspects investigated—mean and high temperatures give negative coefficients, and any increase in accumulated degrees below 60° F. is likely to be accompanied by higher-than-average yields. It is worth noting that this western area is one of blackerth or chestnuterth soils and rather scanty precipitation. Along the whole south margin of the Corn Belt high August temperatures seem unfavorable to corn yield. The north margin, particularly in the more humid eastern two-thirds of the Corn Belt, seems to suffer slightly from lack of enough heat during August.

Corn Yield and Precipitation

Two aspects of precipitation have been correlated with corn yield in this investigation. Total amounts of precipitation by months for the four months of May, June, July, and August have been considered—with enlightening results. The number of days having precipitation of .01 inch or more for each of the months June, July, and August was investigated—without significant results. In general, this study hardly bears out the conclusions of those earlier investigators who found variations in precipitation to be an exceedingly important factor influencing corn yield.

Of the four months for which variations in precipitation were correlated with variations in corn yield, July gave the most significant results. July rainfall correlated positively with corn yield in 49 of the 55 counties studied (see Fig. 7). The negative coefficients are all too low to be significant. This would seem to indicate that in most of the Corn Belt more-than-normal July rainfall has a beneficial effect on the corn crop, though few of the coefficients are extremely high.

As is shown in Figure 8, variation in precipitation for any of the four months, May, June, July, and August, significantly accompanies variation in corn yield in only slightly more than half of the Corn Belt. The correlation is almost wholly positive; i.e. with the exception of early-season precipitation in two small areas, above-average precipitation is significantly accompanied by an increase in corn yield. In the southwest and northwest and in an eastern area variations in precipitation are highly significant or even critical. In general, early-season precipitation is a fairly good indicator of corn yield on the northwest, west, and southwest margins of the Corn Belt. Midseason

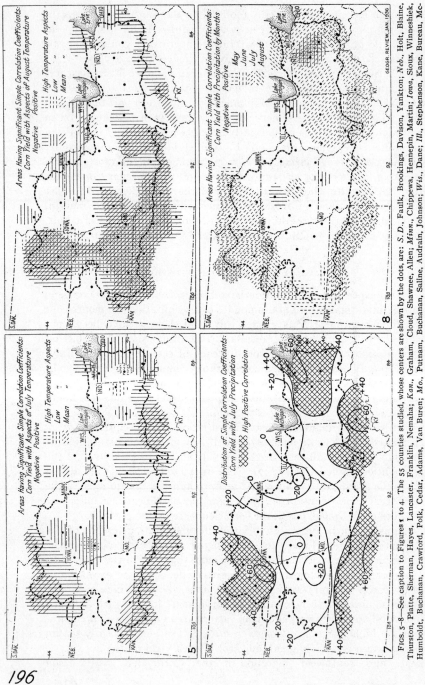

FIGS. 5–8—See caption to Figures 1 to 4. The 55 counties studied, whose centers are shown by the dots, are: *S. D.*, Faulk, Brookings, Davison, Yankton; *Neb.*, Holt, Blaine, Thurston, Platte, Sherman, Hayes, Lancaster, Franklin, Nemaha; *Kan.*, Graham, Cloud, Shawnee, Allen; *Minn.*, Chippewa, Hennepin, Martin; *Iowa*, Sioux, Winneshiek, Humboldt, Buchanan, Crawford, Polk, Cedar, Adams, Van Buren; *Mo.*, Putnam, Buchanan, Saline, Audrain, Johnson; *Wis.*, Dane; *Ill.*, Stephenson, Kane, Bureau, McDonough, McLean, Macoupin, Coles, St. Clair; *Mich.*, Kalamazoo, Washtenaw; *Ind.*, St. Joseph, Huntington, Tippecanoe, Rush, Knox; *Ohio*, Fulton, Ashland, Shelby, Franklin, Clinton.

precipitation, on the other hand, particularly weighted July rainfall, seems significant in about half of the Corn Belt, but more so in the eastern, northwestern, and southwestern parts.

The data here summarized indicate that the role of rainfall variations in affecting the yield of corn is by no means simple or overwhelmingly important. Only locally is precipitation a very significant predictive factor.

Corn Yield Correlated with Miscellaneous Factors

No attempt has been made in this study to correlate with corn yield every possible factor influencing the growth and yield of corn. Other factors than climate have been considered only in an effort to explain the distribution of high and low correlation coefficients between corn yield and climatic factors. Nor have all climatic factors been treated. Temperature and rainfall, presumably the most important, have been treated rather fully. A number of minor factors have also been considered, but with little result. Some of these are of only slight predictive value because basic data for use in computation are as yet largely lacking, others because the correlation coefficients obtained are of relatively little significance.

Insolation data are collected by only a few stations in the Corn Belt. From correlation of yield and insolation for Lancaster County, Nebraska, it may be concluded that insolation in that county either has little effect on corn yield or is so intercorrelated with other factors that its real significance is hidden. Evaporation calculated for Lancaster County—especially evaporation compared with precipitation—correlates negatively with corn yield. For August the correlation coefficient is highly significant (-.78). It is to be regretted that evaporation data are not systematically collected at more weather stations. In general, work on factors of cloudiness gave little return.

Subdivisions of the Corn Belt

A general summary of the number of climatic factors important for any county is presented on Figure 9. Only factors showing significant coefficients over a fairly wide area of the Corn Belt were selected.

On the southwest margin variations in as many as ten climatic factors are shown to correlate significantly with variations in corn yield. The northwestern area has nearly as many, and parts of the southern and eastern marginal areas show no paucity of factors giving significant correlations with yield. On the other hand, very few of the climatic factors studied correlate significantly with corn yield in those samples located near the core of the Corn Belt. In Bureau County, Illinois, not one of the 35 climatic factors or aspects of factors gave a

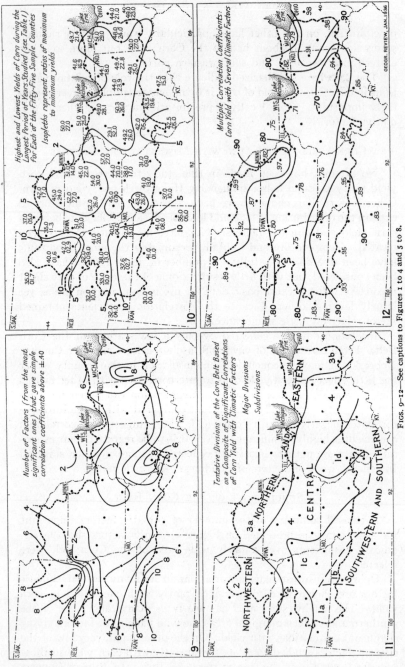

FIGS. 9-12—See captions to Figures 1 to 4 and 5 to 8.

simple correlation coefficient as high as ±.40. This would seem to indicate that climatic conditions near the optimum for corn yield exist in the heart of the Corn Belt but act increasingly as limiting factors toward the margins.

Near the center of the Corn Belt mean yields are comparatively high, and although yields fluctuate from year to year (see Fig. 10), no one factor by itself seems to have much weight in affecting the yield. On the other hand, near the margins yield seems to depend on a very delicate balance of climatic factors, which fluctuate widely from year to year and are seldom very favorable to high yields. Here numerous climatic factors are significant, and any one of them has relatively great effect on yield.

On the basis of the summary maps (Figs. 4, 5, 6, and 8) Figure 11, showing tentative forecast divisions of the Corn Belt, was prepared. The boundaries on it are not to be regarded as placed exactly or as unchanging; they are merely an attempt to present general divisions of the Corn Belt on the basis of the present study.

In area 1 midseason temperatures are critical, precipitation and early-season temperatures being of importance in some parts. This is the area of the Corn Belt that has the highest temperatures and has at the same time, in parts at least, scanty rainfall. Further to complicate matters, in parts of this area some of the blackerths and chestnuterth soils have a heavy subsoil that lessens water-holding capacity. The mean yield of corn to the acre is low, though the soil can produce good yields during the rare years when climate is favorable (see Fig. 10).

In subarea 1A early-season precipitation is significant and early-season temperatures are highly significant or critical. So many climatic factors are significant and generally unfavorable to corn yield in this area that it is a rare year indeed when yields of 30 bushels or more to an acre are obtained. Complete failure here is not unknown.

In subarea 1B midseason precipitation is highly significant. Yields here fluctuate widely.

To the north and east, in subarea 1C, no precipitation factor gives significant correlations. This may be due to slightly greater humidity, and probably the loess soils have considerable effect.

Factors of minor significance in subarea 1D are early-season temperatures and midseason precipitation, especially for July. Midseason temperatures seem to be not so critical here as in other subdivisions of area 1.

Area 2 is also one in which midseason temperatures and both early-season and midseason precipitation are significant or highly significant. Here the yield of corn to an acre is rather low as compared with the Corn Belt as a whole. Yields vary greatly from year to year (Fig. 10). The fact that all the samples show at least one year when the yield was 35 bushels or more an acre means that the soil can produce if other factors, mainly climatic, permit.

Area 3 is one in which early-season temperatures are critical. Corn in this area needs more heat during planting and the time of early growth. Even so, the average yields are more than 30 bushels an acre, in some counties even more than 35 bushels. This is very largely an area of gray-brownerths, but other areas with the same types of soil give no such correlations.

As regards climatic factors of minor significance, subarea 3A shows almost perfect transition from northwest to southeast. In the northwestern part both midseason temperatures and midseason precipitation are significant; in the middle part—northeastern Iowa and northwestern Illinois—only midseason temperatures remain as a factor of minor significance; and in the eastern part there is no minor factor.

In subarea 3B midseason precipitation and midseason temperatures—one or both—are factors of minor significance. Early-season temperatures become less critical to the south but are highly significant near the east margin.

Area 4 is one in which variations in climatic factors do not seem to be critical for corn yield. A variety of factors give significant coefficients, but there is little possibility of generalization regarding climatic factors significant in the area. The westerly protrusion of this area with slightly significant correlations, extending as it does between two areas in which midseason temperatures are critical, is interesting. A suggested hypothesis is that the loess soil found here does not lose its moisture readily even during the hot part of the season, hence the corn plants suffer very little from temperatures that damage the crop severely in areas almost equally humid to the north and south.

The question naturally arises how well it is possible to forecast the yield of corn for the different parts of the Corn Belt. The map of multiple correlation coefficients (Fig. 12) offers summary evidence that in all likelihood corn yields can be very well forecast in the southwest (subareas 1A and 1B), in the northwest (area 2), and in parts of the north and east (area 3). In other parts of the Corn Belt, especially parts of area 4, the coefficients, though helpful, probably will give forecasts containing considerable error.

Conclusions

The correlation of corn yield with climatic factors in the Corn Belt of the United States proves to be a very complex problem, for two reasons. In the first place, climatic variables operate not singly but as many-faceted composites. Secondly, not only climatic factors but other factors of the natural and cultural environment change from area to area. Nevertheless, some climatic factors correlate significantly with corn yield in parts of the Corn Belt. Notable among such factors are precipitation and aspects of temperature for May, June, July, and August. It seems to be an unmistakable conclusion, however, that variation in July rainfall is not everywhere so important a factor in corn yield as earlier investigators believed.

No one climatic factor gives significant correlations for all parts of the Corn Belt; nor, apparently, is any one factor of extreme significance in any part of it. Neither for the Corn Belt as a whole nor for particular areas within it does there seem to be, strictly speaking, such a thing as the critical climatic factor, nor is there much evidence of a critical period. Rather, it seems that corn yield in some parts is to be significantly correlated with several—even ten or more—factors covering much or all of the period of growth and reproduction. In other parts significant correlations with corn yield are found for few or none of the climatic factors investigated.

200

It does seem that of the factors studied variations in temperature are more significant and more critical to corn yield than are variations in precipitation. Also, the midseason period of growth and reproduction is, on the whole, more critical than the early season, except only in the northeastern part.

In general, the significance of the correlation coefficients between corn yield and the factors of temperature and precipitation decreases from the margins toward the center of the Corn Belt. This is true for all margins except the middle of the west one and is outstandingly true for the southwest and northwest margins. It would seem that the south and east margins, fully as much as the north and west ones, are determined by the fact that climatic factors on the margins do not approximate optimum conditions for high corn yield. On the east margin early-season temperatures are commonly too low; on the south margin early-season temperatures are somewhat too high and mid-season temperatures decidedly too high. This suggests that the rather low yields generally returned by corn planted over wide areas south of the Corn Belt may be due to unfavorable temperature conditions that seemingly cannot be counteracted by any amount of precipitation. Coefficients found for three counties in Texas, Tennessee, and Georgia lend substance to this hypothesis.

On the other hand, corn yield in the center or core of the Corn Belt generally fails to correlate significantly with the climatic factors investigated. This is less true for the coefficients of multiple correlations, in which several factors are considered, than for the coefficients of simple correlations. Presumably corn yield in this core area is somewhat affected by the factors significant on the surrounding margins; but, with several factors operative—perhaps first on one, then on the other, side of the optima, and thus with conditions generally favorable—variation in any one factor has little effect by itself.

In general, the areal distribution pattern of significant simple correlation coefficients between corn yield and individual climatic factors shows discordance in its patterns of such natural factors as soil and altitude. It may be noticed, however, that blackerth, chestnuterth, and gray-brownerth areas show several significant coefficients between corn yield and variations in climatic factors, whereas the prairyerth areas show few significant coefficients. This prairyerth area seems to combine optimum soil and climate for corn yield.

The average date of planting and the average yield of corn show only weak correspondence with the patterns of coefficients found. The areas that most lack heat have in general higher yields than areas adversely affected by high temperatures.

There is in most of the cases not much observable correspondence between the pattern of means or the pattern of standard deviations of a climatic factor and the resulting pattern of simple correlation coefficients. This seems to be partly because corn yield depends largely on several climatic variables operating simultaneously during most of the period when corn is growing and reproducing.

It should be possible to forecast the yield of corn with a high degree of accuracy for several of the marginal areas of the Corn Belt. The multiple coefficients found for the core of the Corn Belt should be distinctly helpful in forecasting but will not provide the high degree of accuracy presumably attainable for the marginal areas. It seems possible that higher multiple coefficients might be obtained for this area by successive elimination of less significant factors.

The present program of the United States Department of Agriculture calls for a considerable reduction in the acreage devoted to corn. This reduction in acreage has been applied as a blanket project to the whole of the Corn Belt. One way of preventing any undesirable surplus of corn would be to remove from corn production those areas that produce corn least well.

In view of the facts discovered in this study, large parts of areas 1A, 1B, and 2 might well be withdrawn from corn production and devoted to other uses. This suggestion is based chiefly on the fact that corn yield in these areas, especially in areas 1A and 2, is commonly so adversely affected in a critical manner by several climatic factors as to be well below the average for the United States as a whole and far below the average for the Corn Belt as a whole. Moreover, these two areas are included in the region where wind erosion is especially damaging to soil resources, and cornland is badly exposed to such erosion. The remainder of the Corn Belt can produce, on the average, as much corn as is now needed.

Finally, the areas for which significant correlation coefficients, for either individual factors or groups of factors, were discovered in this study show no respect for state boundaries. It seems, therefore, that the use of sample counties rather than of state averages gives a more informative solution of the problem, especially those aspects of it that relate to areal variations. Not only sampling but also correlation analysis seems well adapted to this problem and, with modifications, to a wide range of geographical problems.

THE GEOGRAPHY OF NORTH AMERICA:
A HISTORY OF ITS REGIONAL EXPOSITION

W. L. G. Joerg

THE appearance of Baulig's "North America," which has just been published,[1] is an event of outstanding importance to American geography. In this work the French school of geography has applied itself to the continent that interests us most. The result is a work that represents the full fruition of the regional method of modern geography.

As regards other continents and major areas of the world this method has already borne choice fruit, as is attested by the other volumes in the series of which this work forms a part and by the number of excellent syntheses that have been produced by professional geographers since the beginning of the modern development of their subject about fifty or sixty years ago. Even as regards North America that development has yielded, as will presently appear, seven or eight works in four languages (three of them within the last three years) that meet the standards of modern regional exposition. But among these, by the amplitude of its canvas, the completeness and balance of its treatment, the penetration of the source material, and the quality and integration of its illustrations, Baulig's work stands supreme.

History of Regional Geographies of North America, 1877-1934

To evaluate the significance of this work properly and to gain perspective, it seems desirable to survey the history of regional exposition as applied to North America as a whole, or to the United States or Canada separately,[2] since the development of modern geography (Table I, p. 659). This may in itself not be without interest, in view of the scattered nature of the publications and the diversity of their origin, as to both the concepts that brought them into being and the languages in which they are written. The inclusion of a work in the table does not necessarily mean, especially for the earlier years, that it is a regional geography in the modern sense of the word, but every work included is thought to have had, in the national group from which it emanated, some significance in the development of the methods of regional exposition.[3] Completeness is, of course, not claimed for the table. As to the present survey, in general it should

---

[1] Henri Baulig: Amérique septentrionale (Géographie Universelle, publiée sous la direction de P. Vidal de la Blache et L. Gallois, Vol. 13), 2 vols. (Part 1, pp. 1–315; Part 2, pp. 317–639), Librairie Armand Colin, Paris, 1935–1936.

[2] It is not the intention in the present survey to consider units subordinate to these in size, though expositions of such units of course exist and are of importance in the methodology of regional geography. On the relation of methods of exposition to size of area see below, pp. 644 and 651.

[3] Works of this kind, which may, for example, deal with only one element of regional geography, or which may be anthologies only, are enclosed in brackets in the table.

be borne in mind that the regional treatment of North America as a rule forms only a part, often only an incidental or peripheral part, of the regional movement in each country concerned. The real mainsprings of regional methodology and its guiding concepts have been centered elsewhere, usually, of course, in the geography of Europe.

MODERN GEOGRAPHY AND THE UNIVERSITIES

Modern geography may be said to date essentially from the establishment of the subject in the universities. In the four countries of Europe that have been the leaders in this development these dates are approximately as follows: Germany, early 1870's; Italy, late 1870's and early 1890's; France, about 1890; Great Britain, late 1890's. In Germany the subject was accorded university status at all Prussian universities in 1874, but at these, as at other German universities, some time elapsed before it was fully under way, owing to the lack of qualified teachers (Richthofen's directive inaugural address at Leipzig is of 1883). Influenced by the German example, modern geography in Italy had an early start. Dalla Vedova's incumbency of the chair at the University of Rome dates from 1875 and Giovanni Marinelli's of the chair at Padua from 1879. However, it was not until about a decade and a half later—the *Rivista Geografica Italiana* was founded in 1893—that the movement proceeded on a broad front. In France in about 1890 the pupils of Vidal de la Blache at the École Normale Supérieure were on the threshold of their own careers, and the *Annales de Géographie*, the organ of the university group, began publication in 1891. In Great Britain, as a result of the Royal Geographical Society's investigation of the status of geography in Europe by Keltie in 1884–1885, Mackinder's readership at Oxford was established in 1887, but it was not until about ten years later that the full effect of the reform movement made itself felt: the School of Geography at Oxford was created in 1899 (Herbertson's appointment as assistant to the Reader dated from that year), and Mackinder's "Britain and the British Seas" appeared in 1902.

In Scandinavia university recognition of geography came rather late, though the subject itself had long been in a high state of development in the whole territory of Scandinavian culture and influence, including Finland. At Swedish universities the modern aspect of the subject may be said to date from about 1910, though there were earlier facets oriented from history and commercial geography; and Otto Nordenskjöld's transition from the professorship of geology and mineralogy at Upsala to that of geography at Gothenburg took place in 1905. In Denmark the date is about 1915, by which time Steensby was progressing fully toward geography from his original interest, ethnography, after having been appointed to the chair of geography

204

at the University of Copenhagen in 1911. The work of his forerunner in that chair since 1883, Ernst Løffler (which was most active at the beginning of his incumbency, an activity that is reflected in Table I), may be said to represent, as did the similar situation in Italy, a response to the early development of geography in Germany.

In our own development in the United States the growth from physical geography, with its special emphasis on physiography, into the fuller conception of the subject to include and stress human geography may be said to have led to two periods of inception in the establishment of the subject as a university discipline.[4] The first falls in the late 1880's and the second in the early and mid-1900's. By the former date the work of Professor Shaler of Harvard had reached the geographical orientation indicated by the publications listed in Table I and discussed later (p. 647), and Professor W. M. Davis, who had been appointed in 1878 instructor in geology as Shaler's assistant, had by 1889 developed the theory of the erosional cycle, from whose development and diffusion the period of modern geography in the United States may be reckoned.[5] The year 1891 provides a cross section that, as has been pointed out,[6] discloses as students of Shaler and Davis six of the men who were to shape the development of geography in the United States in the next decades. The first orientation toward human geography in the early 1900's came through economic geography and centered in the school of commerce at the University of Pennsylvania. Creation of a separate department of geography at the University of Chicago in 1902–1903 ensured the cultivation of the human aspects of geography. Harlan H. Barrows' course on the historical geography of the United States dates from 1904, and in 1906 Ellen C. Semple began her association with the department as visiting lecturer on anthropogeography. In 1906, at Yale, Bowman gave lectures on the regional geography of South America to summer-school students, and in the academic year 1906–1907 he offered a course in the geography of North and South America, which was divided the next year into two separate courses, one for each continent. In 1909 a course in anthropogeography was given there jointly by Bowman and Ellsworth Huntington.

---

[4] As the early history is less familiar and accessible to geographers abroad (it is briefly touched on, with gaps, in G. G. Dept: L'étude et l'enseignement de la géographie aux Etats-Unis, *Bull. Soc. Royale Belge de Géogr.*, Vol. 50, 1926, pp. 119–132), the following references are offered mainly for the guidance of foreign colleagues: C. C. Colby: Changing Currents of Geographic Thought in America, *Annals Assn. of Amer. Geogrs.*, Vol. 26, 1936, pp. 1–37; W. M. Davis: The Progress of Geography in the United States, *ibid.*, Vol. 14, 1924, pp. 158–215; W. M. Davis: A Retrospect of Geography, *ibid.*, Vol. 22, 1932, pp. 211–230; W. M. Davis and R. A. Daly: Geology and Geography, 1858–1928, *in* The Development of Harvard University, edited by S. E. Morison, Cambridge, Mass., 1930, pp. 307–328; A. P. Brigham: William Morris Davis, *Geographen-Kalender*, Vol. 7, Gotha, 1909, pp. 1–73; "The Autobiography of Nathaniel Southgate Shaler," Boston and New York, 1909.

[5] The papers on the Triassic of the Connecticut Valley and on the rivers and valleys of northern New Jersey and Pennsylvania bear the dates 1889 and 1890. The doctrine was made available to the educational world in 1898 in the high-school text "Physical Geography."

[6] *Annals Assn. of Amer. Geogrs.*, Vol. 20, 1930, p. 56, and Vol. 26, 1936, p. 17.

The history of university geography in Canada is brief. Whatever work was done in this field came either from historians (George M. Wrong at the University of Toronto since about 1895) or from economists and sociologists (H. A. Innis at Toronto, C. A. Dawson at McGill, and W. A. Mackintosh at Queen's, since about 1925). Full recognition of the subject has come only in 1935, with the establishment of the first chair of geography in Canada, at the University of Toronto, to which Professor Griffith Taylor was appointed.[7]

SEPARATE DEVELOPMENT OF REGIONAL GEOGRAPHY IN DIFFERENT COUNTRIES

The arrangement of the table by nationalities,[8] in addition to its obviously called-for chronological arrangement, is justified by the fact that, on the whole, the development of regional geography as part of modern geography[9] took place independently in the various countries and that the time of its incidence in each case was a result rather of the stage of internal development of the subject than of external influences. To be sure, the example of Germany in the 1890's is traceable in the concept originating Marinelli's "La Terra," the 8-volume regional geography of the world published between 1883 and 1901 (of which Porena's "North America" forms a part); and there is an early episode, of no developmental consequence, of American contact with German geography in the fact that the first treatment (1883) of North America in Stanford's "Compendium of Geography and Travel" is a translation of the corresponding part of Von Hellwald's "Die Erde und ihre Völker," the United States section being adapted by F. V. Hayden, former head of the U. S. Geological and Geographical Survey of the Territories. But such instances as these are the exception, and on the whole each country's growth was indigenous. Even the English-speaking countries did not exert much influence on one another. The early Canadian and American works, dealing primarily with the physical geography of Canada and the United States respectively, emanated from geological circles and had little subsequent influence on regional geography except as a source of information. Mill's "International Geography" (1899) was to become the first common meeting ground of contributors from all parts of the English-speaking world, as indeed of geographers from everywhere.

[7] *Canadian Geogr. Journ.*, Vol. 11, 1935, pp. iv (Nov.) and 214–216.

[8] The Italian works omitted from the table itself for lack of space are referred to at the bottom of the table and cited by title in the list that follows it. As to range of nationalities, the table, even with this addition, is not necessarily complete; it does contain, however, the leading countries in which regional geographies of North America have been produced.

[9] The phrase "regional geography of" preceding the name of a given area or country is used in this survey to designate a geography of an area written according to modern methods. The slight redundancy involved is deemed permissible to gain this precision. On the other hand, the phrase is here meant to carry no implication as to the organization of region 1 exposition, and specifically it is not meant to designate exclusively expositions organized by regional subdivisions.

That the lists differ markedly in length is not surprising in view of the varying length of time that modern geography has been established in the several countries and the somewhat unequal state of development that it has attained. The number of professionally trained workers resulting from these two factors, many in some countries, few in others, affects the range of regional discussion that they are likely to undertake. Where there are many, there are probably always some who specialize in a given continent or major area. This obvious reflection has special significance where the regional geography of North America is concerned. For, with the possible exception of Australia, no continent has until very recently less engaged the attention of Continental European geographers than North America. Europe, of course, is the homeland; with Asia and Africa there are ties of historical association and colonial interests; and South America still provides a field for scientific exploration both because of unsolved problems and because of a dearth of native investigators. But North America, the home of a modern industrial civilization whose bearing on the affairs of Europe is only of recent realization, could be left to its own scholars. It is with some such considerations as these in mind that many of the Continental discussions of North America up to eight or ten years ago may, not unfairly, be judged. There are a number of notable exceptions, but in the main these discussions owe their existence to the praiseworthy desire to provide a complete survey of the world. In such a scheme it is inevitable that the areas farthest from the center of interest should fare less favorably.

LENGTH OF REGIONAL EXPOSITION AS FACTOR OF ADEQUACY

Such world surveys are usually contained in one or two-volume handbooks by a single author or a group of authors or in a series of volumes in which each continent, generally by a different author, is represented by a separate volume. Manifestly, length is an important factor governing the adequacy of a regional discussion. As with the scale of a map, so in regional description, it is not possible below a certain limit to bring out all the essentials in the portrayal of an area. Because of the importance of this factor in the proper appraisal of a given regional geography, the number of words (in thousands) in the works listed in Table I is indicated in that table. The examination of the works discussed in the present inquiry would seem to show that about the following number of words is needed to deal adequately (from the standpoint of the regional geography of continents) with the areas named: North America as a whole, 90,000–100,000 words; the United States and Canada separately (if preceded by a continental synopsis), 175,000–200,000 and 50,000–60,000 words respectively.

207

GERMAN, FRENCH, AND ITALIAN HANDBOOKS AND REGIONAL SERIES

Of the accounts in the handbooks that by Hettner is a model of concise regional treatment in which the mastery of the background material produces sureness of touch in the selection of essentials and precision in their generalized presentation. The tectonic maps are especially illuminating. The volume of the "Grundzüge der Länder-kunde" of which this account forms a part was not published until 1924, though the volume on Europe had appeared in 1907 and Hettner's text to Spamer's atlas, from which the work derives its origin, about 1897. Of high scientific merit also is Lautensach's treatment (1920) that forms part of a handbook of general and regional geography accompanying Stieler's atlas. The sections on North America, Canada, and the United States in Gerbing's handbook (1927), in method, content, and orientation, are not among the most felicitous in this manual. The accounts by Kergomard and De Lamothe (1914) and by Granger (1922) are contained in two French series that, physically, resemble the "parlor albums" of our own Victorian age. They illustrate, however, as do a number of German accounts, how the high state of development of a subject in a given country makes available a professionally trained authorship even for secondary works. Somewhat similar undertakings, but of more modern orientation, are the German series containing Dietrich's account (1933) and the Italian series containing Errera's (1934). The former benefits from the author's travel and study in the continent he describes, though the work is not devoid of occasional lapses into banality and superficiality. The Italian series, in 8 volumes, is edited by one of the leading geographers of Italy, but the volume on North America unfortunately adheres to a discussion of general aspects and does not advance to a real geographical exposition by regions, nor are the photographs always critically chosen or adequately explained. Treatment by regional subdivision is also lacking in the volume by Michieli (1935) on North America as a whole and Canada; the volume affording amplest scope for such treatment, that on the United States, has not yet appeared in this other Italian series, which is published by the same house as "La Terra" of thirty-five to fifty years ago. On the whole the American reader of these recent Italian accounts misses the touch of field experience that a Calciati or an Olinto Marinelli would have been able to impart.

Among earlier regional series that edited by Sievers and begun in 1893–1895 was outstanding. North America was in the hands of Deckert, a pupil of Peschel. This volume never changed much from the conventional description of the older school and was rather uninspired. Between the second and third editions Sievers published an abridged edition in two volumes in which the entire material was rewritten and reorganized by him on a natural-regions basis (with regional maps). A fourth, condensed edition of this volume on North America, based on the third edition, was published after Deckert's death by Machatschek in 1924. This, in spite of improvement, breathes the same atmosphere, whereas, working under a different plan, the same author has produced (1928) an admirable geography of North America as a unit, critically documented by source material.

ENGLISH ACCOUNTS AND THE INFLUENCE OF EDUCATIONAL GEOGRAPHY

Among British publications the relevant sections in Herbertson's "Handbook of Geography" (1912) are still among the best in the few handbooks written in English by a single author. The considerably shorter treatment in Miss Newbigin's "New Regional Geography of the World" (1929) is also of interest. Such books as these verge closely on school textbooks, a category purposely omitted from the present survey, which aims to deal with the scientific aspect of regional exposition. However, the fact that in Great Britain the rise of modern geography has been closely associated with the school world and that in the secondary system the teaching of the subject reaches into the upper classes has led to the production of textbooks of a relatively high grade and advanced level of information—much more so than in the United States, where the subject in the schools is limited to the elementary and intermediate grades.[10] As a result, especially in further consequence of the greater understanding due to common language and institutions, a British school text on North America may provide a more adequate and accurate representation than an account in a Continental handbook. With Jones and Bryan's "North America" (1924), however, we come to a work of scientific caliber— indeed the first regional geography of the continent in English written by professional geographers from the point of view of modern geography. Although not uniform in its treatment, either topically or regionally, it marked the beginning of a new era in the history of the regional description of North America.

CANADIAN AND AMERICAN CONTRIBUTIONS

The history of Canadian and American accounts is of special interest to us. As pointed out above, the early descriptions, in keeping

[10] Ordinarily it is only at these levels that regional geography is dealt with in American education, high-school and college geography, to the extent that they occur, being concerned with general principles, and, if concerned with regional elements such as the land-type belts of the world, then mainly to illustrate these principles. An exception to this is C. R. Dryer's "High School Geography: Physical, Economic, and Regional" (New York, 1911), in which the world is discussed by natural regions. R. S. Tarr and F. M. McMurry's "North America" (New York, 1900) was a text intended for elementary classes, though its rather detailed content led to its being used by some foreign authors of geographies of North America as a source book. (On these and other American school texts see A. P. Brigham and R. E. Dodge: Nineteenth Century Textbooks of Geography, *in* The Teaching of Geography, *32nd Yearbook Natl. Soc. for the Study of Education*, Bloomington, Ill., 1933, pp. 3–27, and C. R. Dryer: A Century of Geographic Education in the United States, *Annals Assn. of Amer. Geogrs.*, Vol. 14, 1924, pp. 117–149.)

with the development of the times, issued from geologists and dealt mainly with physical geography. But in each country, Canada and the United States, there was a man of broad vision who could not be confined narrowly to one aspect only when reality had so many facets. George M. Dawson, later director of the Geological Survey of Canada, starting with a physical description of western Canada (in his joint account with A. R. C. Selwyn, 1884) expanded this into a physical geography of the whole country in 1897 in the "Handbook of Canada" issued for the British Association meeting in Toronto and into a complete geography of the country in a publication first issued in 1892 and revised in 1904. In the United States, Shaler, social philosopher as well as geologist, in 1884 supplied the introductory chapter, on the physical geography of North America, to Volume 4 of Winsor's "Narrative and Critical History of America." The second, longer part of that chapter is characteristically entitled "Effect of the Physiography of North America on Men of European Origin." The same theme was amplified into a geography of the continent in his "Nature and Man in America" (1891) and "The Story of Our Continent" (1892), which latter, although "for the use of schools," he correctly states in the Preface "departs widely from the ordinary text-books which give an account of North America." The fullest treatment is given in the work entitled "The United States of America" (1894), produced by Shaler and numerous other contributors under his editorship. It deals with the physical setting and the economic and social activities of the American people. There are regional chapters on the East and South and on the West by Shaler himself, and his "Summing Up of the Story" provides a valuable corrective to some of the accounts of social conditions by the Continental geographers.

Contemporaneous with Shaler's works is J. D. Whitney's "United States" (1889), in some respects the first adequate geography of the country by an American in the period under discussion. This book by the former state geologist of California was originally prepared for the ninth edition of the Encyclopædia Britannica. A later (1894), somewhat amorphous supplement deals with population, immigration, and irrigation. Gannett's volume (1898) in Stanford's "Compendium" contains much good geographical material, but it does not rise to the level of a regional geography. The volume of papers by different authors on the physiography of the United States published in 1896 is of high significance in the record because a number of these papers represent the first attempt to portray the physiography of a region as compared with the previous practice of dealing with regional cases merely as examples to illustrate physiographic processes. In it, too, the need for a general orientation and regional classification is squarely met in J. W. Powell's paper and map of the physiographic provinces of the country.

210

Molded by the set plan of the book, W. M. Davis' chapters on North America and the United States in Mill's "International Geography" (1899) transformed general physiography into geographical material by its organization around the regional principle. In complete contrast is I. C. Russell's "North America" (1904), in which different aspects of the geography of the continent as a whole are treated separately, practically without relation to one another; and yet this volume, as an invited contribution to Mackinder's regional series, had the opportunity of being the American counterpart of that editor's classic "Britain and the British Seas." Regional physiography came fully into its own with the publication of Bowman's "Forest Physiography" (1911), in which the great body of relevant geological literature, and especially that of the U. S. Geological Survey, was summarized and set forth regionally. It contains (pp. 108–110) the first adequate statement of the regional principle in an American work on physiography. Fourteen years later appeared the first modern regional geography of North America by an American, J. Russell Smith's "North America" (1925). Here was an account organized sufficiently minutely by regions and of sufficient length to deal adequately with all the essentials—an account benefiting from that intimacy with one's own country and its problems that is only with rare exceptions vouchsafed to the foreigner—and written in an interesting and direct manner, often with brilliance. From the standpoint of historical continuity it is interesting to note that Smith acknowledges his indebtedness to the work of Shaler, "my unseen master." A briefer work of similar trend to Smith's is Miller and Parkins' "North America" (1928), though here the regional units tend to be grouped around the dominant economy of a major section.

RECLUS AND RATZEL

Before passing to a consideration of the very latest books of the modern school, it will be of interest to dwell for a moment on three works from the beginning of the period that arouse expectations because of their major proportions and because, unlike most others at the time, they were written by professional geographers. These are Reclus's "Canada" (1890) and "United States" (1892) and Ratzel's "United States" (1878–1880 and 1893).

Reclus's two volumes form part of the regional geography of the world in 19 volumes that he produced singlehanded in eighteen years (1876–1894). As in the case of most of Europe, North Africa, and parts of South America, his qualifications included personal familiarity with the people and countries he was describing. Having been forced to leave his native France as a result of the *coup d'état* of Napoleon III, he spent more than three years of his young-manhood (1853–

1856) as a tutor in the family on the Fortier plantation near New Orleans. During this sojourn he made a trip up the Mississippi and may have gone as far as Chicago and Niagara Falls.[11] In late middle age, as part of a number of trips made to collect source material, establish contacts, and gain firsthand impressions for the series, he again crossed the Atlantic and in 1889 visited the Middle Atlantic States, New England, and parts of Ontario and Quebec. On the whole, the resulting account of Canada is better than that of the United States, because its organization by six or seven regions affords a realistic framework. In the volume on the United States, on the other hand, the country is divided into only three areas, the Appalachians and the Atlantic slope, the Great Lakes and the Mississippi-Missouri Basins, and the Cordillera and the Pacific slope—large units for so lengthy a book (265,000 words). An attempt to refine the regional characterization of this coarse division is made by following the discussion of each of the three areas by descriptions of the states, one by one, that compose it. The result is barren and encyclopedic. The physical description of the three areas, with its emphasis on river basins and its wholly ungenetic treatment of surface features, distinctly belongs to the old order. On the other hand, there are forward-looking passages, like that dealing with the potentialities of agriculture in the Canadian North, and discerning portrayals, like that of the French Canadians, that make occasional reference to these North American volumes still of interest. The usefulness of the numerous text maps by Charles Perron, illustrating both broad relationships and the detail of critical areas, was attested by the extent to which they were reproduced in Shaler's "United States" (1894). The drawings, numbering in the hundreds, of Perron's text maps for the whole 19 volumes and the source maps used in their preparation were at last reports (1931) in the Cartographic Museum of the University of Geneva, Switzerland.

Ratzel's "United States" is in two volumes, one dealing with the physical, the other with the human, geography of the country. Ratzel was not one of those to whom the United States was merely of marginal interest. Writing in 1878, he deplored the lack of a geography of the country, British, American, French, or German, embodying the advance of knowledge in the last twenty-five years. In German the last comprehensive work had appeared in 1854.[12] And yet, he says, as to physical geography, fully four-fifths of the data on which its principles are based are derived from Europe and North America.

---

[11] Based on Max Nettlau: Élisée Reclus, Berlin, 1928, pp. 57–69. This interpretation of the itinerary seems more plausible than the one given in Guillaume de Greef: Éloges d'Élisée Reclus et de De Kellès-Krauz: Discours prononcé . . . [à] l'Université Nouvelle de Bruxelles . . . 3 novembre 1905, Ghent, 1906. Both publications contain interesting details on the composition of the 19-volume series (Nettlau, pp. 179–184; De Greef, pp. 25–27 and 30–33).

[12] Karl Andree: Nord-Amerika in geographischen und geschichtlichen Umrissen, with atlas of 18 maps by Henry Lange, 2nd edit., Brunswick, 1854.

And on the human side, you must know the United States if you wish to understand the modern world. "Indeed, it may even be asserted that the political insight of a people is directly proportionate to its degree of understanding of what is taking place today in North America and what will take place there in the future." His conviction was based on personal knowledge. Soon after receiving his doctor's degree at Heidelberg in 1868 he served as correspondent to the *Cologne Gazette* (*Kölnische Zeitung*) and in this capacity traveled widely throughout the world. The years 1873–1875 were spent in the United States. The first volume deals with the different aspects of the physical geography of the country as a whole and intentionally avoids any regional division in this part "in order not to interrupt the continuity of the exposition of each physical element." Regional treatment is represented at the end of the volume by a series of short, impressionistic sketches of various areas or aspects of nature throughout the country. It is interesting to note a similar treatment in the latest Swedish geography of North America (Nelson, 1926). In Ratzel, as in Reclus, the description of relief is almost wholly topographical. But it is the second volume, and especially its second edition of 1893, that constitutes a distinctive contribution that is still of value and interest. Under its subtitle of "Political Geography" it deals with such matters as size, space, and boundary relationships, national stocks and race problems,[13] population distribution and growth, immigration, internal migration, agriculture, forest and mineral resources, trade, transportation, commerce on land and sea, administrative systems, educational and spiritual life, social conditions. There is a concluding section on the *Kulturlandschaft* of the United States, accompanied by a general land-use map of the country in 1 : 10,000,-000. The author's personal knowledge and catholic viewpoint pervade the discussion of economic, social, and political conditions and maintain this as one of the best-balanced discussions of these questions in geographical literature by a foreigner. Hence this volume is still of value as a cross section of the economic and human geography of the country more than sixty years ago by a trained observer and as the work in which a number of methodological concepts were introduced that are still being shaped and molded in modern geography.

ORGANIZATION OF SUBJECT MATTER IN THE SEVEN LEADING
WORKS, 1924–1934

In this rapid survey, mainly by nationalities, of the regional geographies of North America that have been published in the last fifty to sixty years it has necessarily been impossible to touch on all the

---

[13] In the preface to the 1893 edition of the second volume Ratzel acknowledges his indebtedness to Miss Semple for help in clarifying certain aspects of the negro question. During the preceding year she had been his student at Leipzig (C. C. Colby: Ellen Churchill Semple, *Annals Assn. of Amer. Geogrs.*, Vol. 23, 1933, pp. 229–240; reference on p. 231).

213

works listed in Table I, since the main aim has been to outline trends of thought and this has consequently involved difference in emphasis.

Of the works listed in the table, exclusive of Baulig's there are seven outstanding ones from the point of view of modern geography. They differ in treatment, as some of them do in the purpose for which they are intended, but they are all regional expositions that meet the requirements of modern standards. It is worth while noting that all the foreign geographers in this group have made study trips to the continent they describe, and several have resided there for a time. In the order of the table the seven works are: Machatschek (1928), Schmieder, Blanchard, Jones and Bryan, Smith, Miller and Parkins, Nelson (1926). Before turning to a closer consideration of Baulig's work it may be of interest briefly to study the organization of their subject matter. In so doing it will be possible to characterize also the first three works, of which only Machatschek has hitherto been mentioned.

Broadly, three types of organization are represented: treatment of the continent as a whole; treatment of the continent as a whole, followed by discussion of its regional subdivisions; treatment by regional subdivisions. Machatschek follows the first method; Schmieder, Blanchard, Miller and Parkins, and Nelson follow the second; and Smith follows the third. The plan of the book by Jones and Bryan is somewhat different, but it tends toward the third type.

Machatschek's book is primarily a text for graduate students of geography and forms one of the regional volumes of a work of which the section on general geography is Hermann Wagner's well known "Lehrbuch der Geographie." For the scale on which the regional volumes are projected treatment by subdivisions is considered too detailed, and regional discussion is by continents alone (except for a brief chapter at the end in which a synopsis of the major natural regions serves as a synthesizing summary of what has gone before).[14] This treatment by continental unit is called *allgemeine Länderkunde* as opposed to *besondere Länderkunde*, treatment by regional units. The corresponding terms in the terminology proposed by James in his excellent discussion of the scale of geographical generalization[15] would be *macrochorography* and *mesochorography*. The treatment by continental unit, provided there is enough scope, as is the case here (90,000 words), makes for a breadth and sweep that are reminiscent of Penck's classic course at the University of Berlin on world regional geography.[16]

---

[14] See the methodological comments in two of the four regional volumes that have appeared so far: by Wagner (Allgemeine Länderkunde von Europa, Hanover and Leipzig, 1915, pp. 179–184) and by Machatschek, p. 169 of the work under discussion.

[15] P. E. James: The Terminology of Regional Description, *Annals Assn. of Amer. Geogrs.*, Vol. 24, 1934, pp. 78–86; reference on p. 85. The terms *microchoric, mesochoric, macrochoric* there suggested as alternatives seem to the writer far preferable to the originally proposed *topographic, chorographic, geographic,* because the first and third of the latter group of terms are already established in other meanings.

[16] The spirit of this is reflected in his opening lecture at Columbia University as exchange professor in 1908–1909: "North America and Europe: A Geographical Comparison," *Scottish Geogr. Mag.*, Vol. 25, 1909, pp. 337–346.

As to the books whose organization follows mainly the third type: The volume by Jones and Bryan is divided into three parts of different scope. One part deals with the main movements of American history and settlement and their geographical setting and thus is predominantly regional; another deals with the main resources and discusses their continent-wide distribution and economy; and a final part is avowedly regional and discusses one by one the regions (except the South) that make up the continent. Smith's book, although organized regionally (the author says, p. 33: "Since a continent cannot be presented as a whole, it must be divided into parts"), has an introductory chapter that gives a continental survey of the questions of economic geography with which the work throughout is chiefly concerned.

Among the books of the second type, Miller and Parkins' "North America," which is intended primarily as a normal-school and junior-college text, has two chapters on the continent as a whole and chapters that discuss the United States, Canada, and Mexico each as a unit. These are respectively followed by discussions advancing to a greater or lesser degree of regional subdivision as the treatment of the dominant economic activities may require.

The combination of continental and regional exposition together is fully developed, however, in the books by Schmieder, Blanchard, and Nelson.

All three are of considerable proportions (150,000–200,000 words), sufficient for a discussion of real scope. Their organization according to the modern viewpoint ensures the utilization of this space so that every page counts, as compared with the diffuse and repetitious treatment of the old encyclopedic and compendium methods. They differ somewhat in ratio of continental to regional part and also in topical emphasis, but these are differences of degree, not of kind. In Schmieder the regional part occupies about seven-eighths of the work, in Blanchard about six-sevenths. Nelson's work is divided into two equal parts, the first being a geography of the continent and the second a series of "regional and environmental descriptions" that, although not systematic regional discussions, in their completeness cover the whole continent. Swedish settlement in the United States and Canada is the subject of particular concern. In Schmieder emphasis is placed on the history of settlement, and each regional section contains an excellent portrayal on a large scale of the development of the natural into the cultural landscape. Blanchard, under each region, brings out the dominant characteristic and orients the discussion of the human geography around the most important economic activities.

These three works in their agreement reflect the tested method of treatment of a large unit in modern regional geography. The culmination of this method, as regards North America, is represented by Baulig's work, to which special attention will now be devoted.

Baulig's "North America," 1935–1936

If the record of what has gone before seems a long one, it is also one that leaves an impression of incompletely fulfilled achievement, of a goal yet to be attained. Sometimes, in the earlier days, professional competence was coupled with a lack of that "predilection" for the area in question that the editor of the North American volume in the first issue of Stanford's "Compendium" wisely considered a desirable attribute of geographical authorship, a conviction that led him at the last moment to assign the section on Canada to a Canadian contributor. Or, where native interest was at hand, the subject had not yet developed the point of view that could have made an adequate treatment possible. Even the few recent works just discussed that truly reflect the spirit of modern geography do not, in spite of their excellence, exhaust the possibilities, in a number of cases as a result of limitations of length, scope, or orientation imposed by the program of the series of which they form a part.

In Baulig's "North America," however, we have a work that is of sufficient length (315,000 words) to permit the adequate discussion of all essential features and topics. And yet this ample scope does not lead to verbosity or looseness of style. On the contrary there is a conciseness and informed restraint that convey a sense of power— the power that comes from consummate mastery of the material. For such it is. Every subject that has a bearing on geography, from geology and physiography to economics and the social sciences, has been drawn on where needed and with complete sureness of touch woven into a composite picture of the region under consideration. This, indeed, is the reconstruction of the totality of truth—real geographical synthesis.

ORGANIZATION OF THE WORK

The work is divided into three parts: North America as a whole (occupying about 30 per cent of the space), Canada (20 per cent), the United States (50 per cent). The ten chapters of the part on North America deal with: general features and relationships; the major lineaments of relief and structure; the surrounding seas; climate; the hydrography of the continent and its regime; vegetation, soils, and fauna; the Indians; the maritime discoveries and the foundation of colonies; the territorial development and peopling of the United States; and the same phenomena for Canada. The two parts dealing with Canada and the United States are organized according to their regional subdivisions; each part is concluded by an appraisal of the national economy and its outlook. Without any formal delimitation the continent is divided into eighteen regions, to each of which one chapter is devoted and in one case two. These are as follows (Arctic

216

Canada is omitted because dealt with under the Arctic in one of the other volumes of the series): Newfoundland and Labrador; the Maritime Provinces; the St. Lawrence Provinces; the Prairie Provinces and Northwest Territories; the Canadian West; Alaska; New England; the Middle Atlantic region; the Great Lakes and Ohio River region (between the Mississippi and the eastern border of the Appalachian Plateau), two chapters; the Prairies and the Great Plains; the Southeast and the Lower Mississippi flood plain; the Southwest (an introductory chapter on the South as a whole precedes these two); the Rocky Mountains; the Lower Columbia and Snake Plateaus; the Colorado Plateau; the Great Basin; California; the Pacific Northwest.

THE PRINCIPLE OF THE PREDOMINANT CHARACTERISTIC

In the treatment of each region the routine consideration of the whole gamut of geographical elements in their systematic order is conspicuous by its absence. Instead, the principle of the predominant characteristic prevails.[17] The salient feature in each region is brought forward, while at the same time the contributing factors are skillfully portrayed as a background. In the South it is cotton; in the Southwest, oil; in the Rocky Mountains, relief and structure; in the Prairie Provinces, wheat on a background of climate, vegetation, and soils. The keynote is struck as a rule in brief introductory paragraphs of characterization.

Take, for example, Southern California, the discussion of which is reached in southward progression through the state:

After their decrease in the southern part of the Great Valley and of the Coast Ranges human activities suddenly take on new vigor south of latitude 35° and, as the Mexican boundary is approached, attain a degree and variety of development that are remarkable. A mild and equable climate, an intensive agriculture, the exploitation of oil, and the utilization of the resources of the sea have here called into being and stimulated the development of a great city, with a busy port, specialized industries, and even a mode of life hitherto almost unknown in the United States.

Or this description of a great mountain system, with its corrective of sometimes loosely made comparisons:

The Rocky Mountains are an orographic and structural unit that is characterized by the persistence of its general alignment; by the definiteness, and sometimes by the abruptness, of its topographical separation from the adjoining Great Plains on the east and the plateaus and Great Basin on the west; by its essentially sedimentary composition and the general absence of volcanic rocks and deep-seated igneous intrusions; by a relatively simple structure and the generally direct expression of

---

[17] In his "Dynamische Länderkunde" (Breslau, 1928) and "Das länderkundliche Schema" (Berlin, 1931) Hans Spethmann makes a vigorous plea for the application of this principle in all regional exposition. In the former he presents outlines, with the corresponding sketch drafts filled in, for the regional treatment of seven areas, for six of which published regional geographies organized according to the conventional "static" method exist. The whole question of method in regional exposition is fruitfully discussed by Hettner and Gradmann in articles called forth by Spethmann's two books (*Geogr. Ztschr.*, Vols. 34, 35, 37, 1928, 1929, 1931).

structure in relief; by usually slight erosional dissection; and by the frequent occurrence at high absolute elevations of the gentle slopes and rounded forms characteristic of *Mittelgebirge*. On the whole, the resemblance of the Rocky Mountains to the Alps is only a distant one; but, on the other hand, they differ distinctly from the Appalachians and the Hercynian mountains of Europe. Their similarities lie rather with mountains of intermediate geological age such as the Carpathians, where the results of early-Tertiary peneplanation go hand in hand with those of recent rejuvenation.

Or this cameo of New England:

With her often refractory soil, her inhospitable climate, her bountiful sea; with her early population of small farmers, seamen, fishermen, and merchants, marked with the deep impress of religious sectarianism and the collective discipline of rural and urban community life; then weakened by the drain to the West and the movement to factory and city and later nearly submerged by an alien flood; frequently ousted from political control of her own destinies and condemned to economic readjustments without end—nevertheless, she has been able to perpetuate that prudent reserve, that civic sense, and that practical spirituality for which she stands and, owing to her cultural institutions, has made the influence of her spirit felt through the length and breadth of the land.

PHYSICAL GEOGRAPHY THE STABLE FOUNDATION

Whereas the principle of emphasis on predominant aspect underlies the organization of the work, physical geography constitutes its stable foundation throughout. The author, like the school from which he stems, is convinced of the truth of the poet's dictum that "to the solid ground of Nature trusts the mind that builds for aye." Of every region, as of the continent as a whole, there is a masterly outline of relief and structure—not a discussion of local physiographic processes or geological history but a description of major surface features in terms of the large-scale forces to which they owe their origin. These outlines are illustrated by superb, critically selected air photographs with trenchant explanatory captions and by a number of physiographic maps, of which the more important are a series of three covering the United States, one from the Atlantic to the Mississippi on the scale of 1 : 8,000,000, another from the Mississippi to the Rockies in 1 : 10,000,000, and the last of the Cordilleran West in 1 : 6,500,000. Here are portrayed with utmost clarity oldlands and coastal plains, cuestas and scarps, mountain massifs of differing structure and age, sunken basins, Pleistocene lakes, edges of the ice sheet, alluvial plains, plateaus, block mountains, faults, lava flows, intermontane parks, desert plains. The symbolism of these maps, like that of a number of earlier maps,[18] incidentally demonstrates the feasibility of devising ground-plan symbols, instead of perspective symbols, for a wide range of physiographic types.

---

[18] De Martonne's physiographic map of the Carpathians, 1 : 2,500,000, *Geogr. Rev.*, Vol. 3, 1917, Pl. IV, and Zaborski's map of the surface features of Poland and Lithuania, 1 : 1,250,000, Warsaw, 1928. The tectonic maps in the different volumes of Hettner's "Grundzüge der Länderkunde" represent a successful solution of the problem on small scales.

Other aspects of physical geography are also constantly taken into account. Although climate and vegetation are discussed in the general part dealing with North America as a whole, these subjects are enlarged on in the regional sections where the special character of the region calls for it, such as the rainfall, grasslands, and soils of the Great Plains, the forests of British Columbia and the Pacific Northwest, the aridity of the Great Basin.

POPULATION AND NATIONAL ECONOMY

It is hardly necessary to say that human geography comes in for its full share of consideration.

In the four general chapters dealing with the peopling and the national economy of Canada and the United States the whole range of questions is discussed—population growth and distribution; natural resources, mineral, water, forest, and soil; agriculture and its problems, especially in their recent aspects; industry, commerce, transportation; international relations and world position. These are chapters of broad sweep and wide horizon, yet supplied with the same wealth of specific facts and figures that characterizes the work throughout and informed with the knowledge and understanding of national problems and trends, even to their minutiae, the foundation of which was laid by the author's long residence and travel in the United States and later by his constant contact with American sources.[19]

Accompanying the discussion of population there is an original, colored distribution map on the scale of $1 : 15,000,000$ based on the United States census of 1930 and the Canadian census of 1931. Rural population is represented by density grades (six in all), which scheme, as the author says in the explanatory note to the map, "better than all other devices of equal simplicity portrays the relationship of man to the earth." Urban population is indicated by city symbols of different sizes and by deeply colored areas for the metropolitan districts.

Cities are accorded special attention. In the discussion of industrial districts the cities are characterized by various criteria, such as size and dominant industries, and, in the case of southern New England, by number of salaried employees in addition (a map with ingenious symbolism shows this). The discussion of major cities, which is illustrated by air photographs, includes a consideration of site, development, and function and, for the largest, a characterization of neighborhoods.

In the field of population questions and forecast two quotations

---

[19] Professor Baulig, who now occupies the chair of geography at the University of Strasbourg, is one of the original group of pupils of Vidal de la Blache. He has specialized in the geography of North America for over thirty years, since he became familiar with the United States from a four-year sojourn as a University instructor at Harvard and elsewhere early in his career. In 1912 he took part in the American Geographical Society's Transcontinental Excursion.

will have to suffice to illustrate the author's treatment. With regard to the future of Canadian population growth[20] he says:

No one still believes in the forecasts that, too confident of the value of extrapolation, predicted a population of several tens of millions for the Canada of the middle of the twentieth century. The probabilities are, rather, that there will be a very gradual increase at a constantly diminishing rate and that stabilization will take place in the relatively near future at a moderate figure. For, here as well as in the United States, or maybe more so, the character of the country and the spirit of the New World call for the availability of large areas and freedom in space relations.

As to Alaska:

If Alaska is not the icy, barren waste it was long imagined to be, neither is it a settler's country for the immediate future, as some have dreamed of it. Owing to its location on the border of the inhabited world, far from the great centers of population, beyond the main currents of trade, Alaska's undeniably valuable resources would come fully into their own only if the world became overcrowded or if constantly increasing consumption reduced the reserve of basic materials to the danger point. In waiting for that day, doubtless far distant, Alaska can continue to furnish regularly, under farsighted management, its quota of products from fisheries, forests, and mines.

In introducing the discussion of the effect of the world crisis on Canadian economy the author gives a clue to his conception of the geographical treatment of economic questions.

It is certainly not the concern of geography to follow step by step a development in which all sorts of financial, monetary, political, and moral factors are operative— for these are certainly devoid of all geographical character. But it is the concern of geography to point out what, in the economic structure of a given country, is in conformity with its nature and what is simply artificial or adventitious. In this respect the world crisis acts as a catalyst, segregating the weak and the strong parts of the structure. We shall see that the strong elements in Canadian economy are usually those that rest on the firmest geographical foundations.

In keeping with this point of view such topics as agriculture, the coal and petroleum industries, forestry and the lumber trade are discussed in their regional setting. Because of the nature of these themes it is difficult to encompass them in a short generalizing characterization, and, for lack of such by the author, no quotations can here be offered to illustrate his method. There are two passages, however, on Southern agriculture that by combination and condensation lend themselves to quotation and, because of their comparison with European conditions, are of special interest. This combined passage is here submitted in conclusion:

On the cultivation of cotton there has been erected since the Civil War what amounts to a financial system whose aim it is to reincorporate the emancipated negro into Southern economy. After unsuccessful attempts to employ negro labor on a wage basis, the solution was found in the institution of tenancy. There were various

---

[20] For an analysis of the elements likely to govern future population growth in Canada see Griffith Taylor: Fundamental Factors in Canadian Geography, *Canadian Geogr. Journ.*, Vol. 12, 1936, pp. 161–171.

degrees, but common to all was the device of large advances in money to the tenant. The system succeeded so well, at least from the point of view of the producer, that it was extended to tobacco, resulting in the same social consequences. Further proof of its success was the fact that it was extended to the whites. In six cotton states white tenancy increased from 30 to a hundred in 1880 to 61 to a hundred in 1930 . . . In short, under one form or another this system has made of the tiller of the soil an agricultural servant without fixed wages, concerned willy-nilly in the success of an enterprise over which he has but little or no control. And as there are no hard and fast lines between cropper, share tenant, and cash tenant, and as even the small owner-operator may in bad years be forced into the ranks of the tenants, there results—a new phenomenon in the United States—a large agricultural proletariat, white and black, already more white than black, a class of peasantry who own their bodies but are held in economic bondage, a class the like of which has for centuries no longer existed in western Europe.

CONCLUSION

With these quotations and this commentary it has been attempted to convey some idea of the scope and method of Baulig's work. Only a perusal of the work itself can give an adequate conception of its significance. On laying it down and looking back over the long list of geographies of North America that have appeared in the last sixty years one is inclined to agree with the doctrine to which in another and yet not wholly unrelated domain the author refers—the doctrine *qui enseigne que la qualité vaut mieux que le nombre.* The present work and the others in the same series seem to prove it.

TITLES AND BIBLIOGRAPHICAL DETAILS OF WORKS CITED IN TABLE I

Reviews are indicated in brackets following an entry. Abbreviations of periodicals: GR *Geogr. Rev.*, BAGS *Bull. Amer. Geogr. Soc.*, GJ *Geogr. Journ.*, PM *Petermanns Mitt.* (Lb "Literaturbericht"). See also next-to-last paragraph in explanation at bottom of table.

German and Austrian

Friedrich von Hellwald: Die Erde und ihre Völker: Ein geographisches Hausbuch, 2 vols., 2nd edit., Stuttgart, 1877 (A, Vol. 1, pp. 3–11, NA pp. 12–203); 4th edit., 1898. [PM, 1878, p. 84]

Friedrich Ratzel: Die Vereinigten Staaten von Nord-Amerika, 2 vols. (Vol. 1: Physikalische Geographie und Naturcharakter, 667 pp.; Vol. 2: Culturgeographie . . . unter besonderer Berücksichtigung der wirthschaftlichen Verhältnisse, 762 pp.), Munich, 1878 and 1880. Second edition of Vol. 2: Politische Geographie unter besonderer Berüchsichtigung der natürlichen Bedingungen und wirthschaftlichen Verhältnisse, 763 pp., 1893). [PM, 1880, p. 237; 2nd edit. of Vol. 2, PM, 1894, Lb 236]

[Scobel 1882] Richard Andree, editor (from 1894 issue on, A. Scobel, edit.): Geographisches Handbuch zu Andrees Handatlas, Leipzig, 1882 (NA pp. 416–515 by A. Scobel); 1st edition edited by Scobel, Leipzig, 1894; 2nd edit., 1895; 3rd edit., 1899 (NA, pp. 673–745); 5th edit., 2 vols., 1910 (NA Vol. 2, pp. 290–383).

Franz Heiderich: Adrian Balbis Allgemeine Frdbeschreibung, 8th edit., completely revised by F. Heiderich, 3 vols., Vienna, 1893–94 (A, Vol. 1, 1893, pp. 385–510, US pp. 511–621, C pp. 762–781). [PM, 1893, Lb 611]

[Deckert 1893] Wilhelm Sievers, associated with E. Deckert and W. Kükenthal: Amerika, Eine allgemeine Landeskunde, Leipzig, 1893 (A, pp. 3–56; NA, by Emil Deckert, pp. 365–606).

Friedrich Ratzel: Geographische Übersicht *in* Baedeker's Vereinigte Staaten: Handbuch für Reisende, Leipzig, 1893; 2nd edit., 1904.

Franz Heiderich: Die Erde, 876 pp., Vienna, 1896; 3rd edit. entitled "Die Erde: Eine allgemeine Erd- und Länderkunde," two parts in one vol., 1923 (A, Part 2, pp. 422–428; NA pp. 428–460). [1896 edit., PM, 1897, Lb 6; 1923 edit., PM, 1924, Lb 28]

Alfred Hettner: text to Spamers Grosser Handatlas, Leipzig [1897?] (NA, pp. 129–138).

Franz Heiderich: Länderkunde der aussereuropäischen Erdteile (Sammlung Göschen No. 63), Leipzig, 1897; 4th edit., 1921 (A, pp. 106–120; NA, pp. 120–136).

(*continued on p. 660*)

TABLE I—REGIONAL GEOGRAPHIES OF NORTH AMERICA, OR OF THE UNITED STATES OR CANADA SEPARATELY, PUBLISHED SINCE THE DEVELOPMENT OF MODERN GEOGRAPHY

(For explanation of abbreviations and symbols, see bottom of table)

GERMAN AND AUSTRIAN	FRENCH	BRITISH (incl. CANADIAN)	AMERICAN	SCANDINAVIAN
Hellwald NA 85* 1877 (2nd ed.; 4th ed. 1898) Ratzel US 550 1878–80 (2nd ed. of polit. geogr. 1893)				Løffler NA 000* 2nd ed. (3rd ed. 1885)
Scobel NA 70* 1882 (3rd ed. 45* 1899; 5th ed. 64* 1910)	Vogel NA 115* 1884	Selwyn C 115* 1883 [Selwyn and G. M. Dawson Phys. geogr. C 20 1884]	Hayden US 95* 1883 Shaler Physiogr. of NA 15* 1884 Whitney US 140 1889 (with suppl. 100 1894)	
Heiderich NA 110* 1893 Deckert NA 145* 1893 Ratzel US 00* 1893 (2nd ed. 1904) Heiderich NA 00* 1896 (3rd ed. 20* 1923) Hettner NA 13* 1897? Heiderich NA 00* 1897 (4th ed. 13* 1921)	Reclus C 145* 1890 (Engl. transl. 1893) Reclus US 265 1892 (Engl. transl. 1893)	Greswell C 42 1891 G. M. Dawson C 00* 1892 (2nd ed. 55* 1904) G. M. Dawson C 00* 1894 (2nd ed. 0000; 3rd ed. 1907; 4th 9* 1922) [Handbook of C, geogr. part 120* 1897] S. E. Dawson C 215 1897 Tyrrell C 15* 1899 (2nd edit. 1908)	Shaler NA 84 1891 Shaler NA 90 1892 Shaler US 00* 1893 (2nd ed. 1899; 3rd 1904; 4th 5* 1909) Shaler and others US, geogr. part 275 1894 [Physiogr. US 130 1896] Gannett US 140 1898 Davis NA 7* and US 31* 1899 (2nd edit. 1908)	Løffler NA 00* 18
Deckert NA 305 1904 (3rd ed. 315 1913) Oppel C 60 1906 Sievers NA 55* 1907 (based on Deckert 1904) Fischer US 45 1908		Herbertson NA 80 1901	Russell NA 140 1904 (2nd ed. 140 1927)	
[Deckert Econ. geogr. US and C 100* 1913 (separate 90* 1916)] Oppel NA 25* 1914 (2nd ed. 1922)	Kergomard US 85* 1914 Lamothe C 33* 1914	Rogers C 80 1911 Herbertson NA 34* 1912? Oxford Survey C 120* 1914 [Brock C 28* 1914] Ami C 315 1915	[Bowman US, regional part 225 1911]	
Oppel NA 20* 1921 Hamilton C 100 1921 [Hassert US 80 1922] Sapper A 75 1923 Hettner NA 32* 1924 (4th ed. 35* 1930) Machatschek NA 150 1924 (based on Deckert NA 1913)	Granger NA 55* 1922 (3rd ed. 1931)	[Handbook of C, geogr. part 125* 1924] Jones and Bryan NA 218 1924 (2nd ed. 230 1928)	Huntington NA 40 1919 [Colby NA 215 1921] [Lobeck Physiogr. map US 1921 and text 20 1922] Smith NA 325 1925	Vahl and Hatt NA 175 Nelson C 45 Nelson NA 160 (2nd ed. 195 1935)
Lautensach NA 90* 1926 Dietrich US 35 1926 [Hassert NA 75* 1927] Lebling NA 10* and US 18* 1927 Hamilton C 12* 1927 Hassert NA 28* 1927 Machatschek NA 90 1928 Ule NA 00* 1929	Allix NA 00* 1926 Cestre US 250 1927	Newbigin NA 22* 1929	Brigham US 87 1927 Miller and Parkins NA 175 1928 (2nd ed. 185 1934)	
Banse NA 35* 1930 Dietrich NA 150* 1933 Schmieder NA 165 1933 Eckert NA 30* 1935	Blanchard NA 155 1933 Baulig NA 315 1935–36		[Fenneman Western US 175 1931] [Jefferson Man in U. S. 29 1933]	Rosberg NA 000*

Works are cited by author, area described, length, and date. Areas are abbreviated thus: A the two Americas, NA North America, C Canada, US United States. Length is given in approximate number of words in thousands (ooos omitted). An asterisk following the number of words means that the account is not an independent unit but forms part of a volume that includes other areas. Works whose length is indicated by ciphers have not been seen by the writer. Works enclosed in brackets are exceptional in that they discuss only some aspects of the given area, such as physical geography or economic geography, or constitute a group of articles by, or quotations from, various authors, or differ in some other way. The chronological placing of a work is by its date of first publication. Later editions are referred to in parentheses.

The area forming the basis of the present survey is primarily English-speaking North America. However, works discussing North America as a whole usually include the whole continent southward at least as far as the Isthmus of Tehuantepec. Mexico may therefore be included in some of the accounts here abbreviated as NA. On the other hand, in the case of works organized by tries, only British North America and the United States (in[cl.] Alaska) have been taken into consideration and, if by th[e] author and in the same volume, have been jointly designated [?] For further details as to the regional structure of the works see following list of titles.

The works cited in the table may be identified in this list o[f] where they are enumerated by nationalities in the same orde[r as] the table. To facilitate identification in the same volume the entry is preceded in brackets by author and date as g[iven in] the table.

Owing to lack of space Italian works have been omitte[d from] the table. They are: Porena NA 100* 1897, Errera NA 175[*] and Michieli, NA 180 1935 (bibliographical details in the list of titles). If inserted in the table they would f[all in the] column between the German-Austrian and French colum[ns in] keeping with the fact that Italy, chronologically, was the [first] nation to introduce modern geography.

Emil Deckert: Nordamerika (Series: Allgemeine Länderkunde), 608 pp., Leipzig, 1904 (designated
2nd edit., i. e. of Deckert 1893 above; 3rd edit., 612 pp., 1913) [BAGS, 1906, p. 332; PM, 1905,
Lb 190; 1913 edit., PM, 1914, II, p. 91]

Alwin Oppel: Landeskunde des Britischen Nordamerika (Sammlung Göschen No. 284), 154 pp.,
Leipzig, 1906. [PM, 1907, Lb 232]

Wilhelm Sievers: Allgemeine Länderkunde, Kleine Ausgabe, 2 vols., Leipzig, 1907 (NA, based on
Deckert 1904, Vol. 1, pp. 152-252). [PM, 1909, Lb 1]

Henrich Fischer: Landeskunde der Vereinigten Staaten von Nordamerika (Sammlung Göschen Nos.
381 and 382), 2 vols. (Vol. 1, 115 pp.; Vol. 2, 103 pp.), Leipzig, 1908. [PM, 1909, Lb 636]

[Deckert 1913] Karl Andree's Geographie des Welthandels. New edition edited by Franz Heiderich
and Robert Sieger, 4 vols., Frankfurt, 1910-21 (US and C, by Deckert, in Vol. 3, 1913, pp. 305-538;
published separately in Die Länder Nordamerikas in ihrer wirtschaftsgeographischen Ausrüstung,
Frankfurt, 1916, C and US, pp. 1-204). [PM, 1914, II, pp. 149-150; 1916 version, PM, 1917,
p. 128]

[Oppel 1914] Ewald Banse: Illustrierte Länderkunde, Brunswick, 1914 (NA, by A. Oppel, pp. 274-
325); 2nd edit., 1922. [GR, Vol. 3, 1917, pp. 84-85, by Jefferson; PM, 1914, II, pp. 284-285; GJ,
Vol. 46, 1915, p. 313]

[Oppel 1921] Oskar Kende, edit.: Handbuch der geographischen Wissenschaft, 2 vols., Berlin, 1914 and
1921 (A pp. 713-716, NA pp. 747-779, by A. Oppel, in Vol. 2).

Louis Hamilton: Canada ([F. A.] Perthes: Kleine Völker- und Länderkunde, Vol. 8), 256 pp., Gotha,
1921.

Kurt Hassert: Die Vereinigten Staaten von Amerika als politische und wirtschaftliche Weltmacht
geographisch betrachtet, 315 pp., Tübingen, 1922. [PM, 1923, Lb 604]

Karl Sapper: Amerika: Eine Übersicht des Doppelkontinents (Sammlung Göschen Nos. 855 and 856),
2 vols. (Vol. 1, Physische Erdkunde, 112 pp.; Vol. 2, Geographische Kulturkunde, 156 pp.). Berlin, 1923. [PM, 1923, Lb 479]

Alfred Hettner: Grundzüge der Länderkunde, 2 vols. (Vol. 1: Europa; Vol. 2: Die aussereuropäischen
Erdteile), joint 1st and 2nd edits., Leipzig, 1923-24 (NA, Vol. 2, pp. 280-351); 4th edit., 1930
(NA, pp. 303-378). [GJ, Vol. 64, 1924, pp. 491-493, by Ogilvie; GR, 1926, pp. 343-344]

[Machatschek 1924] Emil Deckert: Nordamerika, 4th edit. competely revised by Fritz Machatschek
(Series: Allgemeine Länderkunde), 355 pp., Leipzig, 1924. [PM, 1925, Lb 490]

Hermann Lautensach: Ein Handbuch zum Stieler, 2 vols. (Vol. 1: Allgemeine Geographie; Vol. 2:
Laenderkunde), Gotha, 1926 (A pp. 653-672, NA pp. 673-726, in Vol. 2). [GJ, Vol. 70, 1927, p.
310; PM, 1927, pp. 97-99]

Bruno Dietrich: U. S. A.: Das heutige Gesicht, 150 pp., Breslau, 1926. [PM, 1927, Lb 142 (review by
author himself)]

[Hassert 1927] Karl Andree's Geographie des Welthandels, 4th edit., edited by Franz Heiderich, Hermann Leiter, Robert Sieger, 3 vols., Vienna, 1926-30 (NA, by K. Hassert, in Vol. 2, 1927, pp. 585-
757). [GR, 1928, pp. 520-521; PM, 1927, Lb 462]

[Lebling 1927] Walter Gerbing, edit.: Das Erdbild der Gegenwart: Eine Schilderung der Erde und ihrer
Länder . . . , 2 vols., Leipzig, 1926-27 (A pp. 543-544, NA pp. 544-576, US pp. 587-653, all by
Clemens Lebling in Vol. 2, 1927). [PM, 1928, Lb 308]

[Hamilton 1927] Walter Gerbing, op. cit. (C, by Louis Hamilton, Vol. 2, pp. 587-614). [PM, 1928,
Lb 308]

[Hassert 1927] K. Krause and R. Reinhard, edits.: Handbuch [der Geographie]: E. von Seydlitz'sche
Geographie, Hundertjahr-Ausgabe, 4 vols., Breslau, 1925-   (A pp. 425-430, NA pp. 431-496—
photographs pp. 497-528—by K. Hassert in Vol. 3, 1927). [GJ, Vol. 71, 1928, pp. 606-607; PM,
1928, Lb 217]

Fritz Machatschek: Allgemeine Länderkunde von Nordamerika (Series: Allgemeine Länderkunde der
Erdteile, edited by Wilhelm Meinardus, Vol. 4), 195 pp., Hanover, 1928. [PM, 1930, Lb 320]

Willi Ule: Die Erde und ihre Völker: Ein geographisches Handbuch, 2 vols. (Vol. 1: Europa, Afrika;
Vol. 2: Asien, Australien und die Südseeinseln, Amerika, die Polarländer), Stuttgart, 1928-29.
[PM, 1931, Lb 10]

Ewald Banse: Das Buch der Länder: Landschaft und Seele der Erde, 2 vols. (Vol. 1: Das Buch Abend-
land; Vol. 2: Das Buch Fremdland), Berlin, 1929-30 (A pp. 11-16, NA pp. 17-91 in Vol. 2). [PM,
1931, pp. 30-31, by von Drygalski; GJ, Vol. 76, 1930, p. 173]

[Dietrich 1933] Fritz Klute, edit.: Handbuch der geographischen Wissenschaft, 12 vols. in course of
publication, Potsdam, 1930-   (NA, by B. Dietrich, pp. 1-389, in Bruno Dietrich and others:
Nord- und Mittel-Amerika [und] die Arktis in Natur, Kultur und Wirtschaft, 1933).

Oscar Schmieder: Länderkunde Nordamerikas: Vereinigte Staaten und Canada (Enzyklopädie der
Erdkunde, edited by Oskar Kende, Vol. 27), 436 pp., Vienna, 1933. [PM, 1934, Lb 182]

Max Eckert: Neues Lehrbuch der Geographie, 3 vols., Berlin 1931-35 (A pp. 1339-1341, NA pp. 1341-
1402, in Vol. 3, 1935).

Italian

[Porena 1897] Giovanni Marinelli and others: La Terra: Trattato popolare di geografia universale,
8 vols., Milan, 1883-1901 (A pp. 3-14, NA pp. 15-198, by Filippo Porena, in Vol. 7, 1897?).

[Errera 1934] Roberto Almagià, edit.: Geografia Universale Illustrata, 8 vols., Turin, in course of publication since 1934 (NA, by Carlo Errera, Vol. 6, 1934, pp. 4–428). [PM, 1934, Lb 171; GJ, Vol. 84, 1934, pp. 530–531]

A. A. Michieli: America del Nord in generale e Canadà (Terra e Nazioni, Series 1, Vol. 1), 352 pp., Milan, 1935.

French

Charles Vogel: Le monde terrestre au point actuel de la civilisation: Nouveau précis de géographie comparée, 3 vols. in five, Paris, 1877–84 (A pp. 1–71, NA pp. 109–294, in Vol. 3, Part 3, 1884).

Élisée Reclus: Amérique boréale (Nouvelle Géographie Universelle: La terre et les hommes, Vol. 15), 723 pp., Paris, 1890 (A pp. 1–87, Greenland and Arctic Archipelago pp. 89–185, Alaska pp. 187–253, C pp. 255–699). (English translation: North America, edited by A. H. Keane, Vol. 1: British North America (Series: The Earth and Its Inhabitants, [Vol. 15]), 496 pp., New York, 1893).

Élisée Reclus: Les États-Unis (same series, Vol. 16), 847 pp., Paris, 1892. (English translation: North America, edited by A. H. Keane, Vol. 3: The United States (Series: The Earth and Its Inhabitants, [Vol. 17]), 504 pp., New York, 1893). [BAGS, 1892, pp. 379–390; PM, 1894, Lb 5]

[Kergomard 1914] Onésime Reclus, edit.: Grande Géographie Bong Illustrée: Les pays et les peuples, 5 vols., Paris, 1911–14 (US. by J. G. Kergomard, Vol. 5, 1914, pp. 43–136). [GR, Vol. 10, 1920, pp. 116–118]

[Lamothe 1914] Onésime Reclus, op. cit. (C, by H. de Lamothe, Vol. 5, pp. 3–40). [GR, Vol. 10, 1920, pp. 116–118]

Ernest Granger: Nouvelle Géographie Universelle: Le monde nouveau, 2 vols., Paris, 1922 (A pp. 242–250, NA pp. 250–314, in Vol. 2); 3rd edit., 1931. [GJ, Vol. 63, 1924, p. 360]

[Allix 1926] Maurice Allain, edit.: Géographie Universelle Quillet: Physique, économique, humaine, 4 vols. and 2 atlases, Paris, 1923–26 (NA, by [Madame] J. Allix, Vol. 4, 1926, pp. 393–427). [Bibliogr. Géogr., Vol. 33 for 1923, entry 481; Vol. 36 for 1926, entry 735]

Charles Cestre: Les États-Unis, 338 pp., Paris, 1927. [Annales de Géogr., 1929, pp. 175–177]

Raoul Blanchard: L'Amérique du Nord: États-Unis, Canada, et Alaska (Series: Géographie Pour Tous), 399 pp., Paris, 1933.

Henri Baulig: Amérique Septentrionale (Géographie Universelle, edited by P. Vidal de la Blache and L. Gallois, Vol. 13), 2 vols. (Vol. 1: Généralités, Canada, pp. 1–315; Vol. 2: États-Unis, pp. 317–639), Paris, 1935–36.

British (including Canadian)

A. R. C. Selwyn: The Dominion of Canada and Newfoundland, in North America, edited and enlarged by F. V. Hayden and A. R. C. Selwyn (Series: Stanford's Compendium of Geography and Travel, Based on Hellwald's 'Die Erde und ihre Völker'), London, 1883, pp. 289–636. [PM, 1883, p. 357]

A. R. C. Selwyn and G. M. Dawson: Descriptive Sketch of the Physical Geography and Geology of the Dominion of Canada, 55 pp., Montreal, 1884.

W. P. Greswell: Geography of the Dominion of Canada and Newfoundland, 141 pp., Oxford, 1891.

G. M. Dawson: British North America [and] Dominion of Canada and Newfoundland, in Elementary Geography of the British Colonies, by G. M. Dawson and Alexander Sutherland (Macmillan's Geographical Series), London, 1892; 2nd edit., 1904, pp. 1–158.

G. M. Dawson: Geographical and Geological Sketch [of Canada] in Baedeker's Dominion of Canada . . . : Handbook for Travellers, Leipzig, 1894; 2nd edit., 1900; 3rd edit., 1907, pp. xxxiii-xlix; 4th edit., 1922, pp. xxxvi-liii. [1894 edit., PM, 1895, Lb 259; 1922 edit., PM, 1923, Lb 493]

Handbook of Canada [issued on the occasion of the] British Association for the Advancement of Science, Toronto Meeting 1897, Toronto, 1897. (Part I: The Geography, Geology and Biology of Canada, by various authors, pp. 3–102, including The Physical Geography and Geology of Canada, by G. M. Dawson, pp. 3–48; Part II, History and Administration of Canada, by various authors, pp. 105–253, including articles on ethnology and land settlement; Part III: The Economical Resources, Trade, and Population of Canada, by various authors, pp. 257–415).

S. E. Dawson: Canada and Newfoundland (North America, Vol. 1, in Stanford's Compendium of Geography and Travel, New Issue), 719 pp., London, 1897. [BAGS, 1898, pp. 85–86; GJ; Vol. 11, 1898, p. 182; PM, 1899, Lb 247]

Tyrrell 1899] H. R. Mill, edit.: The International Geography By Seventy Authors, London, 1899 (C, by J. B. Tyrrell, pp. 679–707); 2nd edit., 1908 (C pp. 679–707).

F. D. and A. J. Herbertson: North America (Series: Descriptive Geographies from Original Sources), 252 pp., London, 1901. [An anthology]

J. D. Rogers: Canada, Part III: Geographical (A Historical Geography of the British Colonies, edited by C. P. Lucas, Vol. 5), 302 pp., Oxford, 1911. [BAGS, 1912, pp. 55–56; GJ, Vol. 39, 1912, p. 271]

A. J. Herbertson: A Handbook of Geography, 2 vols. (Vol. 1: General Geography, The British Isles and Europe; Vol. 2: Asia, Australasia, Africa, and America), London, 1912? (A pp. 395–399, NA pp. 400–533, in Vol. 2). [PM, 1914, I, p. 39]

son and O. J. R. Howarth, edits.: The Oxford Survey of the British (C, by various authors, Vol. 4, 1914, pp. 1–319). [BAGS, 1915, Vol. 44, 1914, pp. 499–500]

R. W. Brock: The Physical Basis of Canada, *in* Canada and Its Provinces: A History of the Canadian People and Their Institutions, edited by Adam Shortt and A. G. Doughty (23 vols., Toronto, 1914–17), Vol. 9: The Dominion, Industrial Expansion, 1914, pp. 9–91. [*Rev. of Hist. Publs. Relating to Canada*, Vol. 19, pp. 173–174, Univ. of Toronto, 1915]

H. M. Ami: Canada and Newfoundland (North America, Vol. 1, *in* Stanford's Compendium of Geography and Travel, New Issue, 2nd edition), 1069 pp., London, 1915. [GR, Vol. 1, 1916, pp. 150–151 (by Bowman); GJ, Vol. 47, 1916, pp. 58–59, by Unstead]

Handbook of Canada Issued by the Local Committee on the Occasion of the Meeting of the British Association for the Advancement of Science at Toronto, August, 1924, Toronto, 1924. (Numerous articles by various authors illuminating many aspects of the geography of Canada, including The Geology and Physical Geography of Canada, by W. H. Collins). [Mentioned in GR, 1924, p. 663]

Ll. Rodwell Jones and P. W. Bryan: North America: An Historical, Economic, and Regional Geography (Methuen's Geographical Series, Advanced Geographies), 537 pp., London, 1924; 2nd edit., 540 pp., 1928. [GR, 1925, pp. 503–506, by Dryer; GJ, Vol. 66, 1925, pp. 164–165, by Fawcett; *Geogr. Teacher*, Vol. 13, 1925–26, p. 77; PM, 1927, p. 54]

Marion I. Newbigin: A New Regional Geography of the World, London, 1929 (NA, pp. 265–330). [GJ, Vol. 75, 1930, pp. 197–198]

American

F. V. Hayden: North America [i. e. mainly the United States], *in* North America, edited and enlarged by F. V. Hayden and A. R. Selwyn (Series: Stanford's Compendium of Geography and Travel, Based on Hellwald's 'Die Erde und ihre Völker'), London, 1883, pp. 1–285.

N. S. Shaler: Physiography of North America, *in* Narrative and Critical History of America, edited by Justin Winsor (8 vols., Boston, 1884–89), Vol. 4, 1884, pp. i-xxx.

J. D. Whitney: The United States: Facts and Figures Illustrating the Physical Geography of the Country and Its Material Resources, 472 pp., Boston, 1889. With Supplement: Population, Immigration, Irrigation, 324 pp., Boston, 1894. [PM, 1890, Lb 769, by Ratzel]

N. S. Shaler: Nature and Man in America, 290 pp., New York, 1891. [PM, 1893, Lb 550, by Ratzel]

N. S. Shaler: The Story of Our Continent: A Reader in the Geography and Geology of North America, 290 pp., Boston, 1892.

N. S. Shaler: Physiography of North America, *in* Baedeker's United States: Handbook for Travellers, Leipzig, 1893, pp. lxvii-lxxvi; 2nd edit., 1899; 3rd edit., 1904, pp. lxix-lxviii; 4th edit., 1909, revised by T. A. Jaggar, Jr., pp. lxv-lxxiv.

N. S. Shaler, edit.: The United States of America: A Study of the American Commonwealth, Its Natural Resources, People, Industries, Manufactures, Commerce, and Its Work in Literature, Science, Education, and Self-Government, 2 vols., New York, 1894. (Chaps. I-IX in Vol. 1, pp. 1–517, six by Shaler and one each by J. W. Powell, H. P. Judson, and H. H. Bancroft, deal with geographical matters). [PM, 1895, Lb 562, by Ratzel]

The Physiography of the United States: Ten Monographs by J. W. Powell, N. S. Shaler, I. C. Russell, Bailey Willis, C. Willard Hayes, J. S. Diller, W. M. Davis, G. K. Gilbert, 345 pp., published for the National Geographic Society by the American Book Co., New York, 1896. [PM, 1895, Lb 813 (review of monographs as they appeared separately in 1895)]

Henry Gannett: The United States (North America, Vol. 2, in Stanford's Compendium of Geography and Travel, New Issue), 466 pp., London, 1898. [PM, 1899, Lb 247]

[Davis 1899] H. R. Mill, edit.: The International Geography By Seventy Authors, London, 1899 (NA pp.'664–678, US pp. 710–773, by W. M. Davis); 2nd edit., 1908, the same.

I. C. Russell: North America (Series: The Regions of the World, edited by H. J. Mackinder), 435 pp., London, 1904; 2nd edit., 435 pp., London, 1927. [*Geogr. Teacher*, Vol. 3, 1905–06, p. 43; GJ, Vol. 25, 1905, p. 558; BAGS, 1904, pp. 702–704; PM, 1905, Lb 191]

Isaiah Bowman: Forest Physiography: Physiography of the United States and Principles of Soils in Relation to Forestry, 759 pp., New York, 1911. [GJ, Vol. 40, 1912, pp. 208–209, by Herbertson]

Ellsworth Huntington: The Red Man's Continent: A Chronicle of Aboriginal America (The Chronicles of America Series, Vol. 1), 183 pp., New Haven, 1919.

C. C. Colby: Source Book for the Economic Geography of North America, 549 pp., Chicago, 1921. [An anthology]. [GJ, Vol. 60, 1922, pp. 150–151]

A. K. Lobeck: A Physiographic Diagram [i. e. map] of the United States. Scale 1 : 3,000,000. Chicago, 1921. Also text accompanying small-scale (1 : 9,000,000) edition of the map, Madison, Wis., 1922.

J. Russell Smith: North America: Its People and the Resources, Development, and Prospects of the Continent as an Agricultural, Industrial, and Commercial Area, 849 pp., New York, 1925. [GR, 1925, pp. 328–329; GJ, Vol. 67, 1926, pp. 77–78]

A. P. Brigham: The United States of America: Studies in Physical, Regional, Industrial, and Human Geography, 308 pp., London, 1927. [GJ, Vol. 70, 1927, pp. 582–583]

G. J. Miller and A. E. Parkins: Geography of North America, 605 pp., New York, 1928; 2nd edit., 632 pp., 1934. [GJ, Vol. 73, 1929, pp. 85–86]

N. M. Fenneman: Physiography of Western United States, 534 pp., New York, 1931. [GR, 1931, pp. 521–522] (This work is included here and in Table I, in spite of the statement in footnote 2 in the text, because it is to be followed by a companion volume dealing with the rest of the country.)

Mark Jefferson: Man in the United States, 35 pp. of text, 36 pp. of maps, Ypsilanti, Mich., 1933. [GR, 1933, pp. 664–665]

Scandinavian

Ernst Løffler: Haandbog i Geographien, 2nd edit., Copenhagen, 1878; 3rd edit., 1885. [PM, 1886, Lb 199]

Ernst Løffler: Omrids af Geographien, naermest udarbejdet til Brug ved Forelaesninger, 2 vols., Copenhagen, 1893 and 1898. [PM, 1898, Lb 317]

Martin Vahl and Gudmund Hatt: Jorden og Menneskelivet: Geografisk Haandbog, 4 vols., Copenhagen, 1922–27 (A pp. 128–187, Alaska pp. 206–220, C pp. 220–308, US pp. 309–457, in Vol. 1, 1922). [GR, 1924, pp. 676–677]

Helge Nelson: Canada, Nybuggarlandet, 180 pp., Stockholm, 1922.

Helge Nelson: Nordamerika: Natur, Bygd, och Svenskbygd, 2 vols., 526 pp. consecutive pagination, Stockholm, 1926; 2nd edit. entitled Nordamerika: Natur och Kulturbygd, 2 vols., 715 pp. consecutive pagination, Stockholm, 1935. [1st edit., GR 1927, pp. 692–693, by Jefferson]

J. E. Rosberg: Jordens Länder og Folk: Geografisk Handbok, 2 vols., Stockholm, 1935?

OBSERVATIONS ON ALASKAN COASTAL GLACIERS IN 1935

William Osgood Field, Jr.

I N "The Glaciers of the Northern Part of Prince William Sound, Alaska," I described my field observations of 1931 as a basis for comparative study of glacier variations in that area.[1] After an interval of four years I have again visited the region for a second series of observations, which are presented here. The expedition of 1935 was made in collaboration with Professor William S. Cooper, and with two assistants, Russell Dow and Robert L. Stix. Glacier Bay and Holkham Bay also were visited. The position of the various ice fronts in the several areas and the general appearance of the glaciers were recorded by photographs taken where possible from established photographic stations, and the more important topographic features were triangulated where changes were extensive or where the maps were inadequate. After the detailed ground studies in both Glacier Bay and Prince William Sound were completed, members of the expedition flew over many of the glaciers for aerial photographs and additional observations. Professor Cooper carried on his own ecological work as well, especially in Glacier Bay. The results of his study of the general problem in Glacier Bay are given in the preceding pages (pp. 37–62). The present paper is concerned only with the actual changes observed in the Holkham Bay and Prince William Sound glaciers. In neither locality are the variations as well known as in Glacier Bay, and, because of the different conditions prevailing, a much longer period of observation will be needed.

At different times in past geological ages the glaciers of Alaska were greatly enlarged.[2] The last great retreat, at the end of the Pleistocene, began about 30,000 to 60,000 years ago, at which time there were two large centers of ice in Alaska that spread outward from the coastal mountain ranges on the south and from the Brooks Range, north of the Yukon Valley. Since this late-Pleistocene expansion the glaciers have receded and shrunk enormously. In the Brooks Range the present glaciers are very small, but in the southern coastal ranges the glaciers are still among the largest outside the polar regions. Recession, however, has not been a steady and gradual withdrawal. In its course there have been advances of the ice measured in terms of centuries and other, smaller advances lasting for only a few years. It is by studying these lesser fluctuations that we hope to find more adequate explanations of the long-term changes, their causes, and their results.

---

[1] *Geogr. Rev.*, Vol. 22, 1932, pp. 361–388. See also W. O. Field, Jr.: The Mountains and Glaciers of Prince William Sound, Alaska, *Amer. Alpine Journ.*, Vol. 1, 1932, pp. 445–458.

[2] S. R. Capps: Glaciation in Alaska, *U. S. Geol. Survey Professional Paper 170-A*, 1931.

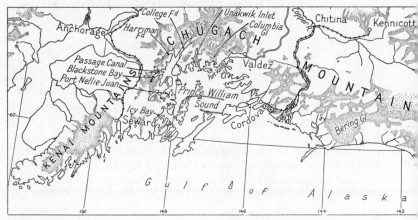

Fig. 1—Map of part of the southern coast of Alaska showing the principal inlets and bays in which coastal glaciers occur. (Based on the U. S. Geological Survey's 1 : 1,500,000 Map of Alaska, 1934. The area about the international boundary north of Mt. St. Elias and Mt. Logan is based on the work of the Wood Yukon Expedition of 1935.) Scale approximately 1 : 5,000,000.

In this report the terms "retreat" and "advance" of a glacier refer to the changes in position of the terminus and not to the motion of the ice itself. The terms "shrinkage" and "increase in size" of a glacier refer primarily to the volume of ice as measured laterally and vertically and are usually applied to the lower parts of the ice stream. Where no precise measurements for advance or recession are available, I have made estimates, based on photographs and direct observations, that tend to be conservative rather than excessive. Such estimates have been used only to indicate the order of magnitude of the change described.

The glaciers will be discussed in geographical order from southeastern Alaska northwestward to the Kenai Peninsula.

THE GLACIERS OF HOLKHAM BAY

Holkham Bay is in Southeastern Alaska, 45 miles southeast of Juneau. It has two fiords, Endicott Arm, 27 miles long, and Tracy Arm, 26 miles long, which penetrate deep into the Coast Range. In Endicott Arm is a magnificent inner fiord known as Fords Terror, so named because of the swift and dangerous tidal currents at its entrance. The principal glaciers are the South and North Dawes Glaciers, at the head of Endicott Arm; Brown Glacier, at the head of the eastern arm of Fords Terror; Sumdum Glacier, opposite the mouth of Holkham Bay; and South and North Sawyer Glaciers, at the upper end of Tracy Arm.

In 1880, when John Muir visited the area, all these glaciers except the Sumdum reached tidewater and were actively discharging ice-

PART OF THE
SOUTHERN COAST OF ALASKA

SCALE : 1:4,840,000

bergs.[3] By 1929 two of them, the North Dawes and Brown Glaciers,
had ceased to be tidal. The greatest retreat has been that of Brown
Glacier, which in 1880 was, as described by Muir, a "glacier of the
first order sending off bergs" (p. 222). In 1935 its terminus had
retreated round a bend in the valley to a point about two miles from
tidewater, and its lower part had shrunk enormously (Fig. 2). North
Dawes Glacier has retreated more slowly. In 1923 it had already
ceased to be tidal, and between 1929 and 1935 it retreated about
800 to 1000 feet. Sumdum Glacier, a much smaller ice stream than
the others, has also receded and shrunk a great deal, especially since
1923.

The other three glaciers, the South Dawes and the South and

---

[3] John Muir: Travels in Alaska; Boston and New York, 1915, pp. 214–232.

FIG. 2—The valley vacated by Brown Glacier at the head of Fords Terror in Holkham Bay.

FIG. 3—Marquette and Beloit Glaciers in Blackstone Bay from near Station 6.

230

FIG. 4—South Dawes Glacier at the head of Endicott Arm, Holkham Bay.

. 5—Blackstone Glacier and part of Northland Glacier in Blackstone Bay from Station 6.

North Sawyer Glaciers, are still tidal, and their termini seem not to have changed position to any great extent in recent years. Compared with their positions in 1923 the termini of the South Dawes and South Sawyer Glaciers are unchanged and the terminus of North Sawyer Glacier has advanced slightly. A comparison of photographs made by the U. S. Forest Service shows, however, that the South

Sawyer Glacier advanced between 1932 and 1934, so that we must assume that minor fluctuations have occurred during the last decade. The vegetation close to the ice of each of these glaciers suggests that they are as far advanced as they have been for some years, and the presence of mature trees near South Dawes Glacier indicates that, for possibly a century, the ice has not been more than a mile farther advanced than at present.

Perhaps the most significant feature of this diversity of behavior is that the three retreating glaciers are much smaller than the three that show little change. Of the latter three, two, the South Dawes and the South Sawyer Glaciers, occupy the trunk valleys of their respective fiords and are long ice streams of moderate gradients. Furthermore, they both terminate in deep water (a depth of 738 feet was found half a mile from the South Dawes Glacier). Certain factors, probably meteorological, seem to be depriving the smaller glaciers of part of their snow supply while not seriously affecting the large glaciers.

FIG. 6—The west margin of the Columbia Glacier ice front from Photo Station G in 1935. Compare with Figures 12, 13 and 14 on pages 372 and 373 in the report in *The Geographical Review*, July, 1932.

There is an interesting similarity in the behavior of these glaciers and those in Taku Inlet and Lynn Canal observed by Wentworth and Ray in 1931.[4] They found that Taku Glacier, corresponding in size to the South Dawes and South Sawyer Glaciers, was advancing and the smaller, nontidal Twin, Norris, Mendenhall, Herbert, and Eagle Glaciers were retreating. This apparent similarity in the behavior of the glaciers of these neighboring districts warrants further

⁴ C. K. Wentworth and L. L. Ray: Studies of Certain Alaskan Glaciers in 1931, *Bull. Geol. Soc. of America*, Vol. 47, 1936, pp. 879–933; reference on pp. 885–896.

investigation. These glaciers are the most accessible in Alaska and are well situated for comprehensive observation.

PRINCE WILLIAM SOUND GLACIERS

For the earlier history of the glaciers of the northern part of Prince William Sound the reader is referred to the papers cited in footnote 1.

FIG. 7—The eastern part of the terminus of Columbia Glacier, 1935. This picture illustrates the value of aerial observations for determining the position of a glacier terminus in relation to nearby topographic features.

The present paper is chiefly concerned with the changes between 1931 and 1935 and their relation to general trends.

Port Valdez. Valdez Glacier has continued the recession observed in 1931. In 1935 the center of the terminus was about 150 feet back of its position four years earlier. The terminus of Shoup Glacier did not change position from 1931 to 1935, but the volume of ice in the lower part of the glacier decreased slightly. Thus the trends that prevailed in both of these glaciers from 1898 to 1931 are continuing.

Columbia Bay. In 1931 the west end of the ice front and the Heather Island terminus of Columbia Glacier were advancing, but all parts of the ice front were several hundred feet back of their most advanced positions reached between 1908 and the early 1920's. In 1935 it was found that the advance had continued actively on all parts of the front. It was measured at various points as follows: at the west end of the ice front, 342 feet (Fig. 6); on Heather Island, 237

233

feet; and on the eastern land terminus, from 100 to 400 feet (Fig. 13). The greatest change had occurred on the east side, where the ice had become very much thicker and far more heavily crevassed. On the west side of the terminus the ice was still more than 500 feet from its recent maximum position. On Heather Island, at one point, it had overridden the terminal moraine of the recent advance and therefore was probably more advanced than for centuries, but at all other points on Heather Island and on the eastern terminus it was still well back of its maximum position.

Since 1899, when the first observations were made, the terminus of Columbia Glacier has fluctuated back and forth between limits 1000 feet apart on the west side and nearly three-quarters of a mile on the east. Less than 300 feet from the outer terminal moraine formed during this period are mature trees, one of which was found to have 420 annual rings. It is evident, therefore, that these fluctuations of the terminus are near the very limit of its most advanced position in more than four centuries.

FIG. 8—Bryn Mawr Glacier from Photographic Station O in 1931. Compare with Figure 11. (See also *Geogr. Rev.*, Vol. 22, 1932, p. 381.)

FIG. 9—Smith Glacier, College Fiord, from Photographic Station K, 1931. (Cf. Fig. 12.)

FIG. 10—View southwest along the eastern terminus of Columbia Glacier from Station 22 in 1931. (Cf. Fig. 13.)

234

Unakwik Inlet. The terminus of Meares Glacier, in Unakwik Inlet, did not change position from 1931 to 1935. Two small changes were noted, however. First, the medial moraine at the ice front was nearer to the middle of the glacier than in 1931. This suggests that the southern part of the ice stream had become relatively stronger than the northern part. Second, a small hanging glacier, which in 1931 terminated above the south branch, had in 1935 become a tributary. The amount of ice this glacier contributes is negligible; but probably this change and the first one are due to the same agents.

College Fiord. The small glaciers on the southeast side of College Fiord, which rise in the low mountain range between it and Unakwik Inlet, all seem to be in a state of recession. Each of their termini is fronted by conspicuous barren zones recently uncovered by the ice.

Between 1931 and 1935 the large Yale Glacier advanced about 200 feet at the east end of the ice front. The ice has covered the small barren zone noted in 1931 and pushed into thick alders. At the

FIG. 11—Bryn Mawr Glacier from Station O in 1935. Note the avalanche ebris on the tributary to the right and the new medial moraine.

FIG. 12—Smith Glacier from Station K in 1935 showing the reduced amount f moraine being carried.

FIG. 13—View southwest along the eastern terminus of Columbia Glacier rom Station 22 in 1935.

west end the advance has been about 50 feet, and a barren zone of about the same distance separates the ice from its most recent extension. The center of the ice front did not change position between 1931 and 1935, but it appears to have been more active in 1935. As a factor contributing to the greater advance of the east margin, it is

Fig. 14—Aerial view of Cascade and Barry Glaciers, 1935, showing the section of the ice front which has advanced since 1931.

perhaps significant that the second tributary on the east side has noticeably increased in volume since 1931.

Harvard Glacier, which on its east side advanced fully 2000 feet between 1905 and 1931, has continued that advance, though at a reduced rate. In 1935 the terminus stood on an average about 100 to 200 feet in advance of its position in 1931. On the west margin of the terminus the ice has continued its invasion of a willow-alder thicket of great age. A tree with 248 annual rings less than 500 feet from the ice shows definitely that the glacier is now more advanced than for at least two and a half centuries. The terminus of Baltimore Glacier, which occupies a cirque above the west side of Harvard Glacier, has come forward perceptibly since 1931, but it is still inside the limits of a recent advance.

Smith Glacier did not change appreciably in volume or in the position of its terminus from 1931 to 1935. The appearance of the ice stream, however, was greatly altered (Figs. 9 and 12). In 1931 its lower course was largely moraine covered and the ice front was dirt

stained. In 1935
this moraine had
been reduced in size
and confined to the
west margin, while
the rest of the ice
stream, with the ex-
ception of a small
medial moraine, was
white, deeply cre-
vassed ice.

Bryn Mawr Gla-
cier advanced slight-
ly and spread later-
ally between 1931
and 1935. The south
margin of the ter-
minus had pushed
forward about 200
feet. A new feature
not present in 1931
was an extensive
cover of surface mo-
raine on the north
branch of the glacier
(Figs. 8 and 11),
which was undoubt-
edly the remains of
an avalanche from
one of the many
oversteepened slopes
above the upper part
of the glacier. This
debris had already
been transported to
the lip of the ter-
minal cascade and
was forming a new
medial moraine. An
unusual opportunity
was thus at hand
for the study over a
period of several
weeks of the ice
motion in this cas-

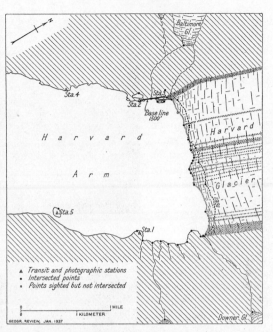

FIG. 15—Map of the ice front of Harvard Glacier, College Fiord,
Prince William Sound, based on the triangulations and data obtained
by the author on the expeditions of 1931 and 1935. (For photos
taken in 1931 see report in the *Geographical Review*, July, 1932.)

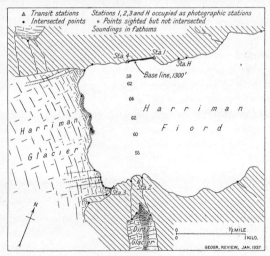

FIG. 16—Map of the ice front of Harriman Glacier, Harriman Fiord,
Prince William Sound, based on the triangulations and data of the
1935 expedition. Photographic Station GG (see Figs. 17 and 20) is
near Station 3.

cading glacier, though, unfortunately, the expedition could not stay.

The moraine-covered terminus of Vassar Glacier shrank slightly between 1931 and 1935, but the white ice above spread laterally, and a small subsidiary tongue on the south side advanced. Wellesley Glacier also expanded laterally between 1931 and 1935, but the position of the terminus has not changed.

The recent lateral expansion of Bryn Mawr, Vassar, and Wellesley Glaciers has not entirely covered the barren zones that mark the limits of the area occupied by the ice since 1909. These glaciers, as well as Smith Glacier are, therefore, not so advanced as they have been within the last quarter of a century. On the other hand, the Harvard and Yale Glaciers are now in more advanced positions than for at least 250 years and 50 years respectively. The other glaciers of the fiord, with the exception of the Baltimore, seem to be retreating. All these recent changes have been gradual and can probably be assigned to slight variations in meteorological conditions affecting one glacier differently from another.

Fig. 17—Eastern end of Harriman Glacier ice front from Station G(1931 with the ice 322 feet away. (Cf. Fig. 20.)

Fig. 18—Toboggan Glacier, Harriman Fiord, from Station E in 1931. (Fig. 21.)

Fig. 19—The most advanced tongue of Toboggan Glacier (see above 1931. (Cf. Fig. 22.)

Barry Arm and Harriman Fiord. The recent history of Coxe, Barry, and Cascade Glaciers has two distinct phases. From 1899 to 1914[5] a retreat took place; since 1914 there has been no significant change. On the south side of Barry Glacier the ice front advanced 150 to 200 feet between 1931 and 1935, apparently because the constant dumping of debris from a heavy medial moraine is reducing the depth of this part of the inlet, curtailing the subsurface melting of the ice, and allowing the glacier to move forward over its own sediments (Fig. 14). Except for this the glaciers remain the same as they have been since 1914.

Serpentine Glacier did not change between 1931 and 1935 except that a small part of the terminus advanced about 50 feet. Probably, as in the case of the advanced tongue of Barry Glacier, this can be attributed to increased protection from tidewater. Between 1931 and 1935 the conspicuous ice tongue of Baker Glacier came forward 150 to 200 feet, the eastern part of the terminus became

[5] In 1914 Dora Keen took photographs of many of the glaciers of these inlets.

thicker and advanced slightly, and the snow-and-ice fan below the terminus increased in size. In a neighboring cirque the lower ice tongue of Detached Glacier has advanced about 100 feet since 1931.

Surprise Glacier advanced slightly at its north side between 1931 and 1935. Although small, the change is interesting in view of the rapid retreat from 1899 to 1910 and the subsequent slower recession from 1910 to 1931. Cataract Glacier changed considerably between 1931 and 1935. The whole lower part of the glacier increased in volume and spread laterally. The terminus advanced from a point 50 to 100 feet above sea level to contact with tidewater in one place. The present advance, however, is still well inside the limits of that of 1909 to 1914. The appearance of Roaring Glacier did not change between 1931 and 1935, and the snow-and-ice fan below the terminus remained about the same size.

Harriman Glacier has apparently been advancing since 1910. From 1931 to 1935 there was a measured net advance of 155 feet at the east end of the terminus (Figs. 17 and 20) and about the same on the west side. A large part of the ice front now rests on a bar that has grown considerably since 1931. On the west side of the valley above the Harriman is a small unnamed hanging glacier, which thickened and advanced slightly between 1931 and 1935. Dirty Glacier has apparently been receding steadily since 1899: between 1931 and 1935 this recession amounted to about 200 feet. Wedge Glacier seems not to have changed during this period.

Toboggan Glacier has apparently been retreating steadily since a short advance that culminated between 1905 and 1909. From 1909 to 1931 recession amounted to more than 900 feet, and between 1931 and 1935 the whole lower part of the glacier continued to shrink in volume (Figs. 18 and 21). The most advanced tongue receded 183 feet in four years (Figs. 19 and 22), and the point where the drainage stream issues receded 72 feet.   .

The changes in Barry Arm and Harriman Fiord are interesting. None of the large glaciers were retreating in 1935, and Surprise Glacier showed a slight advance and Harriman Glacier a considerable one. Four of the six small glaciers rising on the west side of the inlet were advancing, in contrast with the conditions on the east side of the inlet, where two out of three of the glaciers were retreating rapidly. It is possible that the snowfall on the high mountains of the inlet has increased but other factors, such as the rate of melting, have not changed. This would cause a slight advance of most of the glaciers feeding from snow fields on those mountains. East of the inlet the lower mountains and snow fields might receive this increased precipitation not as snow but as rain, and the glaciers would retreat. This oversimplified example may perhaps serve to indicate how nearby glaciers may respond entirely differently to a slight climatic change.

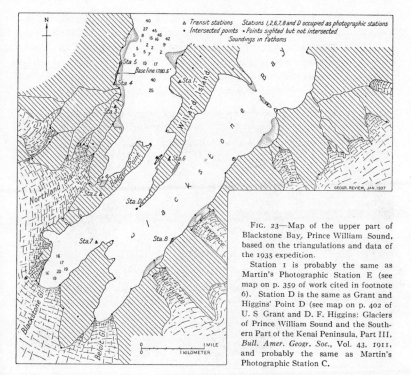

FIG. 23—Map of the upper part of Blackstone Bay, Prince William Sound, based on the triangulations and data of the 1935 expedition.

Station 1 is probably the same as Martin's Photographic Station E (see map on p. 359 of work cited in footnote 6). Station D is the same as Grant and Higgins' Point D (see map on p. 402 of U. S Grant and D. F. Higgins: Glaciers of Prince William Sound and the Southern Part of the Kenai Peninsula, Part III, *Bull. Amer. Geogr. Soc.*, Vol. 43, 1911, and probably the same as Martin's Photographic Station C.

GLACIERS OF THE WESTERN INLETS

The glaciers of Passage Canal, Blackstone Bay, Port Nellie Juan, and Icy Bay have been visited less than those of the northern inlets, and only the broader trends of glacier fluctuations are known. Brief visits were made by U. S. Grant and D. F. Higgins in 1908 and 1909 and by Lawrence Martin in 1910; and in 1925 F. H. Moffit of the U. S. Geological Survey took a series of photographs of these ice tongues. In 1935 our expedition made a rapid reconnaissance of these inlets and noted the conditions of all the principal glaciers.

Passage Canal. The Seth, Billings, Longfellow, and Whittier Glaciers seemed to be receding in 1935, for each had lateral and frontal barren zones. The fluctuations since 1900, however, have probably been slight, for most of the termini are within a few hundred feet of their maximum expansion for the past several centuries.

Blackstone Bay. Of the Blackstone Bay glaciers, the Blackstone and Beloit have tidal fronts, and the Northland, along a part of its terminus, discharges icebergs over a cliff. The changes in the principal glaciers since 1908 are very slight—recession of not more than a few score feet. On the other hand, the hanging glaciers have shrunk in

241

volume, and a comparison of photographs suggests that the upper ridges and snow fields have less snow than formerly. Mature trees grow in different parts of the inlet. One within 6000 feet of Blackstone and Beloit Glaciers, at the head of the bay, was found to be at least 450 years old, an indication that the glaciers have not coalesced to form one large Blackstone Bay glacier within at least 500 years.

FIG. 24—Remnants of an interglacial forest uncovered by the recent retreat of Tebenkof Glacier.

In the channel on the west side of Willard Island the expedition found a submerged terminal moraine whose existence had not previously been established. It proved to be a continuation of the conspicuous moraine in the eastern channel.[6] The western moraine was found to stretch apparently unbroken across the entire channel at an almost uniform depth of about 12 feet (Fig. 23). Its south, or inner, side rises gradually from a depth of 240 feet; its north side slopes very steeply to depths of more than 270 feet.

Tebenkof Glacier, in lower Blackstone Bay, descends from snow fields adjacent to those feeding the glaciers on the east side of the upper bay. It has not been tidal for at least a century. From 1910 to 1935 the terminus retreated fully 1000 feet and the glacier shrank laterally. A comparison of photographs indicates that the surface of the ice for some miles above the terminus has been appreciably lowered. Since 1910 the receding ice has uncovered a rock knoll, on which are remnants of an interglacial forest (Fig. 24). This seems to be the first such forest found in the Prince William Sound area. Its age is un-

---

[6] R. S. Tarr and Lawrence Martin: Alaskan Glacier Studies, National Geographic Society, Washington, 1914, pp. 358–361.

known, but there is no doubt that, as in Glacier Bay, it has grown since the Pleistocene expansion.[7]

Port Nellie Juan. There are no precise measurements available for the fluctuations of the glaciers of Applegate Arm of Port Nellie Juan. All the glaciers have receded fairly recently from a maximum

Fig. 25—The ice front of Nellie Juan Glacier from a point vacated by the ice since 1910. The limit of a recent advance can be seen on the small hill across the inlet.

position very near to mature vegetation. Comparison with early photographs shows that the two largest glaciers, Taylor and Falling, which practically reach tidewater, changed very little between 1908 and 1925 but that since then there has been considerable shrinking in their lower parts. Kings Glacier, which is shown on maps as coalescing near its terminus with another glacier flowing from the east, is now definitely separated from it.

Nellie Juan Glacier is the largest glacier of the inlet and has remained partially tidal in spite of the rapid silting up of the bay into which it discharges. There is more precise information on this glacier than on any other on the west side of Prince William Sound. Its most advanced position for some centuries seems to have been reached about 50 years ago. From 1887 to 1910 it retreated slightly; a comparison of photographs indicates little change from 1910 to 1925; after 1925 a rapid retreat began along the whole terminus. From 1910 to 1935 the total recession at the west end of the ice front was

[7] W. S. Cooper: The Recent Ecological History of Glacier Bay, Alaska, *Ecology*, Vol. 4, 1923, pp. 93–128, 223–246, and 355–365; *idem:* A Third Expedition to Glacier Bay, Alaska, *ibid.*, Vol. 12, 1931, pp. 61–95; see also the present number of the *Review*, pp. 37–62.

1912 feet, nearly all of which occurred in the last ten years. The
east end of the ice cliff receded 1532 feet (Fig. 25); the lobate eastern
land terminus, between 500 and 1000 feet (Fig. 26). Outside the
terminal moraine marking the maximum position occupied by the ice
within the last half century are mature trees more than a century old,

FIG. 26—The eastern terminus of Nellie Juan Glacier showing the barren zone recently vacated by
the ice and the mature trees growing outside this area.

Ultramarine Glacier, a nontidal glacier at the head of Blue Fiord.
receded more than 1000 feet between 1908 and 1935.

Icy Bay. The glaciers of Icy Bay have not been visited often,
and no precise measurements are available. Of its four principal ice
streams, Chenega and Tiger Glaciers have tidal ice fronts, Tiger's
Tail Glacier barely reaches tidewater, and Princeton Glacier ter-
minates some distance back of the shore line. There is evidence that
between 1898 and 1908 there was a two-mile retreat of the Chenega
Glacier, during which Nassau Fiord was opened up. Since 1908 the
Chenega terminus has not changed position. The only differences
discernible are that its surface above the final icefall is lower and the
first hanging glacier on the north side has shrunk to such an extent
that it may no longer be a tributary. The Chenega remains one of
the most active ice fronts of the Alaskan coast, its discharge of icebergs
being comparable to the Muir and the Columbia.

Princeton Glacier may have been a tributary of the expanded
Chenega Glacier some time before 1908, but by that year it was a
separate ice tongue and no longer tidal. From 1908 to 1925 it re-

treated and shrank in volume and the level of its upper snow field became perceptibly lower. This was continued at a still more rapid rate from 1925 to 1935.

Tiger's Tail Glacier seems to have shrunk in volume, and it does not discharge icebergs. Tiger Glacier, at the extreme head of Icy Bay, is slightly in advance of its position in 1910. No lateral barren zones are visible, and the ice is close to what seem to be mature alders. Within a mile of the ice front are mature trees, so that it is improbable that within a century there has been a substantial advance such as that attributed to Chenega Glacier.

In sum, the glaciers of the western inlets show an unusual similarity of behavior. All the glaciers in the vicinity of Passage Canal, Blackstone Bay, and Port Nellie Juan, including the adjacent Princeton Glacier, are retreating or at least showing signs of shrinking. The exceptions are Chenega and Tiger Glaciers, which are the southernmost of the group and as yet remain unaffected.

Conclusion

Although climatic variation is the prime cause of glacier fluctuation, the relationship of the factors involved is extremely complex. Varied and sometimes opposite effects may result from their interaction. For example, as C. E. P. Brooks[8] has pointed out, "the relative position of the snow-line and the level of maximum snowfall are of great importance for the development of glaciers . . ." "The level of maximum snowfall depends on the winter conditions, while the snow-line is determined very largely by the conditions in summer." As the source of every glacier differs somewhat in relation to the snow line and the level of maximum snowfall, and as the relation between these is constantly shifting from one season to the next, it is not surprising to find the glaciers of a locality fluctuating in dissimilar ways.

The study of glacier fluctuations in the United States and Alaska is now commanding widespread attention. The coöperation of additional organizations and government departments has been enlisted, and their studies have been coördinated, largely through the efforts of the Committee on Glaciers of the American Geophysical Union and members of the U. S. Geological Survey. But though a good start has been made to systematize observations in Alaska, there are still many glaciers both along the coast and inland whose recent behavior is totally unknown. Most of these glaciers are not in localities where periodic observations can easily be made. They call for investigation by individuals or by expeditions primarily concerned with the study of that subject and properly organized and equipped to undertake it.

---

[8] Climate through the Ages, London, 1926, p. 183.

RACIAL MAPS OF THE UNITED STATES

Richard Hartshorne

University of Minnesota

ONE of the most difficult problems in the political geography of European countries, that of national minorities, is happily lacking in the United States. We have no areas in which the majority of the residents are both culturally and nationally associated with outside countries rather than with the United States. Indeed, there are few areas in which the language of the majority is other than English (American). However, in place of this problem of national minorities the United States has more permanent problems of racial minorities—problems in a form essentially unknown in Europe. The differences between French and English, Germans and Poles, or even Swedes and Finns, Rumanians and Magyars are essentially cultural, not biological. Germans have become French and Poles have become Germans in two generations. So far as appearance is concerned, the barber and the tailor can make the change in a day. But no amount of education can change into white Americans the descendants of the negroes who arrived in Virginia before the Pilgrims landed at Plymouth, just as no beauty shop can make a fullblood negro look like a white person.

The problems of our racial minorities are regional. The presence of a large proportion of negroes in the population is the feature that most distinguishes the southeastern United States. Indeed, if one considers any of the problems of the South—whether of crop systems, soil erosion, farm tenancy, settlements, or industrial development, not to mention social and political problems—one must agree with the popular conception, that this population characteristic is the single most important factor in the geography of the region.

It is not so generally known, however, that many areas in the South have but few negroes, proportionately fewer than certain areas in the North.[1] Likewise, people who know that there are relatively more Chinese and Japanese in our Pacific States than farther east may have an exaggerated idea of the actual proportions. Probably fewer people realize the importance of another racial problem—that of the Mexican Indians in our Southwest.

The purpose of the accompanying maps is to depict the relative importance of these different races in the various sections of the United States. The chief interest is in the regional differences; conse-

---

[1] The recent Scottsboro case affords an example. Although in Alabama, Scottsboro is in a district of relatively small negro population—less than 10 per cent—but it is near enough to districts of large negro population to have strong racial prejudices, though of a different kind from those in predominantly negro portions of the state. See the discussion in C. L. Carmer's popular "Stars Fell on Alabama," New York, 1934; reference on pp. 74–78.

246

quently the races are not measured in actual numbers but in the proportion that they constitute of the total population in any area.

We shall not enter into the argument regarding what is meant by "race." Our interest is in social and political situations that arise from obvious biological differences, and we can therefore accept the

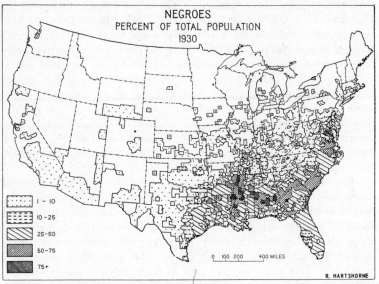

FIG. 1—Negroes in proportion to the total population, by counties.

ordinary interpretation of racial terms as used in this country. In the United States apparently the only definition of a negro is one who is known to be a negro; i.e. one who either because of obvious physical characteristics, chiefly color, or because of known origin, is recognized as having any degree of negro ancestry, regardless of how much white ancestry he may also have. This, of course, is the definition followed by the United States Bureau of the Census, whose data for 1930 were used for the maps.

NEGRO AREAS

The areas that are relatively high in negro population (Fig. 1) lie in the region of hot, humid summers and mild winters—the southeastern part of the country. But it is clear from the map that this is not a direct reflection of climate, as some foreign observers have supposed. The large number of negroes in Northern cities cannot be dismissed as exceptions; nor can the absence of negroes in many Southern districts be explained climatically. Rather the well known concentration in the South can be understood only in relation to certain crop systems, which depended not only on particular climatic

247

conditions but on certain conditions of land surface and soil, and also in relation to a certain historical condition no longer present—the institution of slavery.

The older areas of intensive cotton production, where negroes are still generally a majority, running up to a maximum of six negroes to every white, are clearly apparent. The upper Coastal Plain and the Piedmont of South Carolina and Georgia, the "Black Belt" of Mississippi-Alabama, and the Yazoo-Mississippi flood plain, comprising parts of four states south of Memphis, are familiar areas of relatively finer, heavier, darker-colored soils most suitable for repeated cotton production. The plantations, with their large numbers of slaves, have left their mark in the population make-up, even in those parts where some diversification has since taken place. Undoubtedly this population situation, with the social and economic structure that became associated with it, remains, even after the abolition of slavery, a strong factor discouraging diversification away from the simple, foolproof, cotton-and-corn cropping system.

The smaller proportion of negroes in the Black Waxy Prairie of Texas, now the most important of all cotton areas, is presumably due to its more recent development, largely since the abolition of slavery. On the other hand, negroes form majorities in noncotton areas along the Atlantic coast from Virginia south, areas where slavery was introduced on the tobacco, rice, and indigo plantations of colonial days and where, in part at least, tobacco plantations are still important.

Equally significant are the areas relatively low in negro population in the South.[2] In the poor farming areas of the Appalachians, where plantation culture was impracticable, negroes number generally less than 10 per cent of the population, in some districts even less than 1 per cent, and one county in Georgia records not a single negro. The poor-soiled areas of the highland rims in Kentucky and Tennessee and of a belt in northern Alabama and the sandy-soiled areas along parts of the Gulf coast are similar. The almost complete absence of negroes in the Ozark Highlands of Arkansas and Missouri is most striking; whereas immediately to the north there are large numbers of them, notably in the fertile valley of the Missouri River, where "Southern" settlements were made that kept Missouri among the slave states until the Civil War.

The effect of political boundaries in changing what would have been a transition zone into a sharp line is clearly shown by the distinct break along the historic boundary between slave states and free states —Mason and Dixon's Line and the Ohio River. Significant (more

<hr>

[2] The well known relation between this situation and the alignment by political parties can be seen in detail by comparing this map with the map of "Presidential Elections, 1876–1928," Figure 2 (p. 669) in J. K. Wright: Voting Habits in the United States: A Note on Two Maps, *Geogr. Rev.*, Vol. 22, 1932, pp. 666–672.

than 10 per cent) negro minorities overlap it in but two places. At the west end is the old district of negro population in the river flood plain around Cairo, Ill.—both urban and rural. At the east end negroes have more recently become important in Philadelphia and certain industrial towns near it and in the resort town of Atlantic City.

All told, the portion of the country traditionally "free" now has more than two million negroes, or about one-fifth of the total number in the country.[3] Almost 90 per cent of these are in towns and cities, less than 3 per cent are on farms. Most of them have come in recent decades to the largest cities; nearly half are included in the three largest "metropolitan districts." In New York and Chicago they are so segregated as to constitute almost completely negro districts, but only in Philadelphia do they amount to one-tenth of the total population.

One interesting contrast, not revealed by the map, is that in the cities the proportion of negroes is relatively smaller than in neighboring rural areas in the South but relatively larger in the North. The contrast is probably only apparent, for the cause is the same in both cases: the cities offer employment to many of both races, so that they are simply less homogeneous than the surrounding rural areas.

For legislative purposes it is necessary to consider each state as a whole as well as the component districts, since for most purposes the state is the smallest legislative unit. Practically all the states have white majorities.[4] But the social and political problems that arise out of the population conditions in the counties with negro majorities present legislative problems to the state as a whole. If we consider the states in which two counties or more have negro majorities, we discover a very significant fact: these eleven states form the familiar "Solid South," the Confederacy of 1861–1865. Along their northern boundary are the "border states"—those in which the population of some counties is more than a fourth negro. West Virginia is not a "border state" but is as distinctly free of the negro problem as its parent state, Virginia, is concerned with it. Few of the other states have any serious negro problem except in the large cities. In some of these, however, segregation has produced a situation unknown in the South: individual wards or other electoral districts, for Congress as well as for local offices, have as high as 90 per cent negro population.

MEXICAN AREAS

The second most important racial minority in the United States is the Mexican (Fig. 2). As the Mexicans are practically all Indians,

---

[3] Negroes in the United States, 1920–32, U. S. Bureau of the Census, 1935.

[4] In 1930 Mississippi was the only state that still showed a negro majority—50.2 per cent of the population. But, for the first time, the number of whites of voting age slightly exceeded that of negroes. Apparently the higher death rate among negroes more than balances their higher birth rate; very possibly the total number of whites is already larger than that of negroes.

249

they are recognized on sight as belonging to a "colored" race.[5] Furthermore, unlike the negroes, they speak a different language—Spanish —and have inherited a different culture from outside the United States. Unfortunately the census does not include all Mexicans but

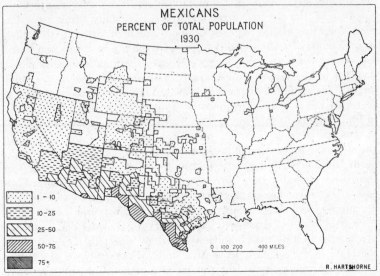

MEXICANS
PERCENT OF TOTAL POPULATION
1930

1 – 10
10 – 25
25 – 50
50 – 75
75 +

0 100 200   400 MILES

R. HARTSHORNE

FIG. 2—Mexicans in proportion to the total population, by counties.

FIG. 3—Border districts in which over half the population are Mexican Indians. Based on statistics for minor civil divisions, 1930.

only those who were born in Mexico or one of whose parents was born in Mexico. However, the number of native-born both of whose parents were native-born is probably small, except in Arizona and New Mexico. In New Mexico the number of descendants from the days when it was a part of Mexico is large enough to make it officially a bilingual state.

The largest proportion of Mexicans, as one would expect, is found in the Southwest. For they alone of all the principal immigrant groups, white or colored, have come in by land and, of course, from that direction. They have been attracted by the need for cheap hand labor—supplied in the older South by the negroes—in cotton fields and sugar-beet fields and on irrigated fruit and truck farms. In general

⁵ For a discussion of the problems introduced by Mexican immigration into this country see P. S. Taylor: Mexican Labor in the United States, *Univ. of California Publs. in Economics*, Vols. 6 and 7, 1928–1932.

they constitute a majority along most of the Mexican border. As the large county units of the West tend to obscure local conditions, the border area was mapped on a township basis, to show this strip of predominantly Mexican population (Fig. 3). It should be remembered, however, that along most of this border the population is very sparse, so that the number of Mexicans is small except in the irrigated districts of the lower Rio Grande and the Imperial Valley and in the city of El Paso. Very much larger numbers are found as minor parts of the population of such cities as San Antonio and Los Angeles.

This large proportion of the population of our southwestern border who are racially and culturally akin to the people of the neighboring country produces a situation that seems to be similar to that found along many European borders. But it would be erroneous to draw conclusions from this similarity. There is no evidence of any Mexican nationalist movement among these people who have been glad enough to emigrate to this country.[6] On the other hand, the presence of this "alien" race, permanently unassimilable because of color, leads to certain social and political problems in these areas similar to those of the old South.

These problems are clearly of importance chiefly in Texas, a state concerned also with the older negro problem. They are increasingly significant for California also and, to a less extent, the other two border states and Colorado.

In the eastern United States, although there are at present no areas with a significant proportion of Mexicans, there are certain suggestive increases, as in sugar-beet districts in Iowa and Minnesota and in two industrial districts around Chicago and Lorain, Ohio. In actual numbers there are many more Mexicans in Chicago itself—in fact, more than in seven mountain states west and north of Colorado.

NATIVE-INDIAN AREAS

The descendants of the aboriginal inhabitants of what is now the United States constitute another racial minority, but one that is sufficiently dispersed so that in only a few scattered areas do they form a majority (Fig. 4). In a sense the map is the negative reflection of the white settlement of the territory of the United States: where conditions were suitable for agriculture, the Indians were driven out; whereas in the Florida Everglades, in parts of the poor cutover lands of the upper Lake States, and especially in the dry lands of the West

---

[6] The Mexican population in the lower Rio Grande area may be seriously affected by the present international controversy over water rights. American authorities predict that, if Mexico should carry into effect its present plans to divert water from the southern tributaries of the Rio Grande, for irrigation in Mexico, this will force abandonment of much land now irrigated on the American side of the river. If that takes place, many thousands of Mexican farm laborers will be forced to return to Mexico for employment, thereby offsetting the new employment offered by the Mexican development.

they remain of some relative importance. Exclusive of the very small reservations scattered from New England to Mississippi, the entire humid half of the country has only one significant area of Indian population. In the eastern half of Oklahoma, once Indian Territory,

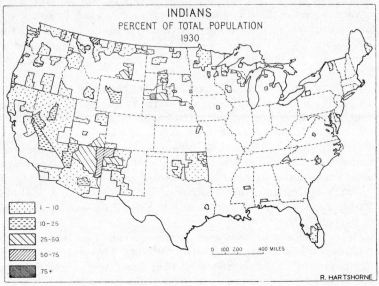

FIG. 4—Native Indians (not including Mexican Indians) in proportion to the total population, by counties.

are concentrated nearly one-fourth of the Indians listed in the census. As in most other areas, these are not descendants of the indigenous tribes but of tribes moved by federal orders from land farther east. This is the only important area of valuable land from which the Indians were not later removed into less valuable regions.

In the western half of the country the map does not give an accurate picture of the location of the Indians, because the counties are far larger than most of the reservations.[7] On the reservations the population is almost wholly Indian, but it is difficult to determine the proportion in other parts of the country. In northern Arizona and New Mexico it is probably large, especially in the mountains.

It is difficult to generalize the area of significant Indian population, because of the method by which the reservations were located—a haphazard, or perhaps purposeful, scattering. Roughly one might say that Indians are of some importance in the northern part of the country west of the Great Lakes, especially in South Dakota west

[7] The Indian reservations (in 1930) are shown in C. O. Paullin: Atlas of the Historical Geography of the United States, Carnegie Institution of Washington and the American Geographical Society of New York, 1932, Plate 36B. They appear on a larger scale in the National Park Service's map "Recreational Areas of the United States" (scale approximately 1 : 4,500,000), 1934.

of the Missouri, in the Southwest from California to New Mexico, and, particularly, in eastern Oklahoma. Politically the problem is different from that of the other minorities because the Indians are defined not as citizens but as wards of the United States.

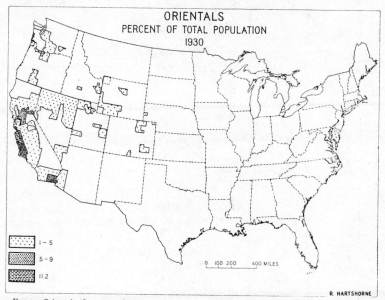

FIG. 5—Orientals (Japanese, Chinese, Filipinos, and others) in proportion to the total population, by counties.

ORIENTAL-RACE AREAS

With one small exception—Monterey County, Cal., where the chief group consists of Filipinos—there is no county or city in the United States in which Orientals amount to one-tenth of the population. Japanese and other Orientals amount to 5 to 9 per cent only in the center of the great valley of California, in the coastal valleys south of San Francisco, and in the Hood River Valley of Oregon (Fig. 5).

Socially and politically the Oriental races are as separate from one another as from the whites; hence they should be considered separately. They are so shown, in round numbers, on the series of dot maps, for the Pacific Coast States only (Fig. 6). Japanese make up most of the Oriental population of the Pacific coast outside San Francisco. They are particularly concentrated in the Los Angeles Plain and the Sacramento Valley. Although the largest group is the 21,000 in the city of Los Angeles, the highest proportion in any political unit—5 per cent—is found in Sacramento County. The city of Sacramento, with 3.5 per cent, has the highest proportion of any

253

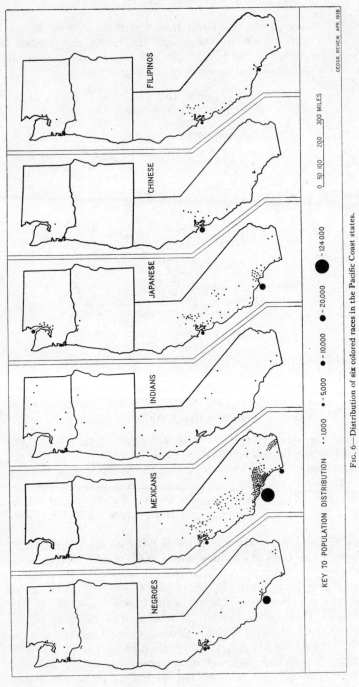

KEY TO POPULATION DISTRIBUTION · = 1,000 •= 5,000 ● = 10,000 ● = 20,000 ● = 124,000

0 50 100 200 300 MILES

GEOGR. REVIEW. APR. 1938

Fig. 6—Distribution of six colored races in the Pacific Coast states.

city of 25,000 or more in the country. The rest of the county has 9 per cent. Japanese farm laborers are found in the irrigation districts of the intermontane region and have reached as far east as those of the Great Plains.

In sharp contrast, Chinese are found chiefly in the cities, most notably in San Francisco, where they number some 16,000—2.5 per cent of the population. These represent a decreasing remnant of the large immigration of the middle of the last century. More than a third of the Chinese residents of the United States are to be found, in almost equal numbers, in the two cities of San Francisco and New York and another third in the remaining eight of the ten largest cities; probably most of the remainder are scattered in smaller cities and towns throughout the country.

Filipinos in California are employed, like the Japanese but in much smaller numbers, in the rural areas. Monterey County seems to have an unusual settlement, amounting to 5 per cent of the population. They are also, like the Chinese, scattered in Eastern cities, in larger numbers than the Japanese.

All told, the eastern half of the country has two-fifths of the Chinese, one-fifth of the Filipinos, and 4 per cent of the Japanese. But there is no single county or city in which these together amount to as much as 1 per cent of the population.

The Pacific coast is the only region that has large numbers of all the colored minorities found in the United States (Fig. 6). Originally the Chinese were the most important immigrant group.[8] The anti-Chinese agitation caused the immigration of Chinese practically to cease after 1882 and led to the concentration in a few cities, chiefly in San Francisco, of those who remained. The need for cheap labor in the rapidly growing fruit and truck industry led to a larger immigration of Japanese, and this in turn led to the development of anti-Japanese attitudes, which brought Japanese immigration virtually to an end by 1908, completely so in 1925. Although most of those who had come remained, the continued demand for labor brought in a very much larger number of Mexican Indians, who now constitute the chief colored element in the orchards and truck farms of California. They are also important in the city of Los Angeles and its suburbs, of which one, Belvedere Township, is composed largely of Mexicans. The frequent reports of difficulties in the Imperial Valley suggest that we may see the development of a movement to exclude this group, in which case there might be more opportunities for negro farm laborers in southern California. As yet the negroes have been confined largely to the cities, particularly in connection with railroad

[8] E. G. Mears: Resident Orientals on the American Pacific Coast . . . : Preliminary Report Prepared for the July 1927 Conference of the Institute of Pacific Relations in Honolulu, New York, 1928; B. Schrieke: Alien Americans: A Study of Race Relations, New York, 1936 (see review in this number of the *Geographical Review*).

work.   The native Indians seem to be restricted chiefly to the undeveloped mountain areas.

COMPOSITE MAP OF COLORED RACES

The composite map (Fig. 7) shows the location of the racial areas
in relation to one another.   Most of them are distinctly separate.   In

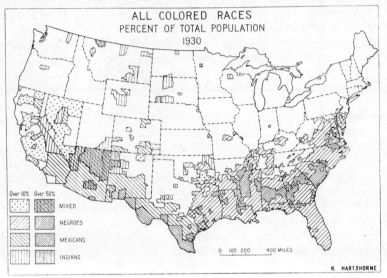

FIG. 7—Map showing the relation of the areas of different colored minorities to each other.

parts of New Mexico and Arizona native Indians and Mexican Indians
are found close together and form a larger part of the population,
than do the whites.   Whether they recognize any community of
race may be doubted, in view of the difference in language and culture,
but continued ostracism by the white population might eventually
lead to such feelings.   However, these areas are sparsely populated
and of little importance.   More important are the overlapping areas
of Mexicans and negroes in southern Texas, where the population
is definitely divided into three social groups: whites, American
negroes, and Mexican Indians.   Finally, in eastern Oklahoma there
is an older mixture of native Indians and negroes.   As many of these
Indians have intermingled with negroes for more than two centuries,
one might well expect active mixture to continue, resulting ultimately
in the cohesion of the two colored races.

FOREIGN-BORN WHITES

In addition to the permanent racial minorities in the United
States there is a temporary type of minority, which, although not

racial, is sometimes treated with similar discrimination. The more recent immigrants from Europe are distinguished usually by their foreign language, often by their clothing, and generally by customs and attitudes unfamiliar to most native Americans, even those of similar family origins. In many respects these foreign-born whites are regarded socially and politically as unassimilated elements, but

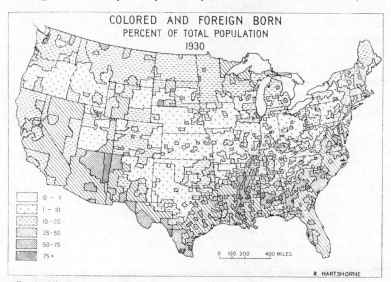

COLORED AND FOREIGN BORN
PERCENT OF TOTAL POPULATION
1930

0 – 1
1 – 10
10 – 25
25 – 50
50 – 75
75 +

0 100 200   400 MILES

R. HARTSHORNE

FIG. 8—All colored races and foreign-born whites, in proportion to the total population, by counties. In the northeastern quarter of the country this is essentially a map of the foreign-born whites (compare Fig. 7).

their children born in this country and educated for the most part in the public schools become full-fledged Americans. This is a very broad generalization, to be sure; many of the first-generation immigrants of English, Teutonic, and Scandinavian stock, especially those who were brought to this country in their early years, are fairly generally accepted as Americans, and, on the other hand, many native-born whites whose parents came from southern and eastern Europe and, who were brought up in foreign-language quarters of our large cities may be discriminated against as un-American. Nevertheless, the generalization that most closely approximates the complicated fact in this case recognizes that in the popular mind those born in other countries are "furriners" and, like all colored peoples, are not included as "100 per cent Americans." Where such foreign-born peoples constitute a considerable part of the population of any area, their presence is one of the significant characteristics of that area and has important social and political consequences.

By comparing Figures 7 and 8 the areas with a significant proportion (more than 10 per cent) of foreign-born whites can be visualized. In actual numbers the most important area is, of course, the manufacturing zone extending from the North Atlantic seaboard west to Detroit and including the Chicago-Milwaukee district. Less important are the zone of Canadian, chiefly French-Canadian, immigration along the northeastern border from Maine to New York, the pioneer fringe in the cutover lands of the Upper Great Lakes region and in the Northern Great Plains, and, generally, the whole West, notably California. In only a few areas, however, do foreign-born whites constitute (in 1930) as much as one-fourth of the population: the urban zone from Boston to Philadelphia; the industrial districts around Youngstown, Cleveland, and Chicago; and the sparsely populated mining and lumbering district of the Upper Lakes.

TOTAL OF ALL MINORITIES

Figure 8 shows the total of all the minorities, cultural and racial; i.e. groups not fully accepted as American by the dominant political population of the areas. In a negative sense it measures the proportion of "100 per cent Americans" in different parts of the country. The areas in which these minorities all together amount to less than one-tenth of the population are those which might be considered as having no important problems arising from their presence. These are, chiefly: the northern interior from eastern Ohio to Nebraska; the Great Plains except at the northern and southern ends; the Appalachians discontinuously from Vermont to Alabama and the Ozarks; and the more sparsely populated steppe and mountain areas of the Northwest. The areas that are more than 99 per cent "American" are especially interesting: the greater part of the Ozarks; scattered districts throughout the Appalachians; certain districts in the Ohio Valley; and a few districts in the northern interior exclusive of the larger cities. Most of these are areas of less desirable land where the native-white population has had all it can do to wrest a meager living from the inhospitable soil, with no chance of developing either plantations or industries requiring immigrant labor. Where coal mining or an industry has developed late in these areas—as in northern West Virginia—the overcrowded native-white population can furnish all the cheap labor needed.

A BIRD'S-EYE CROSS SECTION OF THE CENTRAL APPALACHIAN MOUNTAINS AND PLATEAU: WASHINGTON TO CINCINNATI

John L. Rich

University of Cincinnati

ON a flight on the regular passenger plane of American Airlines from Washington, D. C., to Cincinnati, between 4.35 and 7.05 on the afternoon of May 1, 1938, a photographic record was obtained that shows so many features of geologic, physiographic, and geographic interest and serves so well as a visual cross section of the region that it seems worthy of being made generally available by publication. The cross section was later checked as to interpretation and geologic features on an automobile trip over the route from Cincinnati as far east as the Shenandoah River, during which the site of each picture was visited.

Fig. 1—Route of the flight from Washington, D. C., to Cincinnati.

The photographs were taken through the plane window with a Leica camera using Eastman "background" film with a light-yellow (K-2) filter. Exposure varied with time of day, being $f6.3$—1/60th second from the start to 5.25, then $f4.5$—1/60th until 6.38 (considerable overexposure at first), and $f3.5$—1/60th for the remainder of the trip. All the photographs were taken from the north side of the plane and in directions ranging from northwest through north to northeast. Late-afternoon shadows served to emphasize the topography and to bring out many details that would have been inconspicuous under a noonday sun.

For location, Rand-McNally state maps on a scale of 8 to 12 miles to the inch were used. These maps are especially useful for the purpose because drainage, railways, and towns are clearly shown and the scale is not too large for use in speedy airplane travel or too small to show needed detail. [*Continued on p. 586*]

259

FIG. 2—This landscape of small farms, orchards, and scattered wood lots just south of Vienna and abo⟨⟩ 11 miles west of Washington is typical of the less dissected parts of the Piedmont Plateau as developed on pr⟨⟩ Cambrian schists. (38° 52.7' N., 77° 16.5' W.; Fairfax quadrangle, Va.)

FIG. 3—Twenty-five miles west of Figure 2 the proportion of woodland decreases abruptly along a nort⟨⟩ south line, west of which is open, gently rolling farmland with bright-red soil (Newark Triassic). There⟨⟩ a distinct north-south trend to the topography, suggesting steeply dipping sedimentary rocks. This view⟨⟩ three miles northeast of Haymarket. (38° 50' N., 77° 35.5' W.; Thorofare Gap quadrangle, Va.)

FIG. 4—Bull Run Mountains. Ten miles west of Figure 3 the gently rolling Triassic lowland gives place abruptly along a fault line to parallel ridges of quartzite dipping steeply eastward. These are Cambrian quartzites resting on a series of pre-Cambrian volcanic rocks (Catoctin series). The drainage runs through the ridges without deviation at Thorofare Gap (in the foreground); hence the streams have been superposed on the ridges from earlier and higher courses. (35° 51′ N., 77° 43′ W.; Thorofare Gap quadrangle, Va.)

FIG. 5—West of the ridges of Figure 4 is a rolling lowland developed on the volcanics, which weather int peculiar, irregularly knobby topography, suggestive, under the late-afternoon sun, of hammered silver. vague, roughly north-south trend can be distinguished. This is about three miles south of Marshall. (49′ N., 77° 52′ W.; Thorofare Gap quadrangle, Va.)

FIG. 6—The first outlier of the Blue Ridge, Big Cobbler Mountain, rises as an isolated, wooded cone ab 750 feet above the gently rolling Piedmont Plateau. According to the geologic map the entire area sho is Catoctin volcanic rock; but the monadnock form of Big Cobbler Mountain argues for the presence something locally much more resistant than the surrounding rocks. (38° 50.5′ N., 77° 57.5′ W.; Thorof Gap quadrangle, Va.)

The culture differs considerably from that shown in Figures 2, 3, and 4. Woodland is confined mostly the hills, and there seems to be much pastureland: white fields are presumably recently planted; gray fie with white specks are presumably wheat that was planted among last year's corn shocks (the white do

FIG. 7—About four miles farther on we pass the ragged eastern border of the Blue Ridge, here eroded wn to early old age, with broad valleys between the much reduced residual mountains. The rocks are toctin greenstone and granodiorite, and the peculiar "hammered silver" weathering is still conspicuous. ° 50.5′ N., 78° 2′ W.; Luray quadrangle, Va.)

FIG. 8—The summit and western front of the Blue Ridge are well shown here. This picture, together with ure 7, shows clearly the old-age character of the topography of the Blue Ridge in this area. On the crest he Skyline Drive, leading down toward the town of Front Royal (A). In the background are the Shenan- h Valley and the Shenandoah River. (38° 52′ N., 78° 11.5′ W.; Luray quadrangle, Va.)

Fig. 9—After crossing the south branch of the Shenandoah Valley we see the South Fork of the Shena
doah River, its remarkable meanders entrenched in the steeply dipping Ordovician shales (Martinsbu
at the foot of Massanutten Mountain. The narrow, even-topped ridge crest of the mountain is formed
steeply dipping Silurian quartzite (Tuscarora), one of the most consistent ridge formers in the Appalachia
The Shenandoah has developed a considerable flood plain within its meandering trench. Here, howev
it is cutting on bedrock and does not seem to be actively cutting against its bluffs: this fact suggests that
regimen has recently changed after a stage at grade, when lateral widening was a dominant process. (
52.5′ N., 78° 19′ W.; Luray quadrangle, Va.)

Fig. 10—This shows Massanutten Mountain mass, a compound, synclinal mountain, whose bound
ridges are Tuscarora quartzite. The central lowland at the left of the center is developed on Devonian sha
This mountain mass separates the two branches of the Shenandoah Valley, which unite north of the mo
tain as seen in the background. (38° 53′ N., 78° 21′ W.; Luray quadrangle, Va.)

FIG. 11—This picture shows the valley of Passage Creek north of Seven Fountains, a cultivated low-land in the synclinal area between the two bounding ridges of the Massanutten Mountain mass. Rock structure is clearly revealed by distinct ridges, which are too low, however, to interfere seriously with cultivation. (38° 50′ N., 78° 26′ W.; Luray quadrangle, Va.)

FIG. 12—Immediately west of the western ridge of the Massanutten Mountain mass the north branch of the Shenandoah River shows perhaps the most remarkable series of entrenched meanders to be found anywhere. They are entrenched 100 to 150 feet in steeply dipping soft shales (Martinsburg) and their form, U-shaped, with straight, parallel sides and sharply curved ends, does not seem to have been explained. This view is just north of Woodstock. (38° 53′ N., 78° 28′ W.; Luray quadrangle, Va.)

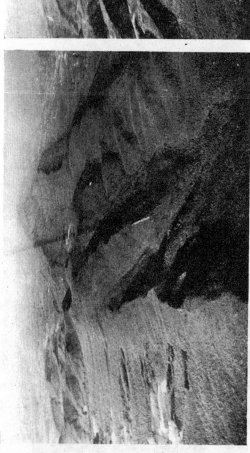

FIGS. 13, 14, and 15—West of the Shenandoah Valley the route crosses a wild mountainous region with ridges of Tuscarora quartzite. Figure 13 (upper left) shows Little Sluice Mountain and Paddy Mountain at the right and North Mountain in the center. Thrust faulting and transverse faulting complicate the structure; a relatively simple anticline is revealed in the right background. (38° 58.5′ N., 78° 36.5′ W.; Woodstock, Romney, and Winchester quadrangles, Va.–W. Va.)

Another ridge of Tuscarora quartzite appears to the left of the center of Figure 14 (upper right). This evidently is faulted off at the north end. Great North Mountain is in the right background, the valley of Trout Run in the right center. (38° 59.5′ N., 78° 39.5′ W.; Woodstock and Romney quadrangles, Va.–W. Va.)

The wooded hills in the upper right of Figure 15 continue Figure 14 westward. Inspection on the ground indicated duplication of some of the ridge-making beds by faulting, probably of thrust type. On the left side of Figure 15 is an anticline, bordered on each side by a ridge of Oriskany sandstone, which can be recognized along the left edge of the picture, extending to the upper margin and thence back to the center. In the center foreground is the sharp, plunging crest of the anticline, revealed by a hard sandstone member of the Clinton formation. (38° 58.7′ N., 78° 45′ W.; Woodstock and Romney quadrangles, Va.–W. Va.)

From this anticline westward to the Allegheny Plateau at the

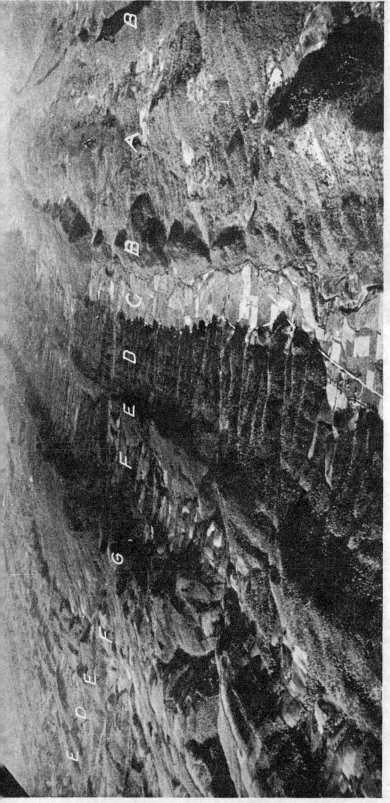

Fig. 16—The Oriskany-rimmed anticline of Figure 15 is seen at the right. It is followed by the Upper Devonian shale and sandstone formations, all dipping to the west (left). Note especially the long, straight strike valley of the Lost River, etched out of the soft Marcellus shale. It is the site of a through highway and of the only considerable cultivation visible in the picture. (39° 1.3′ N., 78° 47′ W.; Woodstock, Romney, and Moorefield quadrangles, Va.–W. Va.)

Figure 17, a sketch cross section through the center of the picture, makes clear these relations.

GEOGR. REVIEW, OCT. 1939

FIG. 18—This figure continues the aerial cross section westward. The physiographic belts of Figure are seen on the right and are given the same lettering. In the lower right-hand corner the steeply dipp bedding of the ridge-making bed, E, is clearly visible. Then come the synclinal mountains, G, in the mid of the picture; a strike valley on the Catskill shales, F, and an anticline rimmed on each side by the ri maker, E, and—as checked on the ground—exposing in its center the Middle Devonian shales, D. (39° N., 78° 49' W.; Woodstock and Moorefield quadrangles, Va.–W. Va.)

FIG. 19—Carrying the aerial cross section still farther west, Figure 19 ties up with Figure 18 at X, on t west limb of the anticline. The rocks, F (Catskill formation), dip westward from the anticline to anot synclinal mountain, Branch Mountain, G, held up by the resistant Pocono sandstone. The synclinal trou on the crest of the mountain is clearly shown, and also the Pocono ledges dipping into it where the stre breaks across the rim. (39° 00' N., 78° 52.5' W.; Woodstock and Moorefield quadrangles, Va.–W. Va.)

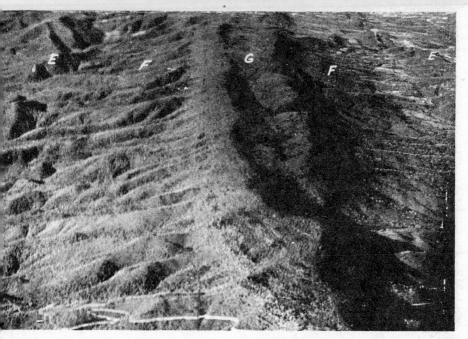

. 20—In the center is Branch Mountain, and at the left are the Devonian formations, *F* and *E* of
e 16, dipping eastward under it. (39° 00′ N., 78° 54.5′ W.; Woodstock and Moorefield quadrangles,
.V. Va.)

. 21—Branch Mountain, *G*, is at the extreme right, and then, in order westward, come the Catskill
s, *F*, the Chemung (?) ridge-making beds, *E*, and the Middle Devonian shales, *D* (Portage and Hamil-
all dipping eastward from a broad anticline, the crest of which, a little to the left of the picture, is broad
w, so that the Middle Devonian shales outcrop in a wide belt near Moorefield. The geology is revealed
almost perfect clearness, though practically the entire area is wooded. (39° 1.5′ N., 78° 55.5′ W.;
efield quadrangle, W. Va.)

FIG. 22—Dendritic drainage developed on Devonian shales on top of a broad anticline southwest of M○ field, a characteristic topographic expression of homogeneous rocks. This picture ties up with Figure 2 the point marked X. (39° 1.5′ N., 79° 3′ W.; Greenland Gap quadrangle, W. Va.)

FIG. 23—A stripped anticline is seen in this view north-northeastward along the southern end of Patte Creek Mountain. The Oriskany sandstone forms the surface of the mountain. Erosion has not yet through the resistant bed but has merely stripped off the weak overlying Marcellus shale. The main is at A; secondary rolls are seen at B, C, and D.

To the west of the anticline is a strike valley on Marcellus shale; beyond, at the extreme left, is a sha syncline on the Middle Devonian shales. (39° 3′ N., 79° 5.5′ W.; Greenland Gap quadrangle, W. Va.)

FIG. 24—The lowland seen at the left of Figure 23 occupies the right half of the view. In detail, the shales considerably crumpled, as was noted on the ground traverse; but they are so uniform in resistance that crumpling is not expressed in the rather intricately dissected topography. At the left appears the western-st anticline of the Ridge and Valley province, or Folded Appalachians, along the line of flight. he first topographic evidence of this anticline, the New Creek Mountain anticline, is a scalloped ridge, obly Mountain, formed by Oriskany sandstone dipping eastward. (39° 4′ N., 79° 10.5′ W.; Greenland quadrangle, W. Va.)

FIG. 25—At the right is the Knobly Mountain ridge. On its west slope and in the strike valley at its e are Lower Devonian and Upper Silurian limestones and shales. Below these is the Tuscarora quartzite t forms the crest of the anticline, stripped bare, so that structure and topographic form coincide. In the e valleys that cross the anticline from the west the Tuscarora ledge can be seen clearly. To the west of anticline is another ridge of Oriskany sandstone, and beyond is the Upper Devonian, dipping steeply tward beneath the Allegheny Front. (39° 4.5′ N., 79° 13′ W.; Greenland Gap quadrangle, W. Va.)

Fig. 26—The Allegheny Front. The front, here at an altitude of about 3500 feet, is the outcropping ed of the resistant Pottsville conglomerate (Pennsylvanian). This great cuesta marks the eastern edge of Appalachian Plateau province. Rock formations shown are Catskill formation at *A*, Pocono sandstone B, lower-Mississippian shales and limestones (Mauch Chunk shales and Greenbrier limestone) on the slo C, and Pottsville conglomerate at the top, *D*. The road shown in the picture is one of those recently b by the Forest Service. The Front in this region is an uninhabited, exceedingly bleak, rocky waste, sw by terrific gales. Near the edge there seems never to have been any forest; farther back, however, a for once grew, which has not been able to reëstablish itself after the ravages of lumbering and fire. (39° 3′ 79° 18′ W.; Davis quadrangle, W. Va.)

Fig. 27—This shows the relation of the Allegheny Front to the Folded Appalachians. At the left is t part of the front seen in Figure 26; at the right is the New Creek Mountain anticline of Figure 25. The vi is looking northeast. (39° 3.5′ N., 79° 15′ W.; Davis and Greenland Gap quadrangles, W. Va.)

FIG. 28—For about 40 miles west of the Allegheny Front the rocks of the Appalachian Plateau are moder-
ly folded in a broad, open pattern. Figure 28 connects in the background with Figure 26 and shows a
low syncline immediately west of the front. The front is at A; Stony Creek Reservoir is in the bottom
the syncline at B; and at C is the west-facing cuesta that forms the eastern rim of the Canaan Valley anti-
shown in Figure 30. Figure 28, although dull on account of haze, shows clearly the barrenness of
Allegheny Mountain crest (compare Fig. 29). In the picture there are no signs of human habitation
my human works except the distant reservoir and an old lumber road in the foreground. (39° 5′ N.,
20′ W.; Davis quadrangle, W. Va.)

FIG. 29—The Allegheny Front as seen from the ground. (39° 3′ N., 79° 18′
W.; Davis quadrangle, W. Va.)

FIG. 30—Immediately west of the broad, shallow syncline of Figure 28 is the Canaan Valley, a high-le (3100 ft.) anticlinal valley. Mauch Chunk shales and Greenbrier limestone (Mississippian) are raised to surface in the center, which has been eroded to a lowland, surrounded, except at the south end, by a rim outward-dipping Pottsville conglomerate. The valley is a fertile island in a rocky waste of brush and seco growth forest on the conglomerate. (39° 4.5′ N., 79° 26.5′ W.; Davis quadrangle, W. Va.)

FIG. 31—A short distance west of the Canaan Valley the barren Pottsville-floored waste is deeply cut the canyon of the Blackwater River. Like other areas underlain by the Pottsville, this region, altho relatively flat between streams, is practically uninhabited except for the coal-mining towns of Thomas and Davis (B), in a shallow syncline where a patch of lower-Pennsylvanian coal beds has been preserv Blackwater Falls and Blackwater Canyon State Park are at the head of the canyon. (39° 6′ N., 79° 32.5′ Davis and Parsons quadrangles, W. Va.)

G. 32—The Pottsville sandstone rises westward to a prominent west-facing cuesta, "Backbone Moun-
" West of this is a broad, flat-topped anticline, which brings the Upper Devonian shales to the surface.
topography of the Devonian area is illustrated in this view, west of Parsons, W. Va. It might well
e as a type of mature topography on homogeneous rocks: ridge divides, narrow, U-shaped valleys, and
dritic drainage pattern without evidence of structural control are characteristic. The relief is 700 to
eet. (39° 7′ N., 79° 47′ W.; Belington quadrangle, W. Va.)

G. 33—The west limb of the anticline of Figure 32 is marked by a ragged ridge or east-facing cuesta,
called Laurel Ridge, formed by the Pottsville sandstone as it plunges beneath the later Pennsylvanian
s of the Appalachian Plateau, not to appear again along the line of flight until east-central Ohio is
hed (Fig. 43). The steep, wooded dip slope of the Laurel Ridge cuesta occupies roughly the left third of
picture. Figure 33 is panoramic in the background with Figure 32, the point X being common to both.
7.5′ N., 79° 50′ W.; Belington quadrangle, W. Va.)

FIG. 34—At the base of the dip slope off Laurel Ridge one is surprised to find an old-age topogra of low relief at about 1700 feet above sea level, which contrasts strikingly with the early mature topogra just east of the ridge where summit elevations are about 1000 feet higher. Evidently here is an interes physiographic problem. (39° 7.7' N., 79° 57' W.; Belington quadrangle, W. Va.)

FIG. 35—This view, about 6 miles west of Philippi, shows part of the Appalachian Plateau province w the texture of the topography is comparatively coarse and a late mature stage has been reached. C topography is well shown in the right foreground, and also the indistinct topographic benches contou the hills and representing the subsoil outcrop of the more resistant rock ledges. The picture also shows sn scale gullying on the middle and lower hill slopes. (39° 9' N., 80° 10' W.; Philippi quadrangle, W. Va.)

FIG. 36—Typical maturely dissected Appalachian Plateau of West Virginia. Ledge terraces on the upper ~~es and gullies on the lower are well shown (compare Fig. 37). Whether the ledge-terrace topography~~out gullies on the upper slopes and the gully topography of the middle and lower slopes are normal ~~ures of erosion or are due to special local causes such as rock resistance or recent physiographic history~~writer did not succeed in determining. It is an interesting physiographic problem. (39° 12′ N., 80° 40′ Vadis quadrangle, W. Va.)

FIG. 37—Ledge terraces and gullies of the spur at *A* in Figure 36 as seen from the ground.

FIG. 38—This is an example of what are perhaps the average topography and culture for the central part of the Appalachian Plateau province in West Virginia. (39° 12′ N., 81° 15′ W.; Harrisville and Elizabeth quadrangles, W. Va.)

ᴵG. 39—About 20 miles east of Parkersburg, W. Va., the monotonous horizontal strata of the plateau are
ᴵrrupted by a remarkable long, straight, steep-sided, and relatively flat-topped fold, the Volcano anticline.
ₛ view is looking northward along the anticline. The steeply dipping western flank, passing through
ₛ revealed, not by the rock ledges, but through their physiographic expression produced by the etching
ᴼf slight differences in resistance of the dipping beds. The eastern flank is revealed at B, passing south-
ᴵ through the town of Petroleum at C. (39° 12.2′ N., 81° 17.2′ W.; Elizabeth quadrangle, W. Va.)

ᴵG. 40—A few miles southeast of Parkersburg is a group of interesting physiographic features associated
ᴵ the lower course of the Little Kanawha River. At its junction with the Ohio River, seen in the distant
ₖground, is the city of Parkersburg, A. Between Parkersburg and the observer, at B, C, and D, are three
ᴵ-level abandoned meander terraces of an earlier stage of the Little Kanawha River. (39° 12.5′ N.,
32′ W.; Belleville quadrangle, W. Va.)

FIG. 41—Typical topography southwest of Parkersburg and east of the Ohio River. The relief is about 300 feet, and valley bottoms are moderately alluviated. Upland cultivation is fairly common.

In this part of West Virginia and in southeastern Ohio as far west as the Scioto River near Waverly, the topography, seen under the late-afternoon sun, has a weird appearance, as if two discordant drainage systems lay crosswise on each other—as is in fact the case. The old "Teays" valley system, draining northward, was blocked by a glacial or morainic barrier, which caused the streams to silt up their valleys to a height that is now between 800 and 900 feet above the sea. On these alluviated flats the streams wandered at random. When, later, conditions permitted them to cut down again, their courses did not correspond to the old valley lines. As the new valleys were deepened, the alluvial fillings were partly removed from the older valleys, so that they, too, now show in the topography. (39° 9.5′ N., 81° 39.3′ W.; Belleville quadrangle, W. Va.)

FIG. 42—Point Rock, Ohio. One of the exhumed "Teays" valleys is seen extend-
ing in a nearly straight line from the lower right corner at *A* to the upper center at
B. Present drainage crosses the old valley at random. (39° 7.5′ N., 82° 17′ W.;
Wilkesville quadrangle, Ohio.)

The crisscross effect of one drainage system superposed on another is caught by
the camera to some degree, but not so clearly or extensively as it appears to the
traveler flying over the region. See also Figure 43.

FIG. 43—Newer drainage superposed crosswise on exhumed "Teays" system near Big Rock, Ohio Incidentally, Big Rock is composed of Pottsville conglomerate, which was last seen dipping beneath plateau at Laurel Ridge (Fig. 33). Note the section lines marked by rows of trees. (39° 5.5′ N., 82° 47′ Waverly quadrangle, Ohio.)

FIG. 44—Seven miles east of Waverly, Ohio. Where the general level is above 900 feet, hence above level of alluviation and possible drainage diversion, the valley system is orderly and normal. This pic shows how an unfavorable topography, even in as well settled a region as south-central Ohio, can caus almost complete wilderness. (39° 6′ N., 82° 52.5′ W.; Waverly quadrangle, Ohio.)

Fig. 45—A few miles southwest of Waverly, Ohio, is a puzzling change in topography, which warrants
ther study. The region has not advanced beyond mid-youth. No prominent rock ledges that might
ve held up this upland appear in the photograph, and none were noted on the ground, though perhaps
 rock may have superior resistance without appearing in conspicuous ledges. Another possible explana-
n—not verified, however—is that the flat upland may be the partly dissected remnant of a till plain of
 of the earlier glaciations. (39° 6.5′ N., 83° 8.5′ W.; Piketon quadrangle, Ohio.)

Fig. 46—Illinoian till plain of southwestern Ohio. Comparison of this picture with preceding ones shows
arly the change caused by glaciation in a region that otherwise presumably would have had a topography
 that of the Appalachian Plateau farther east. (39° 6′ N., 83° 47.5′ W.; Sardinia quadrangle, Ohio.)

The procedure for taking the pictures and obtaining a record from which the subject and location of each could later be determined was first to draw a line on the map along the approximate route to be followed to aid in quickly determining location along the route actually flown (which may vary a few miles on either side of the straight line between terminal points), then to note, at intervals of 15 to 25 minutes, the time of passing over a town, a river, or some other point that could be definitely identified on the map. The time at which each picture was taken was recorded to the nearest quarter of a minute, along with its subject and its number on the film roll.

In the office, later, assuming straight-line flight and uniform speed between control points, each picture was located by simple proportion by using time of taking, time of passing over control points, scale, and slide rule. Its position was first found on the Rand-McNally map, and it was then readily located on the United States Geological Survey topographic map, and the corrected latitude and longitude were recorded on the print.

The route is shown in Figure 1. It crosses the Piedmont physiographic province, the Blue Ridge province, the south and north branches of the Shenandoah Valley, with the synclinal Massanutten Mountain between them, the Folded Appalachians (Ridge and Valley province), the Appalachian Plateau province, the unglaciated portion of southeastern Ohio, and the glacial till plain of southwestern Ohio.

Characteristic physiographic and geographic features of each of these provinces are shown by selected pictures; but over the Folded Appalachians west of the Shenandoah Valley a continuous cross section is shown, broken only by one gap of a mile or two. Matching points on successive pictures are indicated in the captions and by letters in white ink on the prints. Latitude and longitude given is that of the approximate center of each picture.

To the reader who follows this series of pictures and the comments on them it will be evident that with a convenient camera and notebook one can learn much of a region and its geologic and physiographic features and problems by flying over it on a good day, even though these features are passing in panorama beneath him at three miles a minute.

THE PERSONALITY OF MEXICO

Carl O. Sauer

University of California

THE GEOGRAPHIC ART

THIS is an excursion into the oldest tradition of geography. For, whatever the problems of the day may be which claim the attention of the specialist and which result in more precise methods of inspection and more formal systems of comparison, there remains a form of geographic curiosity that is never contained by systems. It is the art of seeing how land and life have come to differ from one part of the earth to another. This quality of understanding has interested men almost from the beginning of human time and requires restatement and reëxamination for each new generation.

Many names have been given to the central and never completed theme of regional interpretation. For this paper a term is borrowed from Sir Cyril Fox's admirable study of the cultural backgrounds of the British Isles.[1] The designation of "personality" applied to a particular part of the earth involves the whole dynamic relation of life and land. It does not deal with land and life as separatè things, but with a given land as lived in by a succession of peoples, who have appraised its resources for their time in terms of their capacities and needs, who have spread themselves through it as best suited their ends, and who have filled it with the works that expressed their particular way of life.

ROOTS OF MEXICO IN A LONG PAST

Mexico, like most lands of Latin America, has its main and living roots in a deep, rich past. The continuity with ages long gone is fundamental in this country. An invasion by the modern, Western world is under way, but this conquest will remain partial, as earlier did the ruder assault of the Spanish conquerors upon native ways.

---

[1] Sir Cyril Fox: The Personality of Britain: Its Influence on Inhabitant and Invader in Prehistoric and Early Historic Times, 3rd edit., Nat'l. Museum of Wales, Cardiff, 1938.

The American motorcar now does duty in remotest villages, but it is loaded with the immemorial goods and persons native to the land. The automobile is accepted as a better means of transport, as, centuries earlier, the pack and draft animals brought from Castile were accepted. It and the other machines, however, are being adapted to native ways and native needs; they will not dominate or replace native culture.

The two most important things to know about Mexico still are the patterns of life that existed before the coming of the white men and the changes that were introduced during the first generation or two of the Spanish period. Although a third period of transformation is under way, we may yet best delineate the basic traits of this land and its peoples from its prehistoric geography and from its geography of the sixteenth century. Our attention may be confined therefore to formative periods in a distant past that distinguish what are still the dominant traits of the country.

THE LINE BETWEEN NORTH AND SOUTH

For unnumbered centuries a narrow frontier has formed the parting line between the North and the South of what is called Mexico today. This is the meeting zone of the high cultures of the South and the ruder cultures of the North. In the east this line reaches the Gulf of Mexico a little north of Tampico. Immediately to the south lies the Huasteca, also called by the Spaniards the Province of Pánuco. Thence the line winds sinuously southward along the eastern escarpments of the tableland to the very margin of the Valley of Mexico. Here it turns westward and then passes more or less along the northern base of the great east-west belt of volcanoes. This northern, aggraded foot slope of the volcanoes is often called the Bajío; and it is extraordinarily fertile, perhaps the best part of Mexico agriculturally. Curiously, at the beginning of historical time the Bajío lands for the most part were held by the Northern barbarians. Near Guadalajara a sharp promontory of Southern high culture reached north-northeastward to include the Cazcán Indians, in the Mixtón or Teul country, on the borders of modern Jalisco and Zacatecas. The Cazcán land is one of high mesas and rich valleys. West of Guadalajara the dividing line turns sharply northwestward and descends through the western sierra to the coast plain of Sinaloa, where it ends on the Gulf of California above Culiacán (see Fig. 1).

The ruder cultures of the North occupied the interior tableland as far south as the base of the central volcanic chain. The advanced cultures held two great prongs extending northward in the coastal lowlands and foothills. The eastern prong (Huasteca) failed to reach

286

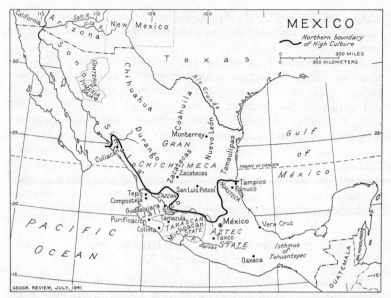

FIG. 1—Map of Mexico showing the boundary between the cultures of the South and the North.

the Tropic of Cancer and ended abruptly against the very primitive cultures of Tamaulipas. On the west coast, the extension of high culture (which I had the good fortune to discover a dozen years ago) reached into northern Sinaloa. In the west also, "islands" of intermediate cultures, especially the Opatería and Pimería Baja of Sonora, formed links to the Pueblo country of our Southwest. In general, the expansive energy of the high cultures was notably greatest in the west, next greatest on the east coast, and least in the center.

In many places the northern limit of high culture archeologically reached scores of miles beyond its historical limit. It seems therefore that the barbarian cultures had been in process of advancing southward.

THE NORTHERN AREA, THE GRAN CHICHIMECA

Climatically, the Northern country is dominantly arid or semi-arid, with wide stretches of mesquite and huisache, of creosote bush, sotol, yucca, and cacti. But it contains also some of the finest and largest alluvial valleys and a great deal of good upland, receiving enough rainfall for summer crops. The position of the line was determined by cultural, not environmental, reasons; and it is to be regarded as the meeting of two very different ways of aboriginal life. The Spaniards made the distinction of *Indios de policía* (polity) to the south and savages, or Chichimecs, to the north. The South was taken over at once by the Spaniards and became the *tierra de paz* (land of peace), whereas the North remained more or less unquiet, the *tierra de guerra.*

The commonest name for the whole North was Gran Chichimeca, which included a large number of very small tribes of assorted barbarians, many of whom, especially in the east, were roving hunters and gatherers (for example, in the states of Tamaulipas, Nuevo León, Coahuila). However, more Northern tribes than have yet been thus recognized in anthropology were at least part-time farmers, especially on the interior plateau (in the states of Chihuahua, Durango, Zacatecas, for example). In the northwest, farming was dominant; in the Ópatería and Pimería Baja at least, agricultural skill was equal to that of the South. These and the Pueblo peoples were excepted by the Spaniards from the general designation of Chichimec.

The Southern Culture Hearth, with Emphasis on the West

The South belonged to Indians who may, with propriety, be called civilized. Here and there, in rain forests or on excessively rugged mountains, primitive groups (mostly relicts) survived. No large, attractive site in the South, however, remained unappropriated by a population of advanced culture, whereas in the North many attractive and commodious areas were poorly, or not at all, used for agriculture.

The South and Southwest of Mexico constitute one of the great culture hearths of the world, in which was created in part, and developed largely, an economic complex that is one of the great achievements of mankind. Perhaps only in the Orient did men elaborate as ample a base for a diversified civilization. Archeology has given most attention to date to the great monumental cultures, which were mostly on the Atlantic side. Behind the named civilizations of Maya, Toltec, and Aztec lie older and more fundamental attainments in plant domestication and other inventions, of which we know only scattered bits. It is possible that greater knowledge of these more ancient beginnings will attach most importance to the Pacific side.

The Pacific slopes have been least regarded by students, yet there is evidence that they may have been the most active front of cultural origins and growth. A few indications may be submitted.

1. The basic traits of the native domesticated plants point to a source on the Pacific margin rather than the Atlantic. The Pacific areas have in general a shorter rainy season, a smaller total rainfall, and a much more sharply marked dry season. Their soils are rarely acid; most commonly they are somewhat alkaline. All the principal native crops show traits that point to an origin in the drier, western

lands. Perhaps we may seek the earliest farming in western alluvial valleys, probably below an altitude of two thousand meters. All the native crops are warm-starting, that is germinate best in well aerated, only slightly moist soils under the rising temperatures of late spring or early summer. Their vegetative growth is made when warm weather and frequent rains coincide, as is characteristic of the summer thundershower period. Short intervals of dry weather are beneficial. Although none of the crops is truly drought-resistant, they have various means, such as hairy leaf surfaces, of protecting themselves against brief dryness. Ripening takes place during the bright, dry season that follows the rains. Some of the beans need a rainy season of only a month; some of the corns may make use of nearly three months of moisture. These climatic qualities of the common crops of Mexico may indicate an origin in the lower levels of the *tierra templada* on the Pacific side.

2. On the Pacific side also, from Guatemala north to Sonora, there is an exceptionally large diversity of ecologically fixed crop types and of subspecies or varieties. Of maizes there are in the west not only a great many kinds of the dent variety but many flour, sugar, pop, and flint corns, which have never been collected or classified. What collecting has been done so far has been chiefly in markets of larger cities and has missed the seeds which are important to native economy but which do not enter into commerce. The result is that the economic botanist does not yet know the wealth of maize, beans, chili, squash, upland cotton, amaranth, and tomatoes that marks the hill lands behind the west coast.

3. It is also noteworthy that the wild flora of the west contains numerous close relatives of the cultivated plants (other than corn).

4. The route of dispersal of crops into the Indian agriculture of the United States also argues for the great age of west-coast culture. This route was almost certainly up the west coast into Arizona and New Mexico and thence east from the Pueblo country to the (middle?) Mississippi Valley and the eastern seaboard of the United States. The Florida–West Indies bridge functioned only slightly, if at all; and there is no indication that any domesticated crops were carried from Mexico by way of the Gulf coast.

5. Bit by bit the work of Southwestern archeologists is producing evidence of the early operation of this western corridor in the diffusion of a variety of culture traits from Mexico into Arizona and New Mexico.

In aboriginal agriculture the lands of highest quality, of most intensive use, of main dependability were the valley bottoms. Many of these lands are used today for a succession of crops throughout the year. During the dry season they may still hold enough moisture for cropping and are then called *tierras de humedad*. In some places water is applied artificially, though neither a main nor an early role can be ascribed to irrigation in Mexico. The valley lands were carefully tended and improved and determined the site of many of the larger villages. However, the frequent summer showers make possible also the growing of one summer, rain-season, or *temporal* crop on hill and mountain slopes. Growth of population soon forced expansion from the narrow valley bottoms to the far more extensive hill slopes.

To this day southern and western Mexico is lost in a smoke haze during spring, from rubbish burning on thousands of mountain deadenings, or *coamiles*, that are being prepared for planting. Many of them are still prepared and planted without the use of a plow, by means of a digging stick (or crowbar) and hoe. The seeds are punched into the ash-covered soil and left to the rains, without further attention except weeding. As no furrows are drawn nor regular fields laid out, the native farmer picks his planting spot chiefly with an eye to the timber. The bigger the tree growth, the easier the clearing, the larger the increment of wood ashes, and perhaps also the better the cash return from charcoal. Slope matters almost not at all, and soil very little; for the crop is grown primarily on the fertility made available by the woody growth, the *monte.*

This untidy method of farming has given remarkable protection against soil erosion on steep slopes. Many such mountain slopes have gone through thousands of years of alternation of clearing (*desmontar*), planting, and regrowth to monte. The process is really a long-term rotation of crops and trees. Under this management fields and settlements have been able to spread over terrain that plow farmers would find impossible. Villages that have a nucleus of permanent *tierra de humedad* appropriate about themselves as well a wide fringe of hill country for their *coamiles* or *milpas.* Also colonization of later generations of villages takes place in mountain terrain, without permanent (valley floor) fields, and all the subsistence is derived from such shifting mountain clearings. In both cases the village is permanent; wandering villages are absent, or at least extremely rare.

American notions of what constitutes suitable farmland, fertile soil, and limits of rural population cannot be applied to such a land and culture as these. These hill areas appear badly overcrowded to us; yet the more we learn of the records of the Spanish conquest and of the archeologic sites far earlier than that, the more it seems that from time immemorial these western hill lands swarmed with villages, as they do today. Indeed, it seems probable that in many hill areas population was more numerous of old than it is now.

This picture of ancient population growth points to a swarming out from the cradle lands of the rich valleys (which I should like to

290

postulate as being on the Pacific versant) to the mountain slopes, gradually encountering higher and colder country. This process of uphill migration made necessary the elimination of some of the more exacting crop plants, occasionally a new domestication (pulque agave), and generally the breeding of specialized forms tolerant of less warmth. The process cannot have been rapid; the *tierra fría*, such as the Valley of Mexico, is not part of the most anciently settled lands. The higher lands are still not very well suited to corn (except a few specialized types); but their agricultural utility has increased with the coming of European crops and domestic animals.

Growth in numbers and in agricultural skills also resulted in spread of the high cultures through the tropical forests of the Atlantic slope. Least of all was the movement northward into the arid lands, except along the west coast, where great and rich valleys invited occupation, even within the desert. Here, on the American side of the international boundary, the Gila and Salt Valleys provide the only known important aboriginal development of irrigation techniques in North America.

In summary, this agricultural civilization seems to have been born of a truly temperate climate with a rich equipment of wild plant materials, suitable for amelioration by breeding. As it acquired more skill in cultivation and plant breeding and more man power, this high Southern (or, as I should prefer to say, western) culture moved up the mountains to the high central volcanic slopes and east across rain forest and savana to the shores of the Gulf, but least of all north into the fringes of the arid country. This statement must be offered as a working hypothesis, not as an established finding.

METALS IN THE SOUTHERN CULTURE

An underestimated element in aboriginal Mexico is the use of metals. In this case also the evidence points strongly westward as well as southward. Gold was one of the most highly prized items throughout the high culture, a main tribute item and a staple of trade, a basic culture trait. The volcanic highlands of the center were barren of gold, which was found chiefly as sand in streams to the south and west in a terrain of older metamorphic and igneous rocks. These outcrop widely south of the central volcanic chain, westward to the Pacific and southward to the Isthmus of Tehuantepec, also in the "old lands" of Central America. There were two such great placer areas, one centering about Honduras, the other and larger one extending from the Isthmus of Tehuantepec north to the Balsas graben and west to the foot slopes of the volcano of Colima. In both these areas almost every torrent concentrated its annual increment of gold sand.

Of the other metals we know much less, but there promises to be a good deal to discover about their aboriginal use. It seems that the first Spanish vein mines previously had been Indian mines; Taxco is an example for copper and tin, and probably also for silver. In the process of looting the Aztec treasure the Spaniards soon found that the metallic wealth of the Aztecs had come mostly from non-Aztec lands and especially that the western neighbors, the Tarascans, were the great purveyors of silver, and also of copper and bronze. Archival and field studies have failed to disclose any silver mining within the territory of Tarascan stock; on the contrary, Tarascan imperialism seems to have been motivated to western conquests by the quest for these metals. Not in Michoacán, the homeland of the Tarascans, but in southern Jalisco have we found, we think, the source of the Tarascan silver and tin and of part of their copper. The trail of aboriginal mining and smelting is now partly marked from the Taxco region of the Balsas, through Tamazula of Jalisco, through the coast ranges of Purificación and the Valley of Banderas, as far north as the Culiacán River of Sinaloa.[2]

Studies under way indicate that in various places in the west smelting skill and alloying practices were rather advanced. We have just begun to explore this subject, which promises to change previous concepts about Indian metal arts. From present evidences we may advance the hypothesis that an Indian metallurgy was developed between Taxco and Culiacán, that it involved the reduction of sulphides as well as of oxides, that hardening, casting, and alloying of copper and silver were practiced, and that the quantity of production of copper and silver suggests the possible beginning of an age of metals, interrupted by the coming of the Spaniards.

AZTEC AND TARASCAN STATES

There were many peoples and languages in this great Southern area of high cultures, but the dominant traits of the civilizations were similar throughout. At the time of the conquest there were only two large political units, the Aztec state of México and the Tarascan state of Michoacán. In geographic design they were similar. Their main areas were at high altitudes, of modest agricultural attraction. The capital of each lay near the northern margin, close to the Chichimeca. On this exposed front both Aztecs and Tarascans were probably no more than holding their own. Both, however, showed a strong expansionist drive into the *tierra caliente*, absorbing more and more subject lands at intermediate and lower altitudes. These lands provided the master nations on the highlands with metals,

---

[2] A report on the Culiacán area by Isabel Kelly, in the *Ibero-Americana* series of the University of California, is in press.

cotton, cacao, varied foodstuffs, dyes, and gums. Both states depended on the subjugation of civilized but weak neighbors for the continuous enlargement of their own power and wealth. Neither ventured on the colonization of the thinly peopled but very fertile Chichimeca immediately adjacent to the north.

THE SPANIARDS FOLLOW THE AZTEC AND TARASCAN POLITICAL PATTERN

Aztec and Tarascan imperialism facilitated Spanish occupation. The Spaniards took over both states and superimposed their own tribute-collecting organization on the native system of tributes. As the Aztecs and Tarascans had been pushing southward and westward, the Spaniards also faced at first in the same directions. In twelve years (1520–1531) they had complete control of the land of high cultures. Millions of native workers exchanged Indian masters for Spanish encomenderos, Indian tribute collectors for the tax collectors of crown and church.

On the whole, the exactions were probably increased; and especially were the Indians required to give more gold. As gold had been brought mostly from the south, from the geologically older and topographically lower lands south of the volcanoes, the Spaniards elaborated a climatic thesis of the origin of gold: This yellow metal has an affinity for the sun and therefore grows in hot lands, in southern lands, in lands of low altitude. The tierra caliente of both coasts was gutted with amazing rapidity. Before 1540 the stream placers, gold sands in terraces, and even concentrations of gold in residual soil had been largely worked out from Vera Cruz to Oaxaca and Colima. Far more serious, the Indian populations of the tierra caliente had melted away to such pitiful remnants that the term "decimation" may be applied literally from Colima to Pánuco. Ten years after the fall of Mexico sober and competent men were discussing the inevitable ruin and depopulation of the country, being emptied of its native workers as it had already been emptied of its treasure.

A NEW FRONTIER FORMED IN THE WEST

Meanwhile a new economic frontier was taking form insensibly, in the western end of the lands of high culture. In 1523 Cortes quietly appropriated for himself the great Tarascan-held silver district of Tamazula (Jalisco). Taxco became a Spanish mining camp at the same time. Nuño de Guzmán's men of the far northwest supported themselves by locating silver properties in the mountains east of Culiacán and in the barrancas of Tepic (decade of 1530). Before 1540 the Spaniards were finding small bodies of silver ore all the way from Taxco to Culiacán. These western encomenderos used their civilized Indians in the service of their mines and engaged also in slave raids into the Chichimec territory beyond. The new silver-bearing West became the scene of furious rivalry between the great captains and officials of New Spain, Cortes, Mendoza, Alvarado, Nuño de Guzmán; and out of this melee grew a frontier government, New Galicia, which really saved New Spain from the fate of the Antillean islands and gave to it its later colonial greatness.

All the earlier silver discoveries were within the area of the civilized Indians. From 1523 into the 1540's a series of now largely forgotten *villas* and *reales* (formally constituted mining settlements) were founded between Taxco and Culiacán. Every one of these Spanish establishments had mining, usually silver, as its basis. Thus was founded the first capital of Nueva Galicia, Compostela. Now drowsing around an ancient church that bears the double-headed eagles of Hapsburg, it is remembered by us only because Coronado collected here the idle young gentlemen of New Spain to ride thence to the plains of Kansas.

The trail of silver led inland and upward, not down the floors of the canyons toward the sea, as the quest for gold had done. The great bodies of silver ore are associated with the lower, or earlier, volcanism of the Mesa Central. The Tertiary volcanics, enriched with metallic sulphides, overlie the older rocks, which may carry the free gold, and underlie the cones, malpais, tuff beds, and mudflows of the young volcanoes, generally barren of precious metals. The western and southwestern rim of the Mesa Central has been deeply trenched by great canyons. Here, along the upper slopes of the barrancas, the silver-bearing, lower volcanic beds were accessible to prospectors. Silver came to connote to the Spaniards high country and cold lands; they even thought of it as in some manner associated with the north, as they had related gold to southern latitudes.

Civilized tribes held the coastal districts of the West and extended inland along the warm floors of the barrancas. Barbarian tribes occupied the high mesas and reached seaward along their shredded fringes between the barrancas. The silver country, therefore, in a measure lay between civilized and barbarian habitats, in the meeting zone of the two major cultures. Thus, especially, the barrancas behind Compostela and Guadalajara became passageways for the Spanish prospectors, leading them back toward the central plateau and into the Chichimeca.

By 1540 the Spanish penetration had created tensions in this frontier zone that gave rise to the most formidable Indian outbreak in the history of New Spain—the Mixtón War. The Mixtón country was the knobby promontory of high civilization reaching north from Guadalajara. Here civilized Indians, mainly Cazcán, were neighbors to barbarian tribes, such as Zacatec, Guachichil, and Huichol. The docile Cazcáns had been badly used by their encomenderos at mining silver in the barrancas. At the same time slave raiding by this group of encomenderos was irritating the nomadic tribes of the highlands. The Mixtón rebellion was the union of desperate civilized Indians with wild hill tribes. The outbreak was suppressed only by the use of the whole military strength of New Spain. In the prosecution of the campaign the Spaniards for the first time broke through this frontier zone and began the occupation of the Chichimeca. Here began the technique of frontier fighting, the establishment of flying squadrons and fortified posts (presidios), that was to mark the occupation of the North for the next two and a half centuries.

To the great good fortune of Spain it so happened that immediately behind the ramparts of the Mixtón country lay the greatest silver country in the world—the land of the Zacatec Indians. Some of these, caught as slaves in the Mixtón War, had been sent down to the mines of Taxco. A number succeeded in escaping and returned home, with some knowledge of silver ores. As Spanish parties from Guadalajara pushed closer to their homes, the Zacatec tried (1546) to gain favor by disclosing the presence of the Veta Grande, at Zacatecas. Soon Zacatecas became the greatest silver producer in the world. In sustained production it has never been equaled by any other silver district.

The Zacatecas strike was followed during the next quarter of a century by the discovery, without parallel in history, of a series of silver districts, first along the western fringe of the Mesa Central, but soon also along its eastern slopes northward through San Luis Potosí. New Galicia, previously a precariously held narrow strip in the northwest, expanded rapidly to absorb the Chichimeca, the unlimited North. The shabby townsmen of Guadalajara and Compostela became the fabulous grandees of northern principalities, built about mines. Guadalajara was the gateway through which miners, merchants, soldiers, ranchers, and missionaries poured northward, carrying in their train docile Southern Indians from Jalisco, Michoacán, and Colima to do the hard work of the new country. Guadalajara became the capital of the North as well as of the West. From this exposed march site—to use the term of Vaughan Cornish—one of the greatest break-throughs of New World history took place, between the fateful date of 1540 and the end of the century. By that time men from the Nueva Galicia march had reached and seized Durango, Chihuahua, New Mexico, Coahuila, and Nuevo León, roughly outlining the present international border. In later years the same breed was to extend its range of operations from Texas to California. The Spanish trails of the American Southwest all lead directly back to the nuclear area of New Galicia.

This land of high steppe and pine-clad mountains has been for four centuries the primary source of the wealth of New Spain–Mexico. Its mining towns became great and architecturally distinguished. Even at the end of the colonial period they were producing, according to Humboldt's estimate, more than half the precious metal of the world. Vast stock ranches developed about the mines, to supply the great and constant demand for pack and draft animals, for meat, hides, and fat. South of the mining country, the rich Bajío lands at the foot of the volcanoes were plowed and planted to foodstuffs for the mining districts and gave rise to a large number of profitable haciendas and a class of overopulent landlords. Mexico City, center of government and trade, grew magnificent and effete, as the ultimate beneficiary of the wealth of the North.

As wealth in unheard-of amount flowed south from the silver mines of the former Chichimeca, the native populations of the North were swept out of existence, except in certain mountain retreats, such as the Tarahumara. Many natives were branded and sold south as slaves. Many more were consumed in the work of the mines. Southern Indians were brought in as free laborers in an unending stream. Thus Tlascalan, Tarascan, Otomi, Aztec, and other colonists were strewn over the North, as farming, ranching, and mining labor. The richer mines imported droves of Negro slaves. Many Spaniards of small means or none at all came north to try their hand at mining, merchandising, or transport of goods. In the course of time all these stocks except the upper-class Spanish fused into a new breed, of no one color. Thus was born the mestizo Mexico of today. Here was the frontier of New Spain, on which finally a new nationality was formed.

This design of New Spain was drawn during the sixteenth century and has persisted to the present. Still the Northern march has dominance in part over the Southern hearth. It is still an area of immigration, receiving labor, foodstuffs, and manufactured goods from the central states for its metals, livestock, and cotton. For the most part, men of the North have made the revolutions and wielded the power, men from Sonora, Chihuahua, Coahuila, Nuevo León, men born to take risks, to the frontier habit of alternation of hard effort and complete laziness. The South still shows its aboriginal fundament of patient, steady toil done by apt craftsmen, who can create things of remarkable beauty if they have the chance. The old line between the civilized South and the Chichimeca has been blurred somewhat, but it still stands. In that antithesis, which at times means conflict, at others a complementing of qualities, lie the strength and weakness, the tension and harmony that make the personality of Mexico.

296

BARLEY IN THE UNITED STATES
A HISTORICAL SKETCH*

JOHN C. WEAVER

BARLEY has a wider ecologic range than any other grain. It thrives beyond the Arctic Circle, in regions where in summer the soil thaws no more than a few inches below the surface, and also on the tropical plains of India. High on Ethiopian mountain slopes barley grows beside frozen pools of water, and it is cultivated beneath the date palm in Saharan oases. It matures on the lower delta of the Nile, where salt water is found at depths of little more than a foot. It provides the native food in the Dangra Yum Basin in Tibet, at an altitude of 15,200 feet, and climbs even higher on the Himalayan slopes, where a form with recurving stalks places the heads of grain almost on the ground in protection from the relentless winds. It grows on the plains of the Argentine Chaco, on the fertile, rolling, glaciated uplands of the American Midwest, on the high plateaus of Bolivia and Peru, on the South African veld, and on the alkaline desert soils of Australia.

Since ancient times barley has played a role in the agricultural economy of Mesopotamia, the valleys of Syria, the Tarim and Amu river basins of Turkestan, and the hills of western China. There are white kerneled barleys from the Caucasus, blue kerneled barleys from North Africa, and strange black seeded types from Iran. Hybridizing and rehybridizing, migrating from environment to environment, tended by the hands of many men through tens of centuries, this grain has been forged into myriad forms and has become identified with a multitude of regions. Drawn from an almost world-wide reservoir of environments, barley as it is known in the United States today is not a single cultivated plant but a polymorphous race of many different plants, each with a long and complex history, each adapted to different ecologic conditions, each serving a unique function and taking a particular place in the agricultural economy of which it has become a part.

Evidence brought to light through extensive archeological work through-

---

* The materials used in this paper have been condensed from a more elaborate analysis of the history of American barley production included in a dissertation presented at the University of Wisconsin in partial fulfillment of the requirements for the Ph.D. degree. The research project, of which this study was but a single phase, had a threefold design: (1) to map and describe, as precisely as available data would permit, the distributional patterns of the barley crop in the United States; (2) to define and interpret the ecologic and human factors that have been influential in creating these patterns; and (3) to portray and examine the regionally contrasted types and purposes of barley production in the various parts of the country.

out the Old World reveals the integral, often dominating, part played by barley in the farming economies of the most ancient agricultural peoples known. Yet kernels of barley associated with sites inhabited as long ago as the beginning of the fifth millennium before the Christian era are practically identical in form and character with the barley grains now harvested in the same regions. In other words, the oldest authentic records of the archeologist do not reach back far enough to give even the slightest clue to the developmental stages in the botanical evolution of this plant. Furthermore, the most distant background of agriculture, as it has been possible to study it so far, finds barley already under cultivation in regions as widely separated as the valleys of the Nile, Tigris and Euphrates, Amu, and Yangtze.

The opinion has long been held that the original home of the barley plant was a single center somewhere in the vast dry-land regions of southwestern Asia, but the far-flung investigations of the Russian Institute of Plant Industry have led Vavilov to another conclusion—that barleys of very different types have originated in two widely separated primary centers: the one, awned and hulled, in the mountains of Ethiopia; the other, hull-less, furcate, awnless or short-awned, in southeastern Asia, in China and regions adjacent to Tibet and probably including Nepal. In an effort to determine how sharply divided the two groups of barley are, attempts have been made to hybridize representatives from the two regions. Vavilov reports that "separate components are, as experiments have shown, differentiated up to the appearance of sterility in crosses. It may be that in a remoter past the two groups of cultivated barley originated in one centre, but about this we can only guess."[1]

Whatever may have been the precise origins and history of this grain in the Old World, in due course it was carried westward to the New World. When considered in relation to the full length of its history, the entire American story of barley growing is only a recent, brief fragment of an integrated whole, but a fragment rich and diversified in experience.

EARLY CULTIVATION OF BARLEY IN THE UNITED STATES

Although the story has not been preserved in detail, existing records show that barley was brought to the Atlantic-seaboard colonies of North America by the earliest settlers. Introduced from England by one Gosnold,

---

[1] N. I. Vavilov: Studies on the Origin of Cultivated Plants, *Bull. of Applied Botany and Plant-Breeding*, Vol. 16, No. 2, Institut de Botanique Appliquée et d'Amélioration des Plantes, Leningrad, 1926, p. 172.

this grain was sown, probably for the first time in this part of the Western Hemisphere, on Martha's Vineyard and the Elizabeth Islands in 1602. Four years later barley seeds were planted by Lescarbot at Port Royal, Nova Scotia, and barley is known to have been growing in Champlain's garden at Quebec as early as 1610.[2] In a letter dated August, 1617, Captain John Mason, writing " 'from the plantacion of Cuper's Cove' " in Newfoundland, said, concerning the plants which he had introduced and was cultivating, that " 'wheate, rye, barlie, oates, and pease' have 'growen and ripened' as well 'as in Yorkshire.' "[3]

The colonists of the London Company were cultivating barley in Virginia in 1611. The Dutch settlers of New Netherland apparently cultivated barley from the outset; in 1626 samples of their harvest from Manhattan Island were shipped to Holland as an indication of their prosperous condition. In New England, the Governor of the Massachusetts Bay Company recorded the introduction of barley in 1629 and reported an exceptionally fine harvest in Lynn in 1633;[4] and it was widely cultivated in Rhode Island.

In these early colonial days barley was grown primarily for the production of malt, used in the preparation of beer, and the varietal forms cultivated were those common in the home regions of the colonists. Neither climate nor soil in the Atlantic-seaboard areas was particularly favorable for the culture of these European varieties, yet cultivation spread steadily, and, owing largely to a strong demand for malt—which had to be met in part by importation[5]—barley maintained an importance among general farm crops which was exceeded only by that of corn and wheat. Chester County, Pennsylvania, and Rhode Island became particularly noted for the production of malting barley;[6] in fact, barley was listed in 1796 as the leading agricultural product of Rhode Island.[7] Barley was also utilized, although to a smaller extent, as a feed for stock, and in years of wheat scarcity barley flour was substituted in the making of bread. It was not until the closing decades of the eighteenth century, when settlement had

[2] E. L. Sturtevant: Sturtevant's Notes on Edible Plants, edited by U. P. Hedrick, *Rept. New York Agric. Exper. Sta. for the Year 1919*, Part II (*27th Ann. Rept. State of New York Dept. of Agric.*, Vol. 2, Part II), 1919, p. 307.

[3] Charles Pickering: Chronological History of Plants, Boston, 1879, p. 935.

[4] H. V. Harlan, M. L. Martini, and M. N. Pope: Tests of Barley Varieties in America, *U. S. Dept. of Agric. Dept. Bull. No. 1334*, 1925, p. 5.

[5] *U. S. Dept. of Agric. Yearbook 1922*, 1923, p. 490.

[6] P. W. Bidwell and J. I. Falconer: History of Agriculture in the Northern United States, 1620–1860, *Carnegie Instn. Publ. No. 358*, 1925, p. 241.

[7] Harlan, Martini, and Pope, *op. cit.*, p. 5.

pushed down the Mohawk Valley to western New York, that the wide-spread occurrence of ecologic conditions truly suited to the growing of high-quality barley was found in the Eastern States.

On these new lands barley quickly came into its own. By 1820 two-thirds of the barley in the United States was being produced in New York, giving to that state a pre-eminence in the culture of this grain that it was destined to hold for several decades. The center of production was in the vicinity of Herkimer County. Albany and Catskill were the leading markets. The estimated receipts of barley at these two points in 1820 were 450,000 bushels, and the trade was greatly facilitated and stimulated by the completion of the Erie Canal in 1825.

Although the exact date is not known, a fall-sown winter variety of barley was introduced from Switzerland or the Balkans at an early date. This permitted the wide extension of barley culture into the Southeastern States, where spring-sown types had been found to be largely unsuitable.[8]

That barley had gained the favor of the scientific agriculturists of the time is clear. Rotations were recommended in which barley was to replace oats, and to a farmer who queried, "Why, how would it be possible to get along without any oats at all?" the retort was simple and direct:

The answer is, that oats are an exhausting crop, and suffer clover to take with them, with great difficulty; whilst barley is one of the choicest grains to accompany with clover, and is as profitable, to every purpose, as oats. Bushel for bushel, it is more valuable: horses, hogs, and poultry, will thrive upon it, as well as upon any grain; and what surplus the farmer has to sell, the malster will buy.[9]

The story of the establishment of barley in the United States is not confined to the eastern seaboard, however. The grain had come to the New World among the plants first imported to Mexico by the Spanish conquerors and had been grown there since the days of Cortes. The Spanish soldier and missionary brought barley to the American Southwest, and it was cultivated wherever settlements were established. No other grain was so well suited to meet the needs of this region for a stock feed, and, as the population of California grew during the early decades of the nineteenth century, its use for malting never acquired a dominance comparable with that in the East.

Unlike the first settlers in the East, the Spanish colonists found themselves in a region well suited to the varieties of barley they had brought

---

[8] *Yearbook of Agriculture 1936*, U. S. Dept. of Agriculture, 1936, p. 319.
[9] *Memoirs Board of Agric. of the State of New-York*, Vol. I, 1821, p. 130.

300

with them, varieties which had been cultivated for centuries in North Africa, from Tunis westward to the Atlantic, and in the Mediterranean climate of Spain.[10] These barleys, which even today are dominant in the western United States, were an immediate success, especially in California.

Thus the history of barley in the United States evolves from two original focuses of introduction, at opposite margins of the continent. In the East were varieties from northern Europe and England, grown in a region of relatively dense population with a strong malting-barley market; in the West were the varieties from the Mediterranean lands, grown in a sparsely settled livestock country with a large demand for feed. In the century that intervened between the census years of 1839 and 1939 the cultivation of this grain spread with agriculture from its eastern centers westward, and from its western centers eastward, to a meeting ground on the High Plains and in the intermountain West.

A CENTURY OF AMERICAN BARLEY CULTIVATION

The earliest detailed and precise record of the distribution of barley production in the United States is found in the census for the crop year 1839.[11] The data provided by this census, and by each of the subsequent agricultural censuses down through 1939, have been cartographically portrayed in a series of thirteen dot maps based on county totals.[12] Through these maps, a number of which are reproduced here (Figs. 1–8), it has been possible to define the essential features of the distributional development of the barley crop in this country over the past century. The story seems to fall logically into four major divisions of time.

THE DOMINANCE OF NEW YORK: 1839–1859

The dominance of New York and the old six-rowed varieties from Europe began sometime between 1810 and 1820; the census records for 1839 present a picture of the distribution of barley about midway in this

---

[10] *Agriculture Yearbook 1924,* U. S. Dept. of Agriculture, 1925, p. 73.

[11] The crops tabulated in the censuses, which are taken at 5 and 10-year intervals, are those of the preceding years; for example, the census of 1840 refers to the crop year 1839. On the maps and in the text the crop year is used in preference to the census year.

[12] The data given on the maps for the years from 1839 to 1869 are shown in bushels of barley harvested and for all subsequent years in number of acres harvested. The discrepancy arises from the fact that before 1879 no acreage data were tabulated by the census enumerators. Rather than follow the possible procedure of mapping bushels harvested throughout the series, it was thought advisable to shift to acreage figures at the point where they became available, since, owing to the wide variability of yields from area to area and from year to year, acreage data seem to provide a more reliable index to the regional importance of the crop.

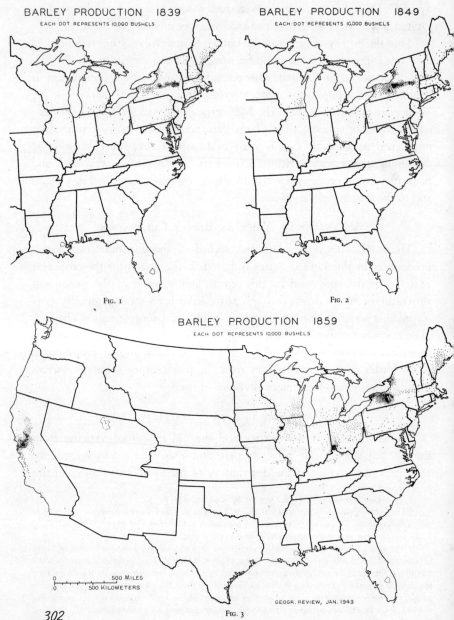

BARLEY PRODUCTION 1839
EACH DOT REPRESENTS 10,000 BUSHELS

Fɪɢ. 1

BARLEY PRODUCTION 1849
EACH DOT REPRESENTS 10,000 BUSHELS

Fɪɢ. 2

BARLEY PRODUCTION 1859
EACH DOT REPRESENTS 10,000 BUSHELS

0   500 MILES
0   500 KILOMETERS

GEOGR. REVIEW, JAN. 1943

Fɪɢ. 3

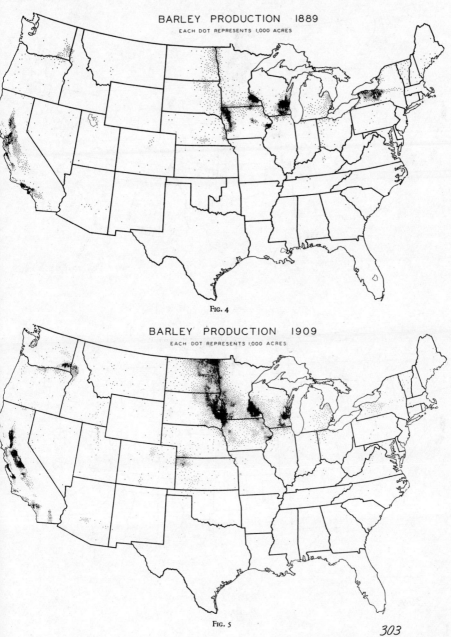

BARLEY PRODUCTION 1889
EACH DOT REPRESENTS 1,000 ACRES

Fig. 4

BARLEY PRODUCTION 1909
EACH DOT REPRESENTS 1,000 ACRES

Fig. 5

303

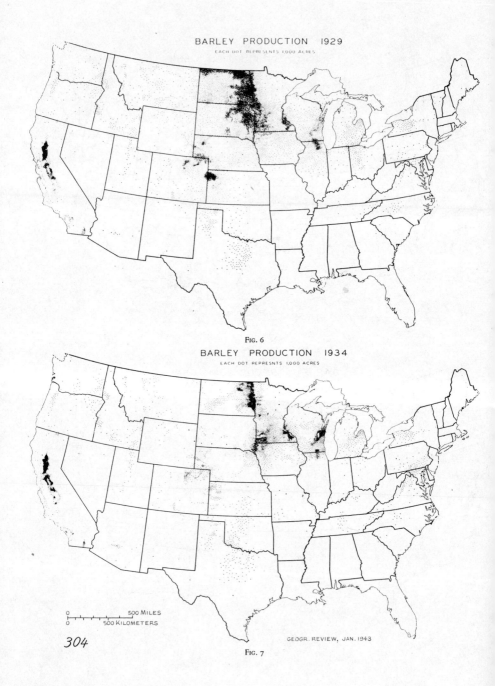

BARLEY PRODUCTION 1929
EACH DOT REPRESENTS 1,000 ACRES

Fig. 6

BARLEY PRODUCTION 1934
EACH DOT REPRESNTS 1,000 ACRES

0   500 MILES
0   500 KILOMETERS

304

GEOGR. REVIEW, JAN. 1943

Fig. 7

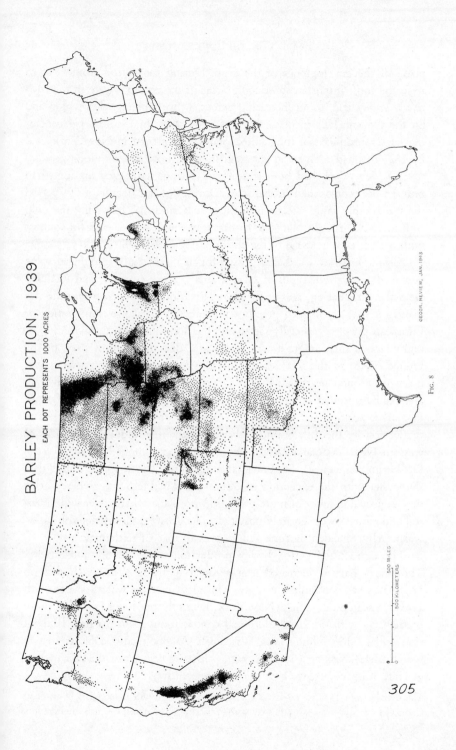

BARLEY PRODUCTION, 1939

EACH DOT REPRESENTS 1000 ACRES

500 MILES

500 KILOMETERS

GEOGR. REVIEW, JAN. 1943

FIG. 8

phase of the development of the crop. During the period from 1839 to 1859 the most important producing areas in the country were in the Mohawk Valley and, to an increasing extent, in the Finger Lakes region and on the Ontario lake plain to the north and west. In 1839, 61 per cent of the barley produced in the United States was grown in New York, and by 1849 this had risen to 69 per cent. In 1859, however, although production in New York had been steadily increasing, its harvest amounted to only 26 per cent of the national total. During the last decade of this period the remarkably rapid rise of agriculture in California, following the gold rush in 1848, brought that state to first rank, with 28 per cent (in contrast with 0.2 per cent in 1849) of the entire barley crop of the country.

Although barley was being grown for its increasingly recognized value as a feed for various types of farm animals, a pre-eminent, and in many areas the dominating, reason for the cultivation of this crop was the demand for malt, a demand greatly stimulated by the large immigration of European peoples, especially Germans. The long-distance transportation of bulky goods such as grain was costly and difficult in most parts of the United States in the forties and fifties. As a result, barley growing was taken up around nearly all the rising centers of population, frequently in areas quite unsuited ecologically to cultivation of the grain. The influence of market position and the difficulty of transport was especially marked in this period by the distribution of barley in the newly developing areas of western New York and eastern Pennsylvania and about Detroit, Toledo, Pittsburgh, Cincinnati, St. Louis, and Chicago. The mapped census data show that with the exception of certain parts of the South, where barley was neglected in favor of more profitable crops and where, over wide areas, soil and climate were entirely unsuited to its growth, the advance of barley was nearly coincident in time and place with that of settlement.

Throughout the period barley production grew steadily and rapidly. The yearly harvest increased nearly fourfold, from 4,161,500 bushels in 1839 to 15,826,000 bushels in 1859. This great increase was associated with a steady rise in production in New York, Pennsylvania, and Maine, but more particularly with the large additional contributions from the new lands of California, Ohio, Illinois, and Wisconsin. As one example of an area in which barley became a leading crop, primarily because of the racial background of its settlers, we have Scott County, Iowa.

The decade from 1850 to 1860 was characterized by a growth in population [in Scott County] from 5,980 to 25,959, this being the period of pronounced German immigration.

306

Farming began on a very extensive scale about 1854. The Germans were mainly grain farmers, and the production of barley, largely for brewing, became important. The soils in many places still show the effect of the continuous cropping to barley.[13]

The Codominance of New York and California: 1859–1889

The national production of 15,826,000 bushels in 1859 nearly doubled in the next decade (29,099,000 bushels) and had quintupled in 1889 (80,-790,000 bushels). At the beginning of this period the two leading producing centers were western New York and the Sacramento Valley of California. Not only had California come upon the scene as a center of codominance with New York, but the spread of agriculture in the interior valley had, as early as 1859, put California slightly in the lead. In the Midwest cultivation was primarily characterized by an intensification of the pattern already established. Barley-growing centers around the malt markets of Wheeling, Cincinnati, St. Louis, Chicago, Milwaukee, Detroit, and other cities persisted. With extending settlement and constantly improving transportation facilities, however, the fading out of these localized areas, associated with a general widening of barley production throughout the North Central States, was a tendency of growing importance.

These decades saw a steady westward advance of the barley frontier of the East. During the sixties barley became firmly established beyond the Mississippi, and in the next decade its cultivation reached the eastern margins of the High Plains. These same years witnessed the decline of barley along the Atlantic seaboard from Maine to Virginia. The new and more suitable ecologic conditions in the lands to the west brought to an end any important production east of western New York. The frontiers of the far western center of barley cultivation also were pushing outward—northward and eastward. By 1869 barley was well established in the Willamette Valley, and by the close of this period it had become significant in the intermountain West, from the Palouse on the north to the Salt and Gila Valleys on the south.

By 1889 California alone was producing 17,544,000 bushels of barley, and Wisconsin had risen to second place, producing nearly twice the amount grown in New York; Iowa was a strong third. The scene of dominance in American barley production was shifting; the stage was set for the opening of a new era.

[13] E. H. Stevens, E. H. Smies, and Knute Espe: Soil Survey of Scott County, Iowa, U. S. Dept. of Agric., Field Operations of the Bur. of Soils, 1915 (17th Rept.), 1919, pp. 1707–1745; reference on p. 1712.

Rise of the Midwest: 1889–1919

The yearly production of barley in the United States rose from 80,790,-000 bushels in 1889 to 225,076,000 bushels in 1918, the harvested acres from 3,352,000 in 1889 to 9,198,000 in 1918.[14] During this period of phenomenal expansion there was also an important regional redistribution of production. The magnitude of the shifts may be appreciated at once when it is realized that in 1909 the total production of the North Atlantic States (including New York) amounted to only 2 per cent of the national crop, whereas the North Central States contributed 63 per cent and the Western States 34 per cent.[15]

The two closing decades of the nineteenth century witnessed the rise of three particularly important centers of barley cultivation: southeastern Wisconsin, southeastern Minnesota, and western Iowa. To these, at the turn of the century, must be added a fourth, namely western Minnesota and the adjoining eastern thirds of North and South Dakota; by 1909 the Red River Valley had become one of the outstanding regions of barley culture in the country.

New producing areas also arose farther west. The most outstanding of these appeared on the plains of western, and especially northwestern, Kansas, in the Palouse region of southeastern Washington and northwestern Idaho, and in the Imperial Valley of southern California. Not so important when judged on national standards but of considerable significance locally was the emergence of producing centers in the smaller irrigated districts of the West, such as the Gallatin Valley in Montana, the Salt River Valley in Arizona, the Wasatch oasis in Utah, and the plains of the Snake in Idaho.

With the exception of the more recent developments associated with the cultivation of winter varieties in the Southeastern States, barley had practically attained its maximum range of cultivation in the United States by the close of this period. Furthermore, the shifts that occurred at this time brought into focus those areas that seem destined to remain, in general at least, the permanent areas of barley culture.

Among the important forces operative during these decades must be listed the final widening phase of settlement. The opening up of the remaining lands of the Midwest, coupled with the final stages of settlement

---

[14] The influence of conditions resulting from the war economy and the passage of the Eighteenth Amendment, prohibiting the manufacture and public sale of alcoholic beverages, made 1919 an abnormal crop year. Barley production amounted to only 131,086,000 bushels, raised on 6,579,000 acres.

[15] U. S. Dept. of Agric. Yearbook 1910, 1911, p. 15.

expansion in the Western States, provided vast new acreages suited to the growing of barley. The development of dry-farming techniques, the construction of large irrigation projects, and the reclamation of saturated and alkali-infested lands, all of great importance during these decades, must indeed be reckoned as potent factors in the extension of barley production. Also of growing and definitive importance was the development of cheap, rapid, and efficient long-distance freight transportation.

Now for the first time the distributional pattern was molded primarily by climatic, pedologic, and biotic considerations, and the farmer was free to choose the optimum combination of these factors from the enlarged agricultural areas of the country.

A major force behind the developments of this period, particularly in the East, was the introduction and selection of new varieties more nearly suited to American conditions. Although scientific work had begun before 1890, its full impact was not felt until these years. For example, in the late 1850's a discovery was made near the Amur River on the plains of eastern Manchuria that was destined to revolutionize barley production in the eastern United States, halfway around the world. A traveler whose identity has long since been lost was impressed by the unusually vigorous growth of a variety of barley native to the Amur and carried samples of the grain with him to Germany. A few years later Dr. Herman Grunow of Mifflin, Iowa County, Wisconsin, observed this remarkable barley in its new environment and, impressed, like its original discoverer, with the possibilities it might have in his own land, brought samples to Wisconsin.

Although the record is incomplete, Dr. Grunow's barley must have fulfilled its promise; for in 1872 he sent some of his seed to the experiment farm at Madison. This Manchurian barley was planted in that year at the Wisconsin Agricultural Experiment Station, and from the ensuing study stems the pioneer agronomic work in the development of barley for which that station became famous and from which the whole nation has benefited. By 1873 selections of the new variety were being distributed to the farmers of Wisconsin. Year after year selections of this remarkable strain were improved and later distributed. It was sent by the Wisconsin station to other state experiment farms, where more selections were made, each better suited to the given local environment. It was grown and distributed under many names and state numbers, such as Manshury, Mansury, Mandsheuri, Manchuria, Minnesota 6, and North Dakota 787.

In 1881 the original stock was again imported, this time from Russia, by the Ontario Agricultural College. Samples of the selections made there were sent in 1894 to the state farms at St. Paul, Minn., and Fargo, N. D., where they became known as Minnesota 32 and Minnesota 105. Over much of the upper Mississippi Valley these types were even more successful than the Wisconsin selections.[16] The popularity of the new, vigorously growing Manchuria barley spread throughout the Midwest, and by the close of the nineteenth century it was firmly established.

There were other outstanding introductions and developments. Unique varietal types permitted expansion into new regions on a plane of improved efficiency; others greatly facilitated the production of high-quality grain in areas where barley cultivation was already strongly developed.

Another factor of prime importance in the rise of the Midwest during this period was the series of events that, in the early nineties, led to the rapid decline of the malting industry and the associated reduction of barley in western New York. The market demand in the region had become so great that, despite the large quantities of barley grown on New York farms, the maltsters were forced to import grain across the Canadian border, from Ontario. In 1890 a tariff imposed a duty of 30 cents a bushel on all imported barley, and the maltsters of western New York suddenly found themselves in an untenable position.

As malt weighs less per bushel than barley the malt houses of Wisconsin and Minnesota could ship to the eastern seaboard more cheaply than it was possible for the eastern malt houses to purchase barley for malting.[17]

Under these conditions, the collapse of the malting industry in New York was inevitable. The center of the industry shifted westward to Wisconsin, Illinois, Michigan, Minnesota, and Iowa. From a harvest of 8,202,000 bushels on 349,000 acres in 1889, production in New York sank to 1,920,000 bushels on 80,000 acres in 1909.

THE MODERN ERA: 1919–1939

Under the influence of a number of closely related factors, American barley production has fluctuated considerably during the last two decades. Involved in the composite picture have been contradictory elements. That factors encouraging an increase prevailed is attested by the rise in total production from 225,067,000 bushels on 9,198,000 acres in 1918 to 260,980,878 bushels on 12,024,208 acres in 1939. Retarding influences, however, are betrayed by the relatively small percentage increase.

---

[16] Harlan, Martini, and Pope, *op. cit.*, pp. 4–5 and 164–165.
[17] *Ibid.*, p. 9.

310

The production curve, which ever since American colonial days has risen swiftly and steadily, has now begun to level off. It may be that barley is nearing its ultimate maximum extension and that regression lies ahead; in fact, production and acreage fell slightly between 1929 and 1939. It seems more probable, however, that the approach of a semipermanent form of stabilization is indicated.

The agricultural frontier, which in preceding decades provided an opportunity for continuing agricultural expansion into new lands, has now practically disappeared. No large untouched blocks of farming country remain, where new and important acreages of barley cultivation might be rapidly developed. Increase of production can come about only through increased yield from the acres currently devoted to barley or expansion of the crop to lands being utilized for some other purpose. The selection, breeding, and introduction of new, higher-yielding varieties, strains more resistant to prevalent diseases and insect pests, and types prepared to withstand other environmental hazards in their particular regions of growth have already done much, and can do more, to bring about increased yield. Associated with this result is the recent growing appreciation of the value of barley as a livestock feed. In some regions the increased competitive power of this grain has gained it a place on lands formerly devoted to other crops.

Perhaps the strongest single factor encouraging an increase in the acreage devoted to barley in the past two decades has been the outstanding advance in varietal improvement. Although a host of widely differing types of barley have appeared since the close of the First World War, those that have had the most profound effect on production are the high-yielding, smooth-awned hybrids of the humid Northeast, the improved strains of winter barley of the humid Southeast, many of which have the smooth-awned character, and the high-yielding Trebi type of the subhumid, semiarid, and arid regions of the West.

The roughly barbed beards have made barley a grain disagreeable to handle, an annoyance to the farmer and an irritation, even sometimes a danger, to his animals. In the last twenty years barley-breeding experiments, carried on particularly at the agricultural experiment stations in the North Central and Northeastern States, have developed a number of high-yielding strains in which the barbed awn has been largely eliminated. These varieties, which gained their smooth-bearded character from a commercially obscure form, are otherwise essentially similar to the dominant Manchuria parent, and they have profoundly affected the extension of cultivation.

311

In the South such barley as had been grown since the early days was largely the old Tennessee winter type. This variety has rough awns, an especially unfortunate characteristic in the Southern States, where barley is grown for forage as well as for grain, and, in addition, it had not proved particularly winter-hardy. Here again selective breeding has done much to remedy both defects. The result is reflected in the following figures. In the decade 1929–1939 barley harvested for grain increased from 71,074 acres to 494,291 acres in Oklahoma; from 9,667 to 176,029 in Missouri; from 12,956 to 67,894 in Virginia; from 9,832 to 59,745 in Maryland; from 11,215 to 53,454 in Tennessee; and from 4,971 to 39,761 in Kentucky.

In the West, of the many new and significant varieties introduced, none has had so wide an effect as Trebi. In 1905 samples of this barley, which was growing under irrigation in one of the small valleys on the south shore of the Black Sea, were sent to the United States Department of Agriculture from Samsun, Turkey. The seeds were tried first on the University Farm at St. Paul, Minn., in 1909, with results of questionable value. Samples were sent to the Chico, Calif., station in 1910, and again the results were not particularly promising. It was sent to Aberdeen, Idaho, for a final trial in that year. Here, under irrigation, the yields produced by Trebi were striking. It took first rank among all the barley forms being tested there. Over an 8-year period Trebi produced the astonishing average yield of 80 bushels an acre, and in 1918 the first farmer to receive seeds of this variety obtained 90 bushels an acre from his 28-acre field. The news of this amazing barley spread rapidly, and its dissemination throughout the irrigated lands of southern Idaho quickly followed. Almost everywhere it gave uniformly fine results, and soon it began to outrank standard varieties from the western Dakotas to Oregon.

Although better suited to irrigated lands, this variety has proved itself capable of giving large yields on dry lands also.[18] During the twenties Trebi occupied an ever increasing acreage in the Great Basin, the northern Rocky Mountain districts, and the northern High Plains. Its remarkable adaptability to so wide a range of environments has undoubtedly been a factor in the expansion of barley cultivation that has taken place throughout these regions.

The Eighteenth Amendment must be counted one of the leading factors connected with the development of barley production during the modern

---

[18] H. V. Harlan, M. N. Pope, and L. C. Aicher: Trebi Barley, A Superior Variety for Irrigated Land, *U. S. Dept. of Agric. Circular No. 208*, 1922, pp. 3–8.

312

era. Undoubtedly the enactment of this amendment in 1918 was a direct cause of the sharp decrease in production in 1919. Decrease was greatest in the North Central States, where the grain had been grown most widely for the malt market. However, in view of the fact that between 30 and 40 per cent of the barley raised in the United States in these years was being utilized by the malting trade, it is remarkable that the decrease in national production was not greater. It is even more surprising that the following decade witnessed a virtual doubling of the national production.

Although large quantities of malt were still used, the expansion that ensued is primarily associated with an increase in the use of barley for feed. Thus, although prohibition played a part in bringing about a temporary decrease in production, it was in reality a major factor in establishing a strong and general increase in barley cultivation on a new and sounder basis. In the years preceding 1918 the Midwestern farmer had been accustomed to sell all his high-quality barley to the maltster; the lower grades, which were not acceptable in the market, he fed to his stock.[19] The virtual disappearance of the malting market forced the farmer to feed his high-quality grain as well, and for the first time the superiority of barley for this purpose was appreciated. The chief malting-barley area, lying to the north and west of the Corn Belt, was situated where corn was a more or less uncertain crop, whereas both environment and farmer training made the culture of high-quality barley a most satisfactory endeavor. The new smooth-awned varieties had appeared at an opportune time. At present only about one-quarter of the national crop is utilized in industry.

The effect of the war economy associated with the opening years of this period is not easy to evaluate quantitatively. An unusually strong rise in barley production in 1917 and 1918 was, of course, related to the stimulation of all crop production in the war years. The marked decrease in the acreage of 1919, moreover, was not a result of prohibition alone.

The war prices of wheat and the campaign to increase its acreage had resulted in a considerable expansion in the area sown to spring wheat in that year. The greatest increase in this crop came in the barley producing sections of North Dakota, South Dakota, and Minnesota.[20]

A decrease in the production of barley in the Palouse region occurred for the same reason; and although barley subsequently re-established itself

[19] H. V. Harlan: Barley: Culture, Uses, and Varieties, U. S. Dept. of Agric. Farmers' Bull. No. 1464, 1925, p. 1.
[20] Harlan, Martini, and Pope, op. cit., p. 11.

in the spring-wheat region of the North Central States, it never regained its former importance in southeastern Washington and in adjacent parts of Idaho and Oregon.

A factor of outstanding significance during the last decade of this period, which not only strongly affected barley production during the thirties directly but also tended to conceal trends that might normally have been observable, was a succession of disastrous drought years. Devastation was particularly intense in the north-central area where barley had become strongly concentrated. In 1931, 1,844,000 acres of barley were sown but never harvested; in 1933, 3,707,000 acres; in 1934, 4,823,000 acres; in 1936, 3,749,000 acres; and in 1937, 1,611,000 acres. It should be added that these enormous losses do not include the hundreds of thousands of acres that were grazed or cut for hay because the yields of grain were too small to warrant the expense of harvesting them.[21] Large amounts of land, especially in the Dakotas, that were formerly devoted to the growing of barley have now been permanently abandoned or turned over to some other use.

Just how strong the effects of the establishment of the Agricultural Adjustment Administration have been with regard to barley is not entirely clear. It is certain, however, that it has had, in some regions at least, a marked influence in bringing about an extension of barley cultivation. The setting of definite limits on the acreage that may be devoted to corn and wheat has had the effect of making farmers substitute other crops on part of the land they had formerly used for these two grains. On many acres the substitute crop has been barley, since it provides a good alternative feed in the presence of a reduced corn supply and is also a potential cash crop to replace wheat.

One remaining item should be included in this summary of the dominant factors influencing the development of barley production in the United States in the modern era. A substantial part of the acreage devoted to oats in regions suited to the production of that grain has been a response to the active demand created by its desirability as a feed for horses. In the decades after the First World War motor power replaced more than one-third of the horses in the United States, and the increasingly significant impact of this development as it affects the competitive relations of barley and oats as feed grains has not yet been fully experienced.

---

[21] *Statistical Abstract of the United States, 1939 (61st Number)*, U. S. Bur. of the Census, 1940, p. 666.

314

THE AMERICAN SCENE

WILMA BELDEN FAIRCHILD

THE past few years have witnessed a steady flow of books that describe, portray, or interpret the American countryside. The flow, in fact, is rapidly assuming flood proportions and is happily indicative of a growing awareness of the beauty and diversity and the colorful historical heritage of the American scene. With the return to their homes of the many men and women who have been serving with the armed forces, the expression of that deep feeling which they share with Touchstone, that "when I was at home, I was in a better place," may be reflected in an even richer regional literature.

The type of regional writing with which this article is concerned is, or should be, important to geographers. "Let anyone recollect the verbal presentations of regions that have stuck fast in his memory. They are, though written by an Alexander von Humboldt, artistic presentations. Can anyone think of the tropical forest without recalling W. H. Hudson's descriptions? . . . Literary art, not systematic description, is the proper medium of regional synthesis."[1] The appreciation of scenery is a facet of the many-sided discipline of geography that has been somewhat neglected among professionals. We are too much involved, perhaps, with minutiae, with the complex of facts necessary to make up what we conceive to be a complete regional description, to capture the personality of the landscape as a whole. The books mentioned in this paper, and others of the same genre, can therefore be read not only with pleasure but with profit by geographers as well as by laymen.

However, for the nongeographer, the books are even more valuable. Since, admittedly, "nothing tends to boredom so much as being uninformed," the postwar motorists and vacationists who make an attempt to learn something of the country through which they are to travel will find their efforts richly rewarded. And even for stay-at-homes an acquaintance with some of the books would be salutary. Joseph Kinsey Howard, a Montana newspaperman, tells of asking a clerk in a Boston shop to forward a package to Howard's home in Great Falls, a city of some thirty thousand persons, only to have the clerk inquire whether the state had regular mail service![2]

The books approach their subject in a variety of ways and from several points of view, but they have one feature in common: each seeks to be a

---

[1] John Leighly: Some Comments on Contemporary Geographic Method, *Annals Assn of Amer. Geogrs.*, Vol. 27, 1937, pp. 125–141; reference on p. 131.

[2] Joseph Kinsey Howard: Montana, High, Wide, and Handsome. vi and 347 pp. Yale University Press, New Haven; Oxford University Press, London, 1943. $3.00. Reference on p. 2.

315

vade mecum and to project the unique quality of the region concerned, whether city, state, river, or mountain range. Some are pictorial—collections of photographs or drawings pointed up with explanatory text.[3] Others are largely or even entirely historical in approach, illuminating the present through examination of the past.[4] Still others[5] are regional in the best sense, the "interpretative writing that shows a man putting down roots deep into the soil of his own place; that takes account of essential geographic and economic differences between one way of life and another lived in a distant region; and that acknowledges the influence upon social behavior of peculiar local conditions."[6]

An enumeration of titles with a brief indication of what kind of material each book contains would be dull indeed, and an attempt to classify them categorically would be an injustice to the immense diversity of interests

---

[3] Outstanding among books of this category are some recent publications of Hastings House, New York. These consist of collections of excellent photographs and include the Visage of America series (for example, Santa Fe, The Missions of California, The Coast of Maine, The Gulf Coast of Mississippi, Natchez: Symbol of the Old South) and the American Landmarks series (camera impressions by Samuel Chamberlain of Gloucester and Cape Ann, Salem, Boston, Nantucket, Lexington and Concord, Marblehead, Portsmouth, Martha's Vineyard, Cambridge).

As regards regional art, two books should be mentioned here. One is Kaj Klitgaard's "Through the American Landscape" (xi and 323 pp. The University of North Carolina Press, Chapel Hill, 1941. $3.50). The other is "Portrait of America," edited by Aimée Crane, which consists of beautiful reproductions of paintings of America by American artists (iv and iv pp., 101 plates. Hyperion Press, New York; distributed by Duell, Sloan & Pearce, New York, 1945. $10.00). "The occupational diversities, the innumerable changes of landscape, the local inhabitants from Louisiana to Minnesota, from Oregon to New England, the richness, the color, the shabbiness, the vitality and the drama—all these are translated vividly into a pictorial language that is unmistakably American."

[4] The Rivers of America series (Farrar & Rinehart) and the American Lakes series (Bobbs-Merrill) are good examples of the predominantly historical approach. Among books entirely historical in character are "The Valley of Virginia in the American Revolution, 1763–1789" by Freeman H. Hart and "The Culture of Early Charleston" by Frederick P. Bowes, both published in 1942 by the University of North Carolina Press, Chapel Hill (xii and 223 pp., $3.50; ix and 156 pp., $2.50), and "Plantation Life in the Florida Parishes of Louisiana, 1836–1846, As Reflected in the Diary of Bennet H. Barrow" by Edwin Adams Davis, Columbia University Press, New York, 1943 (Columbia University Studies in the History of American Agriculture, No. 9; xvi and 457 pp., $5.00).

Also to be included among books of a historical nature is Donald Culross Peattie's "Journey into America," though in this work America's past has been interpreted through stories of great men—Jefferson, Paine, Boone, Bridger, and others—rather than by means of documented data (276 pp. Houghton Mifflin Co., Boston, 1943. $3.00). The "Album of American History," edited by James Truslow Adams, tells "the history of America through pictures made at the time the history was being made" (Charles Scribner's Sons, New York. Vol. 1, Colonial Period, 1944; xiii and 411 pp.; $7.50. Vol. 2, 1783–1853, 1945; xi and 418 pp.; $7.50).

[5] The American Folkways series published by Duell, Sloan and Pearce exemplifies the regional-synthesis type of book. Besides those mentioned in the text of this article, the series includes books on the Ozark Country, Palmetto Country, Blue Ridge Country, Far North Country (Alaska), Golden Gate Country, and North Star Country. The publisher and authors are to be commended on a real contribution to American regional literature.

[6] James Gray: Pine, Stream & Prairie: Wisconsin and Minnesota in Profile. xi, 312, and x pp. (The American Scene.) Alfred A. Knopf, New York, 1945. $3.50. Reference on p. 175.

represented in each. The best way, perhaps, to lure the mind into a desire to experience the adventure and pleasure found in reading them is to sample here and there at random.

RACIAL AND CULTURAL GROUPS

For those interested in sociology or anthropology—or, for that matter, just in people—there are throughout the regional books accounts of comparatively little-known groups. To read about them is to broaden one's understanding of the great variety of races and cultures that make up the patchwork of American life.

One of the most interesting of our not completely assimilated peoples is the Acadians of Louisiana. These French Canadians, expelled for political reasons from Nova Scotia in the middle of the eighteenth century, found a haven in the almost untouched bayou region.

It was the opportunity for which the Acadians had prayed. They were a quiet, rural people, who wanted largely to be left alone. A series of accidents had brought them to one of the few places on the American continent that would permit them to realize that wish.

They had suffered, their families torn apart by hostile outside forces. That must never happen again. Always at the back of their thoughts has been this resolution, that here, in Louisiana, their small part of the world shall remain a citadel. They found themselves in a locale remote from other parts of the colony, and they rejoiced. They had, and still have, twin gifts of simplicity and humor, and they set to work to re-create everything as it was with them before—their small farms, their fields, their holdings of cattle, their meeting places for talk and song. The bayou became their place, their ways fitting to it and changing with it through the years. The product is a culture without parallel in the United States—a curious, untypically American design that is warm and rich in values, fitting no mold but its own.

The world heard little and saw nothing of the Acadian and his bayous. He remained in the back country, developing his own habits, his own economy, his likes and dislikes.[7]

Mr. Kane's book on the Acadians, their life and livelihood in the fecund, watery environment they have made peculiarly their own, is completely delightful.

The Basque sheepherders of the high range country of eastern Oregon[8] and the Belgian farming community on the Door Peninsula of Wisconsin, the only "large rural settlement of Belgians in America. . . , still distinctively

---

[7] Harnett T. Kane: The Bayous of Louisiana. viii and 341 pp. William Morrow & Co., New York, 1943. $3.50. Reference on pp. 10-11. Mr. Kane's more recent book "Plantation Parade: The Grand Manner in Louisiana" deals equally informatively with a phase of Louisiana's past, the great era of cotton, sugar, and slaves (vi and 342 pp. William Morrow & Co., New York, 1945. $3.50.)

[8] For a brief account of these folk see Nancy Wilson Ross: Farthest Reach: Oregon & Washington, Section 2, Chapter 3 (xiv, 359, and xviii pp. [The American Scene.] Alfred A. Knopf, New York, 1941. $3.50).

Belgian with French speech and many customs characteristic of the home land,"[9] are other examples of distinctive racial groups. But it is not necessary to turn to colonies of foreign extraction to discover interesting folk. C. A. Weslager has given us a detailed study of the Moor-Nanticoke people of Delaware, mixed-blood survivors of the original Indian inhabitants of the region.

Today . . . there remains not a single full-blooded Indian on the Delmarva Peninsula. . . . But . . . the Indian blood is still perpetuated in forgotten folk who are neither white nor black nor pure Indian. . . .

The remarkable thing about these . . . people is that they have maintained two distinct settlements about which little is known outside of the state. In fact, the communities are known only vaguely to most of the white residents. One settlement is on the north shore of Indian River in Sussex County, and the second is at Cheswold near Dover in Kent County.

. . . .

The Nanticokes are a group of acculturated mixed-blood folk who have remained deeply conscious of their Indian ancestry and whose social traditions are emphatic and consistent. The Moors, who sprang from an identical racial background, are less aware of native social tradition. Beneath the surface, however, are folkways rooted in the past.[10]

Remnants of the old Indian culture are to be found in the knowledge and use of herbs, weather superstitions, and several industrial survivals such as certain types of traps, fishing devices, tools, and baskets.

There are other excellent studies of the American Indian; for example, a book on the life and economy of the Navahos written by two doctors who "became fascinated with the problem of the mutual adjustment and cooperation between people who are separated by language, skin color, and a whole way of life,"[11] and one on the Hopi community, which "turns out surprisingly to be an 'ideal republic,' a pure, achieved democracy, intensely nurturing an ancient spiritual culture, intensely nurturing and socializing its young."[12]

---

[9] See Hjalmar R. Holand: Old Peninsula Days: Tales and Sketches of the Door Peninsula, Chapter 17 (6th edit. xii and 295 pp. Pioneer Publishing Co., Ephraim, Wis., 1943. $2.50. Reference on p. 233). Another interesting account of the same community is found in Fred L. Holmes: Old World Wisconsin: Around Europe in the Badger State, Chapter 8 (368 pp. E. M. Hale & Co., Eau Claire, Wis., 1944. $2.50).

[10] C. A. Weslager: Delaware's Forgotten Folk: The Story of the Moors & Nanticokes. ix nd 215 pp. University of Pennsylvania Press, Philadelphia, 1943. $2.50. References on pp. 10–11 and 205.

[11] Alexander H. Leighton and Dorothea C. Leighton: The Navaho Door: An Introduction to Navaho Life. xviii and 149 pp. Harvard University Press, Cambridge, Mass., 1944. $4.00. Reference on p. xviii.

[12] Laura Thompson and Alice Joseph: The Hopi Way. 151 pp. United States Indian Service; sales agent, University of Chicago Press, Chicago, 1944. $3.00. Quotation from comment on the book by Ward Shepard: Our Indigenous Shangri-La, Scientific Monthly, Vol. 62, 1946, pp. 158–164; reference on p. 159.

And then there are the Tennessee mountain folk. "Probably no other group of people in the world have been so much caricatured, with so little actually known about them, as our southern mountain people." Alberta Pierson Hannum's fine chapter on the mountain people in "The Great Smokies and the Blue Ridge" helps us to know them better.[13] For instance:

Mountain people are interested in outsiders, feel a natural friendliness toward them, and are famously hospitable—until they feel they are being imposed upon, or made sport of. Then they draw back into a reserve. If the outsider mistakes it for backwardness he is indeed making a foolish mistake. The highlander withdraws into a sense of his own dignity as instinctive as his sense of the dramatic, and regards the less well-bred outsider now with a complete disinterest.[14]

Still another group of people concerning whom misinformation is prevalent is the Mormons.

Though they have been called many things, many hard things, they have never been called bad settlers. They were as indefatigable, obedient, stalwart, and united a people as the world ever saw. Their record in the intermountain region is a record of group living, completely at variance with the normal history of the West.[15]

Wallace Stegner's book traces the epic of Mormon settlement, and another recent book,[16] written by a Mormon, answers the question "Do they really have horns?" Both books contribute generously to an understanding and appreciation of the Mormons and Utah.

EXTRACTIVE INDUSTRIES

The great extractive industries of America have a colorful and romantic history. Although most of us are familiar in a general way with the background against which lumbering, mining, and stock raising have risen to the status of giant enterprises, detailed regional accounts are both stimulating and informative. Several of the books under discussion contain excellent accounts of the lumber industry. In the Pacific Northwest,

though great inroads have been made during the last half century, the remaining timber in Oregon and Washington, largely in the watershed of the Cascades, comprises about half the timber resources of the United States and is by far the globe's largest and heaviest per-acre stand.

[13] Roderick Peattie, edit.: The Great Smokies and the Blue Ridge: The Story of the Southern Appalachians. x and 3–372 pp. [American Mountain Series.] The Vanguard Press, New York, 1943. $3.75. Reference on p. 73.

[14] Ibid., p. 95.

[15] Wallace Stegner: Mormon Country. x and 362 pp. (American Folkways.) Duell, Sloan & Pearce, New York, 1942. $3.00. Reference on p. 62.

[16] Maurine Whipple: This Is the Place: Utah. 222 pp. (The American Scene.) Alfred A. Knopf, New York, 1945. $5.00. This book is illustrated with unusually fine photographs, some in color.

319

The history of the era of "amazing exploitation" that characterized the opening of the Pacific lumber industry is well told in the chapter on giant timber in "Last Mountains" by Robert Ormond Case and Victoria Case.[17]

And the lumber boom of the seventies and eighties in the Upper Peninsula of Michigan also has its story:

All over the peninsula the woods rocked from daybreak to dark with the crash of falling timber, the thunder of breaking rollways, the ring of axes and hum of saws, and the deep long cries of "Timber-r-r-r!" The expanding United States empire simply could not get enough lumber for telegraph poles, for fencing in the new West, for farm buildings and railroad ties that marched across the continent. Softwood from Upper Michigan built a new empire's houses; its hardwood put new furniture into them.[18]

For sheer boisterous and lusty adventure, the story of copper mining in the Butte region is at least a runner-up for the prize; those fabulous early days are ably recounted in "Copper Camp," compiled by workers of the Montana Writers' Program.[19]

No less colorful if less well known is the extraction of borax in the Death Valley–Mojave Desert region of California.

Presumably there is no romance in a cake of soap—or in water softeners, grease solvents, shampoos, deodorants, cosmetics, insecticides—in fertilizers or medicated surgical bandages or rayon fabrics or tanned hides—in manufacturing varnish, artificial gems, ceramic glazes, the slippery surfaces of playing cards, or bathtub enamel. Yet all these, and forty other products, have as an essential ingredient the chief product of Death Valley—namely, borax.[20]

The tale of the discovery and working of the deposits and the mothered-by-necessity development of a unique transportation form (the now famous twenty-mule team) is fascinating.

And another "obscure" industry is the making of pearl buttons from mussel shells.

To another almost clandestine and yet innocent and worthy enterprise I gave some attention. Now and then I saw small mussel boats moving along the Mississippi's shore or coming out of one of its tributaries. They were flat-bottomed, each with a rack over it on which were hung two iron bars with a hundred or more stout crowfoot hooks suspended by short trot-lines. Mussels lie in the mud or gravel of the river's bottom with their valves slightly open; they close them tightly when a hook enters, and are brought to the surface.

[17] Robert Ormond Case and Victoria Case: Last Mountains: The Story of the Cascades. 236 pp. Doubleday, Doran & Co., Garden City, N. Y., 1945. $2.75. Reference on p. 143.

[18] John Bartlow Martin: Call It North Country: The Story of Upper Michigan. viii, 281, and ix pp. (The American Scene.) Alfred A. Knopf, New York, 1944. $3 50. Reference on p. 127.

[19] Writers' Program, Montana: Copper Camp: Stories of the World's Greatest Mining Town—Butte, Montana. xi and 308 pp Hastings House, New York, 1943. $2.75.

[20] Edwin Corle: Desert Country. viii and 357 pp. (American Folkways.) Duell, Sloan & Pearce, New York, 1941. $3.00. Reference on pp. 292–293.

320

So in a sense this industry goes on out of sight, . . . and in fact is little remarked upon. Yet it is important, because every man who has half a dozen shirts and half a dozen suits of underwear in his bureau drawers uses at least a hundred pearl buttons a year. These were once the shells of fresh-water mussels. . . .

In one year more than fifty million pounds of shells, with a value of more than a million dollars, were taken from the Mississippi basin and transformed into buttons and novelties with a value of about eight million dollars. Along the Iowa coast for nearly two hundred miles there are button factories.[21]

CONSERVATION

The conservationist will find much to his interest in these regional books, from the lumber industry of the Northwest and the stock raising of the Great Plains to the muskrat trapping of Louisiana and the wheat growing of the Dakotas.

An anecdote gives a Plains Indian's view of the white man's heedless and wasteful use of the land:

The white man has taken our country, but he is paying for it. He thinks he is pretty smart, but he is not as smart as he thinks he is. The white man came into this country, cut down the trees, and turned the ground wrong-side up. He killed all the animals that would take care of themselves, so that he could bring in animals that he has to take care of. He calls this *civilization!*

When I was a boy the water in the rivers was good to drink, there was plenty of timber in the valley, the grass was knee-deep everywhere, and there was always an antelope or a buffalo to be had for the killing. . . .

But now there is nothing to eat on the prairie. The grass is scanty; the trees are gone. When I drink the water of the rivers, it makes me sick—it even makes horses sick. And the wind has blown away the very earth from under my feet. All we have left is the weather.[22]

But a hopeful outlook is evident in William Van Dersal's challenging book "The American Land"; for he sees in the more recent erosion-control methods of strip cropping and contour plowing a significant change:[23]

Once again the pattern is changing, as the face of the land begins to reflect the ways of the people who live upon it. Here is no patchwork, but a broad and subtle handling of slope and soil, sweeping curves and winding terraces, and fields fitted at last to the rounded rolling contours of the land . . .

It is doubtful whether the new pattern is well understood in its fullest implications, yet it faithfully portrays the ending of one era and the beginning of another. It expresses a profound change in American thought, induced by the realization that this is no longer an

---

[21] Clark B. Firestone: Flowing South. 263 pp. Robert M. McBride & Co., New York, 1941. $3.00. Reference on pp. 181–182.

[22] Stanley Vestal: The Missouri. x and 368 pp. (The Rivers of America.) Farrar & Rinehart, New York and Toronto, 1945. $2.50. Reference on p. 171.

[23] William R. Van Dersal: The American Land: Its History and Its Uses. xvi and 215 pp. Oxford University Press, London, New York, Toronto, 1943. $3.75. Reference on p. 195.

expanding nation, but a country whose future security depends upon the ability of its people to use wisely what they have.

FOOD AND COOKERY

Brillat-Savarin's famous invitation "Tell me what you eat, and I will tell you what you are" might well be amended to "Tell me what you eat, and I will tell you *who* you are," since the regional character of food and cookery constitutes a real index of sectional differences. In "Mainstays of Maine" Robert P. Tristram Coffin, poet, novelist, and essayist, eulogizes the distinctive quality of down-East food, including lobster, baked beans, berries, and codfish chowder. Maine, says Mr. Coffin, "is bayberry and sweetfern and fern-brake and balsams, and I like to think its people and their foods are pungent and sharp-flavored also."

Our farm was a saltwater farm, so apples crowded clams, and herring jostled bees as the feeders of the family. My mother had to be an amphibian cook. She had to put the sea and the woods, clamflats and pastures together. . . .

Town was far away and once a week. Ready-made foods, outlandish concoctions, and short-cuts to a full man or boy or girl were not for us. We had no refrigerator. My mother shied away from canned goods as she shied away from the Old Boy. We had to make the most of what was at hand. . . . .

We made out with plenty. We had the whole ocean, the sky, as well as the usual land, on our table. We had the wild and the tame. My mother's dishes swept a wide arc. Some of them came from fifty fathoms down, some from a hundred feet up, some from pens, and some from woods where the sun came only in long, thin golden fingers.[24]

The sea and the woods replenish the larder in the Pacific Northwest also:

There are famous dishes in the Northwest indigenous to this part of the country: Geoduck steaks cut from a gigantic clam; Captain Doane's famous oyster pan roast, made from the little native Olympia oysters—a dish, accompanied by whisky, which played its part in many an informal political caucus of the early days; barbecued hard-shelled crab, served with curry sauce; pies of wild blackberry and salal; Oregon grape jelly; smoked brook trout prepared over a willow fire; goat's milk cheese from Pistol River or the rich creamy American cheddar from Tillamook.[25]

The beef-and-potato diet of the Great Plains States and the hog-and-hominy diet of the South are proverbial. But the fare is not always monotonous. Here, for example, is a verbatim account of a Kentucky meal:

Hot biscuits, fried chicken, gravy made with cream; slaw, pickles, new lima beans, hulled October beans cooked long with bacon and hot pepper; squash baked; light mashed potatoes,

---

[24] Robert P. Tristram Coffin: Mainstays of Maine. xviii and 185 pp. The Macmillan Co., New York, 1944. $2.00. References on pp. ix and 22–23.

[25] Ross, *op. cit.*, pp. 10–11.

candied sweets; cream and corn; turnips diced and buttered; tomatoes sliced and stewed; four preserves and jellies; black jam cake, mincemeat pies; coffee, tea, milk.[26]

And a "Georgia products dinner" as described in Hal Steed's book "Georgia: Unfinished State" offers further proof of variety and abundance.[27]

Cultural as well as physical differences are reflected in cookery. Harnett Kane tells an anecdote from the Mississippi-delta country of Louisiana of a Yankee husband who watched his Delta wife in the kitchen:

She was trying to follow his suggestion that she prepare something he remembered from boyhood, a New England boiled dinner. She cut the vegetables, she washed them, she put them in the pot; and then she added tomatoes, bayleaf, thyme, onions, and five or six other items without which she was sure no dish was complete. The husband, grinning, told her: "Bébé, no matter what you put on that stove, it's going to come out French—your own kind of French."[28]

THE WEST

Those who appreciate what one author has called the "gay and un-buttoned spirit" of the West will find delight in a number of recent books. It is impossible to sample them all, but several recommend themselves as true exponents of the special Western flavor. One of these is Ladd Hay-stead's "If the Prospect Pleases."

The West itself is the place where you climb for water, dig for wood, look farther and see less, and the Powder River runs uphill from Texas. It's a land of fable, myth, tradition and the lack of it, extremes of heat and cold, wetness and dryness, lowness and highness, of promise and bitter disappointment . . . It's a land that has been exploited worse than almost any other part of the globe; and a land still incredibly rich in resources.[29]

Another is Richard Lillard's "Desert Challenge."

The "Old West" was the hardships of camping. It was unbalanced diet, uncouth manners, midwives and quacks, casual homicide, too little water and too much whisky, and an un-stable population that half built a town and then stampeded off somewhere to start another.[30]

Howard's "Montana, High, Wide, and Handsome," with its emphasis on social and economic problems arising from a long history of exploitation, and Nancy Wilson Ross's "Farthest Reach," both mentioned in other connections, should also be included here. Edward Everett Dale's "Cow

---

[26] Firestone, op. cit., p. 138.

[27] Hal Steed: Georgia: Unfinished State. xvi, 336, and viii pp. (The American Scene.) Alfred A. Knopf, New York, 1942. $3.50. Reference on pp. 102–103.

[28] Harnett T. Kane: Deep Delta Country. xx and 283 pp. (American Folkways.) Duell, Sloan & Pearce, New York, 1944. $3.00. Reference on p. 77.

[29] Ladd Haystead: If the Prospect Pleases: The West the Guidebooks Never Mention. xiii and 208 pp. University of Oklahoma Press, Norman, 1945. $2.50. Reference on pp. 7–8.

[30] Richard G. Lillard: Desert Challenge: An Interpretation of Nevada. (The American Scene.) viii 388, and ix pp. Alfred A. Knopf, New York, 1942. $4.00 Reference on p. 7.

Country,"[31] Towne and Wentworth's "Shepherd's Empire,"[32] and Winifred Kupper's "The Golden Hoof"[33] provide full accounts of the great stock-raising enterprises that have been so large a part of the life and economy of the West. The first of these is particularly entertaining and contains, besides a vivid and informative picture of the cattle empire, an amusing chapter on the humor of the cowboy.

THE EMERGENCE OF PERSONALITY

One of the most satisfying effects of a concentrated dose of regional literature is the manner in which various elements of the American life and landscape come alive and assume distinct personalities. The element may be a town or a river or a mountain range, or even a "country."

All over the United States there are "countries" of people, and in each there is a central force that has molded the thought and behavior of the people of the region. That force may be the newness of the land, or the difficulties imposed by nature, the physical contact with desert and plain, or a religious idea as impelling as that of the Mormons, but always some dominant power creates man's folkways.[34]

Whatever the particular feature, it will long be remembered by the reader in terms of the personality that has been evoked.

Butte, for example, emerges as "a painted, old trollop waking up after a wild night."

The barren, gray mine dumps with faded cottages in clusters at their feet; the huge steel and wooden gallows frames of the mines; the smoke-belching stacks; the crooked, crazy dirt roads and crumbling sidewalks leading up the hill to the mines; the rickety, unpainted, bulging and leaning brick and frame buildings—all look as if they had been there for generations. Yet Butte is relatively young. To quote an old-timer: "If you had lived as hard and excitin' a life as old Butte has, you'd be a bit prematurely aged yourself." That is Butte—prematurely aged, but tough and defiant.[35]

The Missouri River is an erratic, sly, cantankerous fellow with a pro-digious appetite. It is the only river "that goes traveling sidewise, that inter-feres in politics, rearranges geography and dabbles in real estate."

It is eating all the time—eating yellow clay banks and cornfields, eighty acres at a mouthful;

[31] Edward Everett Dale: Cow Country. ix and 265 pp. University of Oklahoma Press, Norman. 1943 (1st edit., 1942; 2nd printing, 1943). $2.75.

[32] Charles Wayland Towne and Edward Norris Wentworth: Shepherd's Empire. xii and 364 pp. University of Oklahoma Press, Norman, 1945. $3.50.

[33] Winifred Kupper: The Golden Hoof: The Story of the Sheep of the Southwest. xi and 203 pp. Alfred A. Knopf, New York, 1945. $2.75.

[34] Clarence M. Webster: Town Meeting Country. ix and 246 pp. (American Folkways.) Duell, Sloan & Pearce, New York, 1945. $3.00. Reference on p. 3.

[35] Writers' Program. op. cit., p. 22.

winding up its banquet with a truck garden and picking its teeth with the timbers of a big red barn. Its yearly menu is ten thousand acres of good, rich farming land, several miles of railroad, a few hundred houses, a forest or two and uncounted miles of sandbars.[36]

The New England mountains become venerable old men, "matured and wise," "ancient and time-scarred," and "because of their age and experience they make conversation with each other which is full of philosophy."[37]

And what could more realistically portray the essential quality of New England and its people than this passage:

Though Town Meeting Country is old, not very often does the visitor smell the musty odor of dry rot that hangs over many ancient towns and cities. It is beautiful, but never flamboyant or seductive. It is a sober country that disdains gallant gestures and the glorification of wild deeds. We rejoice that the turbulent Miz-zou-rye does *not* flow through our pastures, and we would put a Hatfield or McCoy or Wild Bill Hickock in the county jail along with the vagrant ballad singer and the cowboy who disturbed the peace with his loud talking. It is a sensible land where romance does not flourish, and the picturesque froo-fraw of life is not appreciated. Scarlett O'Hara was not a neo-Puritan maiden, and a Congregational Deacon would rent Tara Hall to the summer folks. Practicality is the motto of this country. We would drain a bayou and use all the Spanish moss for bed ticking.[38]

THE BEAUTY OF THE LAND

Aside from the pleasure of making friends with America, the most lasting impression derived from these regional books is of the infinite beauty and variety of the land—a kaleidoscopic pattern of color and line shifting and crystallizing before the mind's eye. One moment it may be an image of some dramatic, untamed Western landscape such as eastern Oregon:

There is some curiously compelling quality in this land. There are places where it seems to break and flow like vast turbulent waters. . . . It is as though the ocean has left its rhythm here, with tides of hills and mesas, breaking surf of buttes and rocks.[39]

At another moment it may be a scene of calm contentment, a settled farmland, rich and productive, as in the valley of the Shenandoah:

a long green trough between two mountain ranges, a checkerboard of green and brown and gold, on which the silver river writes in flowing curves.[40]

---

[36] Vestal, *op. cit.,* pp. 8 and 13–14 (quoting George Fitch).

[37] Roderick Peattie, edit.: The Friendly Mountains: Green, White, and Adirondacks. xii and 13–341 pp. [American Mountain Series.] The Vanguard Press, New York, 1942. $3.50. References on pp. 16 and 17.

[38] Webster, *op. cit.,* p. 8.

[39] Ross, *op. cit.,* pp. 78–79.

[40] Julia Davis: The Shenandoah. x and 374 pp. (The Rivers of America.) Farrar & Rinehart, News York and Toronto, 1945. $2.50. Reference on p. 11.

Or the pattern shifts once again, and we recall the hushed serenity of the Minnesota north woods in winter:

The pond was a small circle of flawless white, ringed by steep hills. The black pines and spruces were veiled in frost and the birches and aspens were blooming with ethereal, gauzy flowers . . . The cliff behind them was white instead of black, shining like old silver, . . . and the shore, where the level whiteness broke up into frosty tangles of slim branches, was like silence broken by faint music.[41]

We have dwelt more particularly on the pleasure to be found in examining the American scene. Perhaps it would be well to end on a deeper note: the meaning of the "thousand environments—forests, deserts, prairies, plains, mountains, with all their climates—all at work molding men, shaping their bodies, brains, habits, characters, occupations, attitudes, scales of values, social organizations." Exploration and understanding of these thousand environments surely constitute the first step toward resolution of the American "predicament," toward the creation of "an ordered harmony, an integrated unity, which will be the United States."[42]

---

[41] Florence Page Jaques: Snowshoe Country. viii and 110 pp. The University of Minnesota Press, Minneapolis, 1944. $3.00. Reference on p. 100. For an equally beautiful description of the same region in summer see Mrs. Jaques' earlier book "Canoe Country" (78 pp. The University of Minnesota Press, Minneapolis, 1938. $2.50).

[42] T. K. Whipple: Study Out the Land: [A Collection of] Essays. xxii and 215 pp. University of California Press, Berkeley and Los Angeles, 1943. $2.00. References on pp. 36 and 41 (in the essay entitled "The American Predicament").

WESTCHESTER – FAIRFIELD

PROPOSED SITE FOR THE PERMANENT SEAT OF
THE UNITED NATIONS*

CHARLES B. HITCHCOCK

O N October 3, 1945, the Executive Committee of the United Nations, meeting in London, voted on two proposals concerning the location of the permanent seat for the United Nations: Should it be in the United States of America or in Europe? By a vote of 9 to 3 the United States was chosen (Australia, Brazil, Chile, China, Czechoslovakia, Iran, Mexico, Union of Soviet Socialist Republics, and Yugoslavia in favor; France, the Netherlands, and the United Kingdom against; Canada and the United States abstaining from expression of opinion.)[1]

On January 5, 1946, a seven-man Inspection Group arrived in New York City to examine sites for the permanent United Nations headquarters. For a period of one month, under the guidance of an American secretary, the Inspection Group followed instructions to explore the general areas "within 60 miles of Boston; between 25–80 miles from New York City, in the Hudson Valley; or east of the Hudson River in New York State or Connecticut; and in the Princeton, N. J., district."

" 'Essential criteria' for the selection of sites included local political conditions and general character of local press and public opinion in harmony with the tenets of the United Nations Charter, including freedom from

* This article, prepared on short notice, illustrates the lines on which a full study of the region might proceed. The collection of data presented in the notes was made by members of the Society's staff (Wilma B. Fairchild, Raye R. Platt, O. M. Miller), with the exception of the sections on an airport water supply, and sewage disposal, which were contributed by Mr. William E. Rudolph. Other members of the staff (W. O. Field, Jr. and Stanley F. Smith) took most of the photographs. The three detailed regional maps were drawn by Stanley F. Smith and the remainder prepared by John Forsyth, Gustav Schweizer, and E. D. Weldon.

Thanks are due to the Regional Plan Association, and in particular to Mr. C. McKim Norton of that organization; to Mr. Chester E. Wheeler of the Westchester County Department of Planning; and to others whose assistance is acknowledged in the body of the text.

[1] Report by the Executive Committee to the Preparatory Commission of the United Nations, 1945, p. 132.

racial and religious discrimination; accessibility to the world at large, and
unrestricted and uninterrupted contact with all countries of the world,
including a radio station, and an airport available on or near the site.

" 'Desirable criteria' included 'climatic conditions which would not
entail hardships likely to affect the health or efficiency of permanent or
temporary residents connected with the United Nations; favorable cultural
conditions, high public service standards, suitable living accommodations,
educational, health, and recreational facilities within reasonable distance;
sufficient facilities for the establishment of the necessary offices, and the
possibility of acquiring, on satisfactory terms, such land or buildings as the
United Nations may need.'

" 'Other points to be considered by the Inspection Group were 'sufficient
distance from nearest large metropolis, reasonable accessibility to metropolitan cultural, medical, and recreational centers, and beautiful country
and setting for site, including route to and from metropolis, and protection
of amenities in surrounding areas.' " [2]

On February 2, after examining fourteen localities, the Inspection
Group picked an area lying within Westchester County, N. Y., and Fairfield County, Conn., referred to as the North Greenwich–North Stamford
area, as the site to be recommended to the full Interim Committee on Headquarters of the United Nations in London.[3] For their guidance in the selection of a site in the Westchester-Fairfield region, the Inspection Group had
been furnished with rather detailed reports on three general areas, referred
to as Westchester-Amawalk, Ridgefield-Poundridge, and North Greenwich–North Stamford.[4] In their report to the General Assembly, they indicated that "the considerations which have influenced us particularly in the
choice of sites" had been: (1) distance and accessibility to a large metropolis;

[2] C. McK. Norton: The Hunt for a World Headquarters Site, *Amer. City*, Vol. 61, 1946, pp. 86–87 and 91; references on p. 86.

[3] Reference from the *New York Times*, February 3, 1946.

[4] See the reports (mimeographed) prepared for the Interim Committee on Headquarters of the United Nations: H. M. Lewis: Report on Westchester-Amawalk District as a Site for United Nations Headquarters, 1946; *idem*: Report on Ridgefield, Conn.-Poundridge, N. Y., District as a Site for United Nations Headquarters, 1946; E. P. Goodrich: United Nations Organization Proposed Permanent Head-quarters Site at North Greenwich-Stamford, Connecticut and New York, n.d. See also "General Data, New York Metropolitan Region and Sites under Consideration for United Nations Headquarters," Regional Plan Association, New York, 1946 (manuscript); and a memorandum to the Inspection Group from F. P. Clark and C. E. Morrow, "Prospects for Further Territorial Expansion of New York Metro-politan Region," Regional Plan Association, New York, Feb. 1, 1946 (manuscript), in which one of the conclusions is that "of the various districts under consideration in the New York area, all would seem to be beyond the probable ultimate limits of metropolitan and suburban growth except in the North Greenwich-North Stamford area which may be reached by expanding development within the next 25-50 years."

(2) climatic conditions, especially during the summer; (3) natural features and danger of urban development; (4) possibility of constructing a city; (5) availability of educational facilities; and (6) accessibility to recreational facilities such as seacoast and mountains.[5]

After presentation of their findings to the General Assembly meeting in London on February 14, it was resolved that "the permanent headquarters

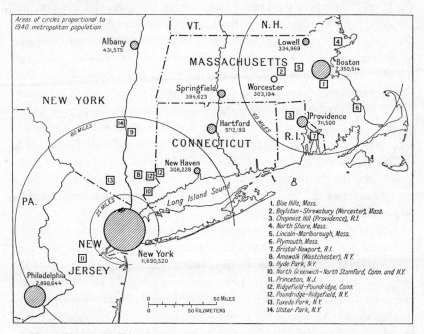

FIG. 1—Districts visited by the Inspection Group, Interim Committee on Headquarters of the United Nations. (After map by Regional Plan Association.)

of the United Nations should be established in Westchester (New York) and/or Fairfield (Conn.) counties, i.e. near to New York City." [6]

The Headquarters Commission was instructed to "proceed as soon as possible to the region . . . with a view to carrying out an exhaustive study thereof and making recommendations to the General Assembly in the second part of its First Session regarding the exact location to be selected

[5] Report and Recommendations of the Inspection Group on Selecting the Permanent Site and Interim Facilities for the Headquarters of the United Nations (mimeographed), p. 10.

[6] Resolution Adopted by General Assembly February 14, 1946, as to Procedure for Selecting a Site in Westchester County, New York and /or Fairfield County, Connecticut, in Documents Relating to the Selection of the Site for the Permanent Headquarters of the United Nations in the United States and the Arrangements for the Control of the Area Comprising the Site (mimeographed), n.d., pp. 1-2.

within the aforementioned general region." [7] They were furthermore instructed to draw up plans on the assumption that the United Nations would acquire about 2, 5, 10, 20, or 40 square miles of territory.[8]

The following resolution was also adopted by the General Assembly: "Considering that appropriate assurance should be given to the residents and neighbors of the site finally chosen as the permanent headquarters of the United Nations in the United States, to the effect that this selection will not cause injustice to be done to them, it is *resolved* that the United Nations shall give all due and friendly consideration to any problems that may arise in connection with the possible displacement of residents or with tax, revenue, and other problems affecting the localities involved, when a final decision is taken with regard to the exact site of the permanent headquarters of the United Nations." [9]

Local reaction to the selection of the North Greenwich–North Stamford area was varied. Citizens' committees in Greenwich and North Castle voiced opposition, and residents in Poundridge were polled on their opinions. Although the majority of those registering their feelings were against establishment of the United Nations capital in the area, a strong minority favored it.

One obvious reason for objection was the natural desire to retain possession of personal property.[10] Such a feeling is common in cases of land condemnation for public use. Perhaps another reason lay in the size of the proposed initial area, 42 square miles, and in its proposed future northward extension to include 172 square miles. Furthermore, little or no publicity was given to the resolution adopted by the General Assembly assuring "residents and neighbors of the site" that the selection would not "cause injustice to be done to them." However, be it said on the other side that no

---

[9] Resolution adopted by the Headquarters Committee of General Assembly February 13, 1946 as to Assurances against Injustice to Residents and Neighbors of Site, *in* Documents Relating to the Selection of the Site for the Permanent Headquarters of the United Nations (*op. cit.*), p. 3.

[10] A "Draft of Convention between the United Nations and the United States Regarding Establishment of Headquarters" (in "Documents Relating to the Selection of the Site for the Permanent Headquarters of the United Nations," *op. cit.*, pp. 13–21) was transmitted by the General Assembly to the Secretary-General for discussion purposes only, since the United States was not committed to that draft. The tentative outline includes such matters as ownership of the UN site; expropriation and compensation of interests in land and buildings conveyed to the United Nations; subsoil rights; airport, radio, and railroad station facilities; matters of jurisdiction within the zone; communications and transit to and from the zone; privileges and immunities of resident representatives; police protection; and public services. At the time of writing, these matters are still subject to study, and no final treaty has been negotiated. A note added to the draft by the United States Department of State indicates that "if the zone comprising the headquarters should be more than a few square miles in area, the changes to be discussed in negotiating the final convention would include appropriate provisions as to the rights of private residents" (p. 13).

concrete picture of the extent and nature of the United Nations community was furnished, and suggestions ranged from a university-campus type of development to a city of 50,000 people.[11] The preliminary report on buildings and facilities was couched in words too general to permit even an overall picture of requirements. It would seem essential that the nature of the permanent headquarters be defined before final negotiations are begun on selection of acreage, whether it is to be in the Westchester-Fairfield region or elsewhere.

Conversation between a Visitor and a Resident

Westchester-Fairfield is a new name to most of the world. What kind of place is it, this pleasant countryside of rolling hills and valleys? It has been settled long enough to have acquired a personality, or, rather, personalities; for through it runs a boundary as old as white settlement in these parts, the boundary between "Yorkers" and Yankees. Should the UN confirm its initial selection of a Westchester-Fairfield site, the representatives might well find of interest this local example of the influence of a boundary on the lives and customs of the inhabitants!

Adequately to describe the Westchester-Fairfield region would require a monograph. One way of getting a rapid impression would be to "listen in" on a conversation between a visitor (V) and a resident (R) living in Westchester County a stone's throw from the Connecticut boundary:

V. This is only my second trip to the United States, and yesterday was my first chance to see something of your countryside. We drove out from New York into Westchester and Fairfield Counties. Wonderful rolling country, and surprisingly wild in many parts for a region so near to your great metropolis. Those fine parkways make it so accessible.

R. Too accessible on a week end! Almost everybody with a car seems to seek the parkways on a sunny Saturday or Sunday. Incidentally, with one major exception, the Westchester parkways were largely planned and financed by the county. Of course, there are federal and state-aid and town-maintained roads as well.

---

[11] Bearing in mind the recommendation that each delegation be composed of 5 delegates, 5 alternates, and staff, and assuming a future enlarged membership of almost 60 nations, the Executive Committee had stated that the main buildings should contain a large hall with seating facilities "for no less than six hundred Delegates, alternates and principal members of their staffs" and additional seating capacity for others, including "a large gallery . . . for the accommodation of accredited journalists, representatives of organisations connected with the United Nations, and the general public" (Report by the Executive Committee to the Preparatory Commission of the United Nations, *op. cit.*, pp. 117 and 118).

331

V. You mean to say that each town has its own local road department? And just what do you mean by a "town?"

R. I should explain that we use the word "town" rather loosely, commonly referring to a minor civil division, and this can be rural, urban, or a combination of both. The local road commissioner is one of the most important and highly paid elected town officials. Each town has considerable autonomy and self-management. We have a supervisor, corresponding to a mayor, a town board, and such officials as town clerk, tax collector, welfare commissioner, and a board of assessors, all of whom are elected by popular vote of the property owners. We take considerable pride in running our local affairs, and see to it that our tax money is spent properly. The supervisor also represents us at county meetings in White Plains, where county affairs are settled.

V. Well, my friend from Connecticut must have been misinformed. He told me that the counties have no significant governing power and that local government is vested in the towns and cities.

R. On the contrary, he was right in so far as Connecticut is concerned. Counties don't have the same significance there. There is a strong movement in the state for city and town consolidation in order to avoid duplication of officials. By using separate taxing districts, they have worked out a system whereby people of the entire area pay for the general costs of the town, while only those in the urban areas pay for their special urban services. Greenwich, New Canaan, and Ridgefield are all consolidated towns.

V. Much more local autonomy than I realized. Somewhere I remember having read of a former feudal system in the New York region, with huge land grants and lords of the manor.

R. In the eighteenth century the English government encouraged the organization of manors, but these were freehold manors without any titular rank for the proprietors. Under this semiaristocratic system, the owners were assessed only a small annual quitrent payment by the provincial government and could run their estates under the laws of the land as circumstances required. Frederick Philipse and Stephanus Van Cortlandt controlled a large part of Westchester in the early part of the eighteenth century. Van Cortlandt acquired virtually all the northern part of the county from Indians and white settlers—over eighty-six thousand acres. Sale of land to strangers was extremely rare. The settlers merely held the land as tenant farmers, and change-over to small land ownership was slow.

V. Quite different from your ordinary homestead lots taken up in bona fide settlement; but surely things must have changed during your Revolution.

R. Strangely enough, some of the leading land owners were not Tory in spite of a system made possible through monarchical institutions. Long before the Revolution tenants had commonly been given the right to purchase "soil rights," but with low rentals there was apparently no great tendency to acquire ownership.

V. Didn't the Revolutionary government seize these great properties at once?

R. In some cases, yes. Philipse Manor, for example, which extended south from the Croton River to Spuyten Duyvil and was bounded west and east by the Hudson and Bronx Rivers, was seized and divided up by the state during the Revolution, then sold off in cheap parcels. Cortlandt Manor didn't go out of existence until 1788 when the county was divided into townships.

V. But at least you had no boundaries to be settled after the war.

R. Hardly! New York and Connecticut started squabbling about boundaries almost as soon as the English had taken over from the Dutch in 1664. The dispute only lasted a couple of hundred years. There was even a period when Rye and Bedford were up in arms about being ceded by Connecticut to foreign territory. For a time residents in the disputed area didn't know whether to pay taxes to New York or Connecticut, so judiciously refrained from paying either.

V. I trust they have it fixed up so that you know which state levies the taxes now.

R. To add to the confusion, Connecticut has no state tax—and thereon hinge many differences on either side of the border.

V. Speaking of finances, one thing which struck me most forcibly was the large, modern schools, sometimes out in full country—orchards and cows on one side; playground and athletic field on the other. How do you support your educational system—by federal aid?

R. Out in Westchester by local property owners' tax. But there is additional state assistance in some instances, in both New York and Connecticut. Only a few years ago, the traditional one-room school still was common; now they are largely consolidated, and the children are brought by bus. Let me tell you, there is nothing the youngsters like better than a good winter snowstorm when the busses can't get through on the back roads!

V. Sufficient snow to stop traffic? I have heard of your continental climate, but when I was in New York last winter, it never occurred to me that the weather could be so severe.

333

R. Probably not. After all, it takes a commuter—and I say this with feeling—to appreciate the big temperature differences in up-county Westchester. Not that I wish to imply that we have really severe winters, but zero temperatures are not uncommon. Rain in the city and ice or snow in the commuting area. In addition, the lay of the land may create local climatic differences within short distances in our hilly country. One valley may have its local summer fogs, while its neighbor remains crystal-clear.

V. Quite a difference between your winter and the present midsummer scene! Frankly, as an amateur landscape painter, I was rather disappointed by the lack of color contrast. Everything a uniformly lush green; but from what I have read, it must be a glorious riot of color when autumn brings its reds and yellows to the woods that seem to be everywhere.

R. "The colors of autumn stream down the wind, scarlet in sumach and maple, spun gold in the birches, a splendor of smoldering fire in the oaks along the hill." I welcome an opportunity to quote from the lyric proclamations of Connecticut's Governor Cross. And you must not overlook the brief beauty of our springtime—"the flight of a season that came with snowy petals of dogwood drifting, spray beyond delicate spray, in the early luster of Spring."

V. Delightful! But there is one aspect of your woodland that is not so pleasing. I was rather amazed to note how unkempt it looks as soon as one leaves the parkways. I rather expected a more pruned landscape—something more like Sussex.

R. No insult. We don't practice silviculture as we should. Back in the sixties, lumbering was still an important industry, but it was largely a matter of cutting down the good trees, and letting the second growth come back as it pleased. In many places, we haven't gotten around to clearing out the old chestnuts killed off by blight back around 1914. Then of course there is the matter of abandoned farmland.

V. Yes, I noticed that. Almost everywhere I went there seemed to be a network of stone walls running off into second-growth woods.

R. Foreigners often seem impressed by that. A visiting European geographer once asked if they had been built by slave labor. Plenty of Yankee farmers must have turned in their graves at that question! You probably noticed the tree succession in recently abandoned pasture—poverty grass, volunteer red cedar, and gray birch. Farmers are gradually moving out, what with increased taxes and high labor costs, but there is still some nice farmland, particularly in northern Westchester and in parts of Fairfield beyond the commuter belt. And then there is also a patchy distribution of farms in the commuter area.

V. It must have been quite a farming country once.

R. As a matter of fact, it still is. Fairfield had over twice the agricultural production of Westchester according to the 1940 census, but even so Westchester produced more than a million dollars in crops, largely nursery products. Agriculture used to be the backbone of Westchester's economy. You can see that by the even distribution of the population around 1800.

V. You mean to say that New York City didn't have much influence on local population distribution?

R. No. For example, Poundridge, in northern Westchester, with an area slightly smaller than Yonkers, had about the same population at the beginning of the nineteenth century. At the present time it has around 800 inhabitants and Yonkers over 142,000. Improvement in transportation and the coming of the railroads in the 40's changed things. People started moving out from New York along lines of cheap, rapid transportation. New towns were even developed. Mount Vernon is an interesting case in point, started in 1850 by a cooperative group rejoicing in the title of New York Industrial Home Association Number One!

V. One of those money-making schemes.

R. On the contrary, an honest movement by tradesmen, employees, and others of small means to secure homes free from the depredations of the hungry New York landlords. With its present population of around 67,000, Mount Vernon has proved a distinct success.

V. I suppose if your railroad network were more extensive you might have even more of this kind of development. You know, one of the things which impress me is your sparsity of railroads as contrasted with your close network of good auto roads. Not at all like the train facilities around some of our larger European cities.

R. I suppose that is true, although I must confess I have never given it much thought. However, in spite of the number of automobiles and good roads, the railroads continue to carry the greater part of the commuters. As train schedules improve there is bound to be an even greater movement of New Yorkers away from the city.

V. Surely you don't mean to suggest that the automobile has had little effect in that direction?

R. No such sweeping assertion implied; automobiles have obviously made it possible for people to commute from greater distances to stations, but even at that, only about one per cent of recent residential building has been more than two miles from rail facilities. Aside from New York City, many people have found it possible to carry on part-time farming and still work in near-by towns.

V. That must have a decided effect on standards of living in up-country areas away from the manufacturing towns. One of these days I must take a good cross-country hike and get a better feeling of the land.

R. Well, you'd better plan your trip beforehand. Otherwise you will probably be questioned as a trespasser.

V. What use do they make of all this vacant land? Except for its accessibility to New York, I can't see how it could have great value.

R. You are quite right in implying that there is ample room for residential expansion, and that is exactly what goes on today. But you raise two rather touchy points of definition—what is vacant land and what is value. In the first place, what isn't taken over for urban, public, and semipublic uses and agriculture is residential.

V. Vacant land could be defined as land without structures, or large-acreage tracts with only a few scattered buildings not particularly related to an integrated residential-estate development.

R. That is practically the definition of a local land-use report, but in addition, it included parts of exceptionally large estates which people acquainted with the properties felt were more accurately termed "vacant." It's a relative matter, and probably everyone wouldn't agree. The same with values. Certain areas carry exceptional values on account of the financial position of the present owners, but even the average farm or residence is high in comparison with, say, its equivalent in New Hampshire.

V. I was noticing some of the good old New England names over the village shops—Bricceti, Minozzi.

R. Quite so. Actually, many of the residents are descendants of original settlers. Then again, about 20 per cent in both Fairfield and Westchester are foreign-born—Italians in the majority, with Germans, Poles, and Irish in substantial numbers. One often thinks of a concentration of foreign-born in our eastern cities, but the percentage difference in the rural areas is very slight.

V. Well, you certainly must live in a heterogeneous community. Has there ever been a type study prepared showing the different occupations?

R. I recall one of Wilton, Connecticut, with a map showing those working in New York or elsewhere—an amusing mélange of physicians, butchers, brokers, house painters, lawyers, professors, farmers, and artists, with an opera singer, a mail-order salesman, and a wire drawer thrown in for good measure.

V. Are you getting facetious?

R. Not at all, and I would say that in so far as my region is concerned,

336

you could not ask for a more cooperative group. Perhaps not as closely knit as in the old days before the commuters began to come in. It takes one of those outsiders quite a while to become a local man, but if he stays long enough, he is educated into being a decent citizen. Almost everybody seems ready to lend a hand to his neighbor. The town wouldn't run without its garage mechanic and vice versa.

V. One thing that strikes me as peculiar is the abundance of wooden houses. You don't make as much use of brick and stone as we do.

R. Cheap, readily available lumber undoubtedly accounts for that, but many of the houses date back to Revolutionary days. All these earlier structures were built largely from timbers and lumber from the near-by woods. Many of the houses built recently are none too attractive to look at. To my eye, the older ones fit into the landscape better, but maybe that is pure prejudice on my part. An English friend once told me it took him some years to tell a "good" house, but his eye is as trained as mine now on good doorways.

V. I didn't even notice the doorways. The houses all look so boxlike and frail. With your hard winters it must be a problem to keep warm.

R. Not so bad now, with a furnace and storm windows, but I agree it must have been quite a struggle in the old days with nothing more than fireplaces. Stay around a while, and you will learn a lot about our peculiarities! Incidentally, when the United Nations Headquarters Committee recommended the Westchester-Fairfield region as their choice for the permanent UN headquarters, I started to look into the literature on the region.

V. There must be a tremendous quantity.

R. Plenty, but scattered through all manner of books and magazines. I have notes on some of the stuff here in my brief case. Why don't you take them along and look them over at your leisure?

V. Thanks. Incidentally, I was rather disgusted at the unfriendly reception the UN received in some quarters.

R. Well, I suppose you can blame that partly on the novelty of the idea and the rather abrupt way in which it was introduced. People often seem to react unfavorably to something new, particularly when they don't know much about it. They are apt to get upset and play "follow the leader." With a carefully thought-out plan for permanent site requirements, the committee should be able to find what it needs, whether they finally decide on Westchester-Fairfield or on some other location.

V. I agree. The residents would probably give more mature consideration then, too.

FIG. 2—Northern Greenwich, looking west to the Hudson River and Palisades. To left, Merritt Parkway, with Putnam Lake reservoir of the Greenwich water

Fig. 3—Farming country in Yorktown, looking east into Somers. Yorktown Heights is a short distance to right (south) of the photograph. In upper right, Amawalk Reservoir. In foreground, Taconic State Parkway. (Region of Amawalk site, 8 on Fig. 1.)

FIG. 4—Danbury, Conn., looking southwest. Double-track freight route of New Haven Railroad running from left in center of photograph (dark line). Hills in background reach over 1000 feet above sea level; relative relief more feet. (Immediately north of the Ridgefield-Poundridge, Conn., site, 12 on Fig. 1.)

FIG. 5—Cross River Reservoir, part of the New York City Croton system, looking north over Bedford and L Village in right center is Cross River. (Region of Poundridge-Ridgefield, N. Y., site, 12 on Fig. 1.)

. 6—Continuation of Figure 4 to the west. Right foreground, West Lake Reservoir, part of Danbury water-supply system.

. 7—View to west from Ridgefield, Conn., 1½ miles north of South Salem, looking over parts of the towns of Lewis-
d North Salem in Westchester County. Lake Waccabuc in distant center. (Region of Poundridge-Ridgefield, N. Y., site,
ig. 1.)

Fig. 8—Winter scene near Danbury. (Photograph by Helen R. Olson.)

Fig. 9—Young second growth in abandoned fields, northern Stamford, Conn.

Fig. 10—General farm land, typical barns. In distance, plowed land. North Castle, N. Y., about 1¼ miles north of the village of West Middle Patent.

Fig. 11—Heavy ice storm; serious damage to maples and elms. March 3–4, 1940. Poundridge, N. Y.

Fig. 12—Well constructed stone wall running through abandoned field, North Castle, N. Y.

Fig. 13—Manufacturing town of Georgetown, Conn., looking west. In foreground, wire screen mill employing between 300 and 400 workers.

343

FIG. 14—Dairy farm, Poundridge, N. Y., looking north. In left background, part of county-owned Poundridge Reservation.

FIG. 15—Cattle in pasture, Somers, N. Y., ¾ mile east of Yorktown Heights.

FIG. 16—Village green, Bedford, N. Y. White building to left of modern brick block is the old county courthouse (1787); to the right is the Bedford Library.

FIG. 17—Spring plowing, Norwalk, Conn., about 2 miles east of New Canaan.

FIG. 18—Public Central School, Somers, N. Y., a 12-grade school including both elementary and high; enrollment 335. Facing the school, to left of picture, are dairy farm and orchard.

FIG. 19—Shopping center, Ridgefield, Conn., looking north.

345

Fig. 20—Former inn, Somers, N. Y., owned by town and used to house its offices.

Fig. 21—Abandoned farm, Somers, N. Y., near Amawalk.

Fig. 22—Late-eighteenth-century white-clapboarded, central-chimney house, near Salem Center, N. Y.

Fig. 23—First Presbyterian Church, Yorktown, Y., founded 1738.

Fig. 24—New York–Connecticut granite boun[d] pillar, Banksville. Detail of monument in Figure

Fig. 25—Mid-Victorian architecture, house type c[om]mon to the 1860–1880 period. Note storm wind[ow]

Fig. 26—Presbyterian Church, South Salem, N. Y., founded 1752.

Fig. 27—Banksville, looking south. Photograph taken from New York side of boundary, with boundary marker in center (see Fig. 24).

Fig. 28—White-clapboarded house with central chimney, Redding, Conn. More elaborate trim than house in Figure 22.

347

FIG. 29—Main Street, New Canaan, Conn.

FIG. 30—Yorktown Heights station, on the Putnam Division of the New York Central Railroad. Compare with Figure 33.

FIG. 31—Merritt Parkway. Typical view in Norwalk, Conn., looking east. The dividing strip between eastbound and westbound traffic is safety feature characteristic of recent parkway design.

FIG. 32—Yorktown Heights. Postoffice and garage filling station, near station. Looking south.

FIG. 33—New Canaan station during commuting hours. Compare with Figure 30, taken at about the same time of day.

FIG. 34—Looking south on Route 124, Lewisboro, N. Y. Two-lane connecting concrete highway. Bouldery pasture reverting to red cedar. Lowlands under cultivation. Across valley, Poundridge Reservation.

349

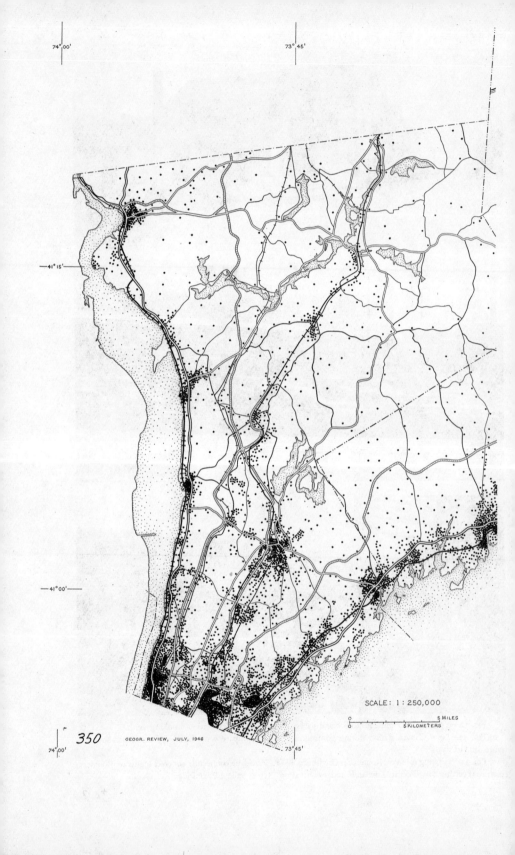

SCALE: 1 : 250,000

5 MILES

5 KILOMETERS

350   GEOGR. REVIEW, JULY, 1948

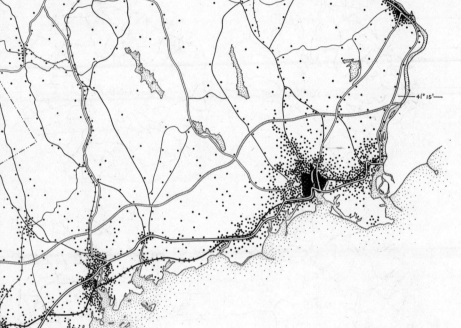

WESTCHESTER – FAIRFIELD
TRANSPORTATION AND POPULATION

Transportation

Four tracks	Two tracks	One track	
├┼┼┼┤	┤┼┤	┼┼┼┼	Passenger and freight railroad, electrified
├┼┼┼┤	┤┼┤	┼┼┼┼	Passenger and freight railroad, steam
├┼┼┤	┤┤	┼┼┼┼	Freight railroad, steam

Parkway (non-commercial passenger traffic)

Main highways and important
connecting roads (mixed traffic)

Population (1940 CENSUS)

Each dot represents 100 persons

Densely populated urban areas

TRANSPORTATION

Westchester County, N. Y., and Fairfield County, Conn., form one of three principal, and essentially rural, residential areas for those who work in New York City but "sleep" outside. Another is Long Island, to the east; and the third lies west of the Hudson River in New Jersey and in Rockland and Orange Counties in New York State. Rail intercommunication between the three is virtually impossible at present except by way of New York

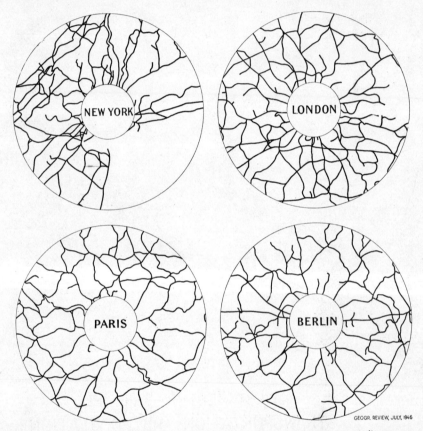

FIG. 36—Passenger and freight railroad network in the 15-to-55 mile zone surrounding metropolitan centers.

City, but bridges and ferries make it possible to go by automobile from one to another and avoid the heavy traffic in the city, though links are few and far apart.

This isolation of suburban areas is probably unique so far as the very large metropolitan centers of the world are concerned, and its effect on the pattern of transportation routes is well illustrated on maps showing the railroad network surrounding New York, as compared with London, Paris, and Berlin (Fig. 36). Even within the Westchester-Fairfield region connecting railroad lines are conspicuously lacking, and this situation, too, is somewhat distinctive (see, for instance, the comparison in Fig. 37). Two main railroad routes border and define the V within which the counties lie. The New York Central main line, or Hudson Division, which runs along the east bank of the Hudson River, connects New York City with Albany, the state capital, and provides through communication to Chicago, the West, and Canada. The main line of. the New York, New Haven and Hartford Railroad is the gateway into New York City for all of New England and also provides through communication from Canada.

White Plains and Danbury are the only sizable towns in the region that do not lie on either of the two main railroad lines. They are served by secondary through lines, the Har-

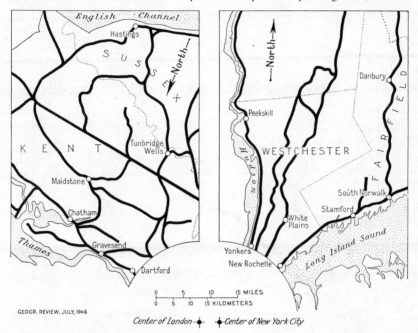

GEOGR. REVIEW, JULY, 1946

Center of London -◆- -◆-*Center of New York City*

FIG. 37—Comparison of passenger railroad facilities in Westchester and Fairfield Counties and similar facilities in Kent and Sussex, England.

lem Division of the New York Central and the Pittsfield line of the New Haven Railroad respectively. The Harlem Division is the oldest line in the region, having started operation in 1842.

Three purely local passenger lines also serve the two counties. The prosperous residential community of New Canaan is served by a branch line of the New Haven Railroad that connects with the main line at Stamford. Through businessmen's trains run to and from New York in the morning and evening, and frequent connections at Stamford are also provided. Another line is a short branch of the Harlem Division to Lake Mahopac, an old-established summer resort. The third line is the Putnam Division of the New York Central. This starts at Brewster, where it connects with the Harlem Division, and runs south between the Harlem and Hudson Divisions, to connect with the latter at High Bridge, on the Harlem River. It is single-track and does not boast through trains to Grand Central Station, the terminal for all the other lines.

353

The Putnam and Lake Mahopac lines are steam-operated; the New Canaan Branch is electrified. The Hudson Division is electrified to Croton-on-Hudson, the Harlem Division to White Plains, North Station, the New Haven main line to New Haven, and the Pittsfield line to Danbury.

Commuting traffic is heavy on the two main routes and on the Harlem Division (see Fig. 38 and Table I) and seems to be increasing in spite of bus and automobile competition.

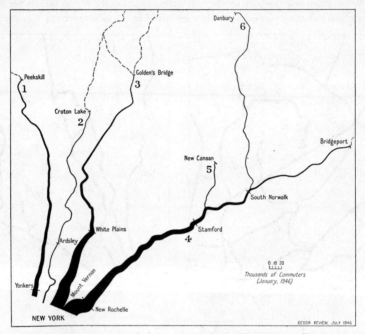

FIG. 38—Daily commuter flow into New York City. The thickness of line is cumulative. See Table on facing page.

The New Canaan Branch also has considerable commuting traffic, though many residents in the area prefer to drive to Stamford and take one of the more frequent express trains there. The Lake Mahopac branch caters mainly to summer visitors, being too far from New York to maintain year-round commuting traffic.

The Putnam Division, nicknamed the "Put" or "Putput," has a commuting traffic, but it is not comparable in magnitude with that of the main routes and the Harlem Division. Its infrequent and somewhat inconvenient service is largely the cause of a condition in the Westchester countryside comparable in many respects with one often commented on by visitors to New York City—the anomaly of poorly developed avenues paralleling adjacent prosperous and fashionable ones. Although the country through which the Putnam runs is in no way less picturesque or intrinsically less desirable as a residential area than that of the Harlem Division, it is still comparatively undeveloped. As a consequence, land values on the whole are lower than elsewhere for the same distances from New York. This rather curious situation is not likely to last, however, because of the enormous development of good highways throughout Westchester and Fairfield.

A tance in miles to Grand Central Station;   B Time in minutes to Grand Central Station;**
mber of train services to New York City per day (Monday to Friday);   D Number of commuters.***

NEW YORK CENTRAL RAILROAD

HUDSON DIVISION

Station	A	B	C	D
…ill	40.6	84	15	623
…ose	38.1	86	12	69
…rs	36.7	81	10	5
…ana	35.7	78	11	13
…n-on-Hudson	33.9	70	29	123
…on	32.7	63	35	489
…ng	30.2	59	33	763
…rough	28.7	56	25	120
…e Manor	25.8	52	26	181
…own	24.5	48	33	908
…ton	22.0	48	26	252
…y-on-Hudson	21.0	45	25	167
… Ferry	20.0	43	26	457
…gs-on-Hudson	18.7	40	26	771
…one	17.2	38	22	56
…ood	15.6	38	30	573
…rs	14.5	34	37	1301
…w	14.0	33	28	1001

PUTNAM DIVISION

Station	A	B	C	D
Croton Lake	38.8	90	10	5
Kitchawan	37.8	87	11	7
Millwood	35.7	82	11	10
Briarcliff	32.3	76	11	68
Graham	30.6	76	7	0
East View	27.1	69	9	0
Beaver Hill	25.1	66	1	0
Elmsford	24.8	60	11	56
Worthington	23.3	61	8	11
Woodlands	22.3	58	8	8
Ardsley	21.4	53	11	210
Chauncey	20.5	52	7	0
Mount Hope	19.7	51	9	64
Nepera Park	18.7	47	9	40
Gray Oaks	18.0	46	10	110
Nepperhan	17.3	44	9	91
Bryn Mawr	16.2	40	10	225
Dunwoodie	14.8	38	10	31
Lincoln	13.1	34	9	106

HARLEM DIVISION

Station	A	B	C	D
Golden's Bridge	43.5	87	17	44
Katonah	41.1	81	18	275
Bedford Hills	39.1	76	17	188
Mount Kisco	36.6	70	18	486
Chappaqua	32.4	65	17	624
Pleasantville	30.5	61	17	720
Thornwood	29.3	60	15	93
Hawthorne	28.3	56	15	253
Mt. Pleasant	27.2	54	6	3
Kensico Cemetery	26.3	52	6	3
Valhalla	25.4	50	15	201
N. White Plains	23.9	49	45	450
White Plains	22.4	43	46	4370
Hartsdale	20.6	46	29	1355
Scarsdale	19.0	43	30	3485
Crestwood	16.8	40	29	1287
Tuckahoe	16.0	38	28	1107
Bronxville	15.3	36	31	3379
Fleetwood	14.3	33	29	1751
Mount Vernon	13.2	30	50	1213

NEW YORK, NEW HAVEN, AND HARTFORD RAILROAD

NEW CANAAN BRANCH

Station	A	B	C	D
…Canaan	41.0	70	18	392
…dge Hill	38.8	67	18	13
…way	37.8	64	16	..
…dale Cemetery	37.0	59	5	..
…dale	36.7	61	18	51
…ook	35.3	58	18	..
…rd	33.1	..	..	..

DANBURY BRANCH

Station	A	B	C	D
Danbury	64.8	115	5	13
Bethel	61.9	109	5	19
Redding	58.6	103	3	1
Branchville	54.0	95	5	20
Georgetown	53.1	93	3	20
Cannondale	50.1	88	3	13
Wilton	48.6	84	5	64
South Wilton	46.2	..	..	..
Norwalk Mills	45.0	79	1	1
Wall Street	42.8	75	1	..
Norwalk	41.0	..	..	..

MAIN LINE

Station	A.	B	C	D
Bridgeport	55.6	91	39	483
Fairfield	50.6	86	10	64
Southport	48.9	82	9	62
Green's Farms	47.2	78	6	3
Westport	44.2	71	16	580
East Norwalk	42.1	71	4	·2
Norwalk	41.0	66	35	716
Rowayton	39.2	69	4	29
Darien	37.7	62	17	806
Noroton Heights	36.5	62	4	43
Glenbrook	35.2	59	2	162
Stamford	33.1	60	63	1792
Old Greenwich	31.3	58	28	231
Riverside	30.3	58	27	144
Cos Cob	29.6	56	27	150
Greenwich	28.1	50	33	920
Port Chester	25.7	47	49	1204
Rye	24.1	44	43	1073
Harrison	22.2	44	41	633
Mamaroneck	20.5	40	42	1279
Larchmont	18.7	36	44	3417
New Rochelle	16.6	33	48	4610
Pelham	15.2	32	41	2033
Columbus Ave.	14.5	29	42	1462
Mount Vernon	13.8	25	42	2277

his table has been compiled from figures obtained through the courtesy of the New York Central and the New York, ew Haven, and Hartford Railroads.
ean between fastest and slowest commuting trains.
e New York Central Railroad issues, in addition to regular commuting tickets, 26-round-trip tickets valid for three months. take into account this type of commuting travel, the figure in Column D is the number of regular commuting tickets d plus one-third of the number of the 26-round-trip tickets sold.

Two other lines, which before the days of good roads and automobiles used to have passenger service but now handle freight only, are the Ridgefield branch of the New Haven Railroad and the important through cross-country line of the New Haven between Danbury, Brewster, and the Poughkeepsie railroad bridge over the Hudson. The second line enables the heavy coal traffic originating in Pennsylvania and destined for New England to be routed so as to avoid New York City.

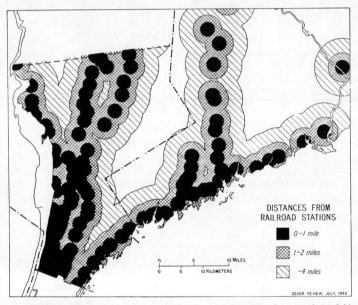

DISTANCES FROM
RAILROAD STATIONS

■ *0-1 mile*

▨ *1-2 miles*

◸ *-4 miles*

GEOGR. REVIEW, JULY, 1946

Fig. 39—Distances from passenger railroad stations in Westchester and Fairfield Counties. The areas four miles or more from railroad stations, especially in Fairfield County, are larger than they were two decades or so ago.

Other lines have been proposed, but most of them did not get beyond the planning stage, though a few were surveyed and graded before the projects were dropped. Two were actually constructed, and service on them was discontinued only recently—the electrified branch of the Putnam to Yonkers and the New York, Westchester and Boston Electric Railway. The latter, in spite of its name, never succeeded in pushing farther from New York City than White Plains, with a branch to Port Chester, on the New Haven main line. Its failure was due largely to poor terminal facilities on the Harlem River in New York. It is of interest, however, that in the not too distant past it was proposed to extend this line from White Plains to Danbury, an extension that would have passed through some of the areas for the suggested UN sites, not at present adequately served by railroads. Another proposal, as part of a scheme for an outer belt line around New York City, was the construction of a connecting line between the New Haven main line at Greenwich and the Hudson Division at Tarrytown, with a tunnel under the Hudson to connect with the New Jersey railroads. It is not beyond the realm of possibility that interest in the second of these proposals will revive when peacetime conditions finally return. In any event, should the

UN site be the North Greenwich–North Stamford or Ridgefield-Poundridge area, a suitable branch line would have to be built from either the Harlem Division or the main line of the New Haven.

On the other hand, if the Westchester-Amawalk area is chosen, the Putnam Division could be double-tracked and electrified as far north as desired, or a short connection might be constructed to the Harlem Division near Hawthorne, where the two lines come very close together. If the latter plan were adopted, electrification would be necessary only above North White Plains. It should be noted here that the principal reason for not giving the Putnam through connection to Grand Central Terminal is that the four-track approach into this terminal is already loaded to capacity during rush hours. However, this reason would probably not hold with respect to train service to and from the UN site, since the useful trains for visitors would be in the morning and early afternoon and the bulk of the return service in the afternoon and early evening—a flow in the opposite direction to that of the heavy commuting traffic.

New York City and vicinity is the pioneer region for the development of parkways; its system "may well be a nation's pride," as an English visitor once put it. The distinguishing characteristic of a parkway is that land in considerable width on each side is owned by the state or county. Thus there is no private building development alongside the road or access from private property to it; furthermore, such ownership permits extensive and beautiful landscaping. Other roads cross over or burrow under the parkway; hence they do not impede flow of traffic. These roads are connected with the parkway by "clover leaves" or other ingenious loop and spur roads that eliminate most crossovers at grade. Traffic on a parkway is fast and uninterrupted and is restricted to light private passenger cars.

In the Westchester-Fairfield region the two main radial parkways from New York City are the Saw Mill River–Taconic State system, which runs north and passes close to the Westchester-Amawalk area, and the Hutchinson River–Merritt system, which runs northeast and passes close to the North Greenwich–North Stamford and Ridgefield-Poundridge areas. Other parkways lead into, or form cross-country connecting links with, the two main arteries, and more are proposed. Of special interest in connection with the UN site location are the authorized northerly branch extension of the Saw Mill River Parkway close to the Ridgefield-Poundridge area and the proposed cross-country parkway between the Merritt and Taconic State Parkways, which would pass through or close to both the Ridgefield-Poundridge and the Westchester-Amawalk areas. Excellent connections exist from the present parkway system into New York City, to New Jersey and the Newark Airport via the George Washington Bridge over the Hudson, and to Long Island and the La Guardia Field and Idlewild Airport via the Whitestone Bridge, and they will undoubtedly be made even better in the near future.

Technically a parkway is a class of expressway, and an expressway is defined as any motor-vehicle roadway designed to carry large volumes of through traffic with speed and safety. Another type of expressway now coming into existence in the Westchester-Fairfield region is the freeway. A freeway is open to all kinds of traffic, but, as with a parkway, right of access from abutting property is denied.

In addition to the parkways and freeways, Westchester and Fairfield Counties abound in first-class through highways and connecting roads, many of which have concrete surfaces and are sufficiently well constructed to carry high-speed traffic. Even the secondary roads are usually well surfaced and well maintained.

On most of the main roads other than the parkways bus lines run. Some of these give through service to New York, but most of them are local, converging on such centers as Yonkers, Peekskill, Mount Vernon, White Plains, and Danbury, and on the towns along Long Island Sound.

In spite of the excellent road system, most of the commuter traffic into New York City is by railroad, even when the commuter's residence is as much as ten miles away from the nearest railroad station (see Fig. 39). In normal peacetime many commuters in the Westchester-Fairfield region own two cars, one for family use, the other to be driven to the station in the morning, left parked all day, and driven home at night. This calls for extensive parking facilities at the stations, and the scene in the morning when commuters are arriving, consistently reaching the station with few seconds to spare, is a lively one.

There are many reasons why the average commuter prefers to travel by railroad into the city. The most important are the difficulty of parking in the city, the fatigue of driving, and the opportunity that the train ride affords to read one's newspaper or otherwise relax before and after a day's work.

THE QUESTION OF AN AIRPORT [1]

Throughout the early discussions of the UN site there has been a general feeling that either an airport should be included in the original layout or provision for a future airport should be made in the initial planning. The function and type of the airport obviously will depend largely on the size and ultimate function of the UN establishment. Will it begin and remain a meeting place of nations, a small community built up much like a college campus, with meeting hall, library, research center, and the like? Or will it grow into a true world capital, with executive offices capable of supervising all international relationships? The latter would mean a city the size of Washington and a major airport able to accommodate the largest transoceanic planes of the future. However, the present planning problem so far as the Westchester-Fairfield region is concerned would seem to hinge on a community of perhaps some 5000 permanent employees and their families and the required subsidiary services—a population of about 50,000. Such a community would hardly require a major airport; indeed, the expense of maintenance alone would be out of proportion to the value.[2]

A secondary airport for shuttle service to New York City's Idlewild or some other major airport in the vicinity would involve considerably less expense, though it would still require more than a million dollars. Grading for airport facilities might be rather costly because of the uneven terrain and the prevalence of rock outcrops. On the other hand, there already are several good airports within the two counties. Westchester County Airport, at Purchase, near White Plains, is a Class 4 airport; Bridgeport, Conn., also has a Class 4 airport (runways 4500-5500 feet long). Danbury, Conn., has a Class 3 airport (runways 3500-4500 feet). An express superhighway could make one or more of these ports accessible to the UN site by a motor trip of half an hour at the most.

---

[1] The writer acknowledges the cooperation of Mr. C. McKim Norton of the Regional Plan Association, New York, and Mr. James C. Buckley of the Port of New York Authority, New York, in the compilation of these data.

[2] A single runway with taxiways for a future heavy plane has been estimated at $7,000,000 ("Military Airfields—A Symposium," *Trans. Amer. Soc. of Civil Engineers,* No. 110, New York, 1945, p. 751).

However, certain considerations make desirable an airport within the jurisdiction of the UN itself—World War II is not so far behind that the difficulties of air travel from such a place as Madrid, for instance, have been forgotten. To satisfy these considerations should not be too formidable a task. A take-off and landing strip could be coordinated with a highway at the site; the requirements would be a width of 500 feet and a length of 2000–4000 feet laid out so that planes would not be subjected to strong prevailing cross winds and would be protected from the interference of surrounding structures. Planes of foreign representatives could be housed near by, and arrangements could perhaps be made that their movements in and out of the site would not be subject to restrictions other than the usual safety requirements. The French are said to have built and operated strips of this kind for many years in connection with the colonial air services in Africa.

Whatever plans for an airport or landing strips may be made at this time, consideration must be given to the great uncertainty regarding the types of planes that may be operating in the future. In a recent study of this situation one engineer suggested future lowering of runway length as catapults, tricycle landing gear for cross-wind landings, and better air and ground brakes are developed. Another engineer suggested that the great planes of the future may be like ocean liners—not expected to land under their own power but brought to the ground position by auxiliaries comparable to tugs. The tendency will probably be toward smaller airports rather than larger ones.

POPULATION

The original inhabitants of the Westchester-Fairfield region were Indians belonging to the Wappinger division of the Mohicans. It was from these Indians that the Dutch, spreading northward from New Amsterdam, and the English, filtering into the Sound area from their colonies in Massachusetts, bought land for settlement in the middle years of the seventeenth century. Just how numerous the Indians were at the time of European penetration is uncertain, but there is no doubt as to the rapidity with which they disappeared thereafter. A letter written from Rye in 1708, a little less than half a century after the settlement of the village, states that "we have now in all this parish twenty families [of Indians], whereas not many years ago there were several hundred," and a later correspondent, in 1720, indicates that the Indian population had then been reduced to four or five families.[3] This situation may be taken as typical of most of the region.

Early colonial enumerations, predating the first federal census, show a correspondingly rapid increase in the white population. In Westchester County, for example, the 25 years between 1698 and 1723 witnessed a fourfold increase, from 1063 to 4409 inhabitants, and by the time of the provincial census of 1756 the second figure had tripled, reaching 13,247.[4] A census of Connecticut taken in the same year (1756) lists the population of Fairfield County as 20,560.[5]

By 1790, the year of the first federal census, the division of both counties into "towns"

---

[3] F. Shonnard and W. W. Spooner: History of Westchester County, New York, from Its Earliest Settlement to the Year 1900, New York, 1900.

[4] A Century of Population Growth: From the First Census of the United States to the Twelfth, 1790–1900, U. S. Bureau of the Census, Washington, 1909.

[5] Evarts B. Greene and Virginia D. Harrington: American Population before the Federal Census of 1790, New York, 1932.

was fairly well defined, and the statistics were returned by minor civil divisions. In general, the towns with the largest acreage had the largest population, a fact that reflects the dispersed agricultural character of settlement, without reference to the urban center. The towns of Bedford and North Castle, for instance, each had almost as many inhabitants as the smaller towns of Westchester and Yonkers together, though situated at a much greater distance from New York City.

A steady but less spectacular population growth characterized the first years of the nineteenth century. Emigration to the West, particularly heavy from Connecticut, accounted for the slowing up of the rate of increase. By 1840 the population of the two counties stood at 48,686 for Westchester and 49,917 for Fairfield and was still fairly evenly dispersed. With the construction of railroads in the forties and fifties, however, a considerable change, both in the growth and in the concentration of population, became evident. Within ten years, from 1845 to 1855, the population of Westchester County jumped more than 68 per cent, the increase being greatest in the towns within a relatively short and inexpensive railroad journey of New York. Figures for Fairfield County for the same period are not available, but it is likely that a similar trend occurred, though possibly not to such a marked degree. In short, the era of suburbanism had begun. The statistics of the eighth census, 1860, show the Westchester towns of Yonkers, Cortlandt, and Morrisania leading in population, all having made substantial gains over the figures of the previous census (1850); outlying towns, however, such as Bedford, North Castle, and Poundridge, had remained virtually static or, as in the case of Poundridge, had fallen off slightly. The same situation prevailed in Fairfield County. The towns on the railroad along the Sound had increased rapidly: Bridgeport had almost doubled between 1850 and 1860, and Norwalk, Stamford, and Greenwich had increased markedly. The interior towns of Ridgefield and New Fairfield, on the other hand, each showed a slight decrease.[6]

After 1900, as motor transport developed and highways were improved, and particularly with the construction of parkways after 1920, the suburban character of the two counties was intensified.[7] Another wave of population growth appeared, the crest of which was reached in the decade 1920-1930. In Fairfield County during this period, for example, the town of Greenwich showed a percentage of gain in population of 49.7, and Stamford of 41.7,[8] though it should perhaps be remarked that the greater part of the increase was concentrated in the urban areas of the towns and was to some extent due to the flourishing industrial activity growing up concurrently with the cities. In the following decade, the percentage of gain was much less, largely as a result of the general economic depression and the correlative curtailment of building. For Norwalk, Stamford, and Greenwich, the percentage of gain dropped to 7.2, 7.8, and 10.6 respectively. For Westchester County as a whole, the figure was 10 per cent, as compared with 51.2 per cent for the previous decade;[9]

[6] J. D. B. DeBow: Statistical View of the United States . . ., Being a Compendium of the Seventh Census . . , Washington, 1854; Eighth Census of the United States, 1860, Washington, 1864.

[7] For comparison of changes in population density in the significant years 1850 ,1900, 1920, see maps in "Regional Survey of New York and Its Environs," Vol. 2, Population, Land Values and Government, Regional Plan of New York and Its Environs, 1929. pp. 68–70.

[8] Population Growth in Connecticut. Statistical Bull. 2, Conn. State Dept. of Education, Division of Research and Planning, Hartford, 1941. Map following p. 7.

[9] W. A. Anderson. Population Trends in New York State, 1900 to 1940. Cornell Univ. Agri. Exper. Sta., Bull. 786, Ithaca, 1942.

for the New York metropolitan region as defined by the Regional Plan Association, the figure was 7 per cent as compared with 28 per cent for the 1920–1930 period.[10]

A study by the Westchester County Planning Survey[11] finds that following the depression of 1837–1840 the rate of population increase in the county fell off 13.7 per cent; during the decade of 1870–1880, which included the panic of 1873, the rate of increase dropped 18.9 per cent, and so on. There is also evident a drop in the rate of population increase, as might be expected, after periods of spectacular growth. From an analysis of the trends, the Westchester County Planning Survey estimates the average falling off of population increase following periods of depressions and spectacular growth to be 22.95 per cent.

With respect to the composition of the present-day population, statistics of the 1940 census indicate that 18.2 per cent of the total population of Westchester County is foreign-born; in Fairfield County the figure is 20 per cent. Numerically, the greater part of the foreign-born population live in the urban areas, but proportionally, there is a surprisingly small difference between urban and rural areas in the percentage of the population that is foreign-born.[12] In Westchester, for example, the foreign-born in the town of Yonkers constitute 20 per cent of the population; in Mount Vernon, 18 per cent; and in New Rochelle, 18 per cent; in rural towns such as Bedford, North Castle, and Lewisboro, the percentage of foreign-born is nearly as high—20, 19, and 13 respectively.[13] The same situation obtains in Fairfield. In the town of Bridgeport the proportion of foreign-born is 23 per cent; in Norwalk, 17 per cent; and in Stamford and Greenwich, 21 per cent; whereas the proportion in the rural towns is again very much the same—Ridgefield, 22 per cent; Fairfield, 19 per cent; and New Canaan, 16 per cent. In both counties, Italians form the largest single group of foreign-born, and there are relatively large German, Polish, and Irish representations.

The 1940 population of the two counties stood at 573,558 for Westchester and 418,384 for Fairfield; the distribution is shown in Figure 35.[14] In Westchester, the concentration of population at the south end of the county, the section nearest New York, is evident, and the sparsity of persons in the rural towns of the northeastern part of the county is likewise apparent. In Fairfield, the outstanding features in the distribution are the agglomerations of dots representing the cities along the Sound and the light scattering of dots in the rural towns and the inland portions of the urban towns.

In "Population Changes and Their Significance in New York and Its Environs," the Regional Plan Association estimated that the population of Westchester County would

---

[10] Population Changes and Their Significance in New York and Its Environs. *Regional Plan Bull. No. 55.* July 14, 1941.

[11] The Westchester County Planning Survey, A Report of Progress From June 1, 1934, to April 15, 1936. Westchester County Emergency Work Bureau, White Plains, 1936.

[12] For more detailed discussion of this point and illustrative maps, see: Nathan L. Whetten and Henry W. Riecken, Jr.: The Foreign Born Population of Connecticut, 1940, *Storrs Agric. Exper. Sta. Bull. 246,* 1943.

[13] Percentages derived from figures in the Sixteenth Census of the United States, 1940. Population, Vol. 2, Characteristics of the Population. Table 28, p. 98, Pt. 5; Table 28, p. 836, Pt. 1.

[14] Sources used in the compilation of the population dots: Map of Population Distribution, 1940 U. S. Census, Westchester County, N. Y., 1 : 72,000, Westchester County Planning Commission, 1943; [Map of] Population Distribution, 1940, 1 : 62,500, Greenwich Town Plan Commission, 1944; General Highway Map of Fairfield County, Connecticut (various scales), Connecticut State Highway Department, 1938, which locates and classifies buildings. Location of dots was based on the assumption of 4 persons per dwelling unit and modified, where necessary, to agree with the 1940 census.

reach 690,000 in 1950, 800,000 in 1960, and 850,000 in 1970—an increase for the thirty-year period of 48 per cent. For that part of Fairfield County included within the New York metropolitan region, the estimates show a probable increase to 552,000 in 1970, or a 49 per cent gain for the period. As for the New York region as a whole, the population is expected to increase from the 12,308,350 of 1940 to more than 13½ million by 1950, more than 14½ million by 1960, and 15,190,000 by 1970.

CLIMATE

The Westchester-Fairfield region is characterized by an abundant precipitation well distributed through the year (see Table II). Thunderstorms, which may occur at any time in the year, are particularly frequent in the summer and account for the high percentage of rainfall in July and August. The hottest months are July and August, the coldest January and February; temperatures decrease gradually inland from the coast. Average maximum temperatures for July, the hottest month, range from 82.9° at Bridgeport and Bedford Hills to 81.7° at Carmel, average minimum temperatures for February from 21.3° at Bridgeport to 17.6° at Bedford Hills and 16.4° at Carmel.[15] Temperatures as high as 102° have been officially recorded in the region, but these are rare. Subzero weather is not uncommon from November through February.

The climatic differences between New York City and upper Westchester and Fairfield, only 30–50 miles away, are striking. They are well illustrated by average maximum and minimum temperature variations (Table III). Below-zero absolute minimums are recorded for three months in New York, four in Bedford Hills, and five in Carmel. For the three subzero months recorded for New York, December, January, and February, the temperatures are −13°, −6°, and −7°; for Bedford Hills for the same months, −17°, −17°, and −15°; and for Carmel, −23°, −20°, and −23°. The climatic differences between New York and its northern suburbs are even more strikingly illustrated by the average dates of the first killing frost of autumn and the last of spring: November 6 and April 11 in New York, October 13 and May 1 in Bedford Hills, and October 14 and April 28 in Carmel. This represents an average growing season of 209 days for New York, but of only 165 to 169 days for the inland stations.

Although such climatic differences between New York and the adjoining region to the north and northeast are representative, they by no means tell the whole story of local climates in the two counties. Temperature inversion in this hilly country is a common feature. In certain places valley and swamp conditions brew summer fogs, whereas their neighbors may remain fog-free. These marked variations over short distances have an important bearing on selection of house sites and undoubtedly will be borne in mind in connection with any studies for future airport development. At the present time there are not nearly enough Weather Bureau stations in the Greater New York area to permit a microclimatic study. Perhaps it is not too optimistic, however, to dream of such a large carefully planned study for the metropolitan and outlying areas, carried out with the cooperation of the United States Weather Bureau and an ample number of volunteer weather observers.

---

[15] Unless otherwise indicated, data are from "Climatic Summary of the United States," U. S. Weather Bureau, 1934, Section 83, Eastern New York; Section 86, Massachusetts, Rhode Island, and Connecticut.

TABLE II—AVERAGE MONTHLY AND ANNUAL PRECIPITATION

In inches

STATION[*]	JAN.	FEB.	MAR.	APR.	MAY	JUNE	JULY	AUG.	SEPT.	OCT.	NOV.	DEC.	YEAR
Carmel	3.70	3.74	4.11	3.74	3.89	3.76	4.94	5.00	4.17	3.85	3.68	3.74	48.32
Bedford Hills	3.55	3.47	3.46	3.48	3.98	3.67	4.63	4.66	3.81	3.68	3.40	3.56	45.35
Bridgeport	3.80	3.89	4.07	3.91	3.74	3.24	4.34	4.51	3.52	3.89	3.58	4.04	46.53
New York	3.52	3.71	3.60	3.33	3.17	3.33	4.35	4.39	3.38	3.53	3.12	3.36	42.88

TABLE III—AVERAGE MONTHLY TEMPERATURES—MAXIMUM, MEAN, AND MINIMUM

In °F.

STATION	JAN.	FEB.	MAR.	APR.	MAY	JUNE	JULY	AUG.	SEPT.	OCT.	NOV.	DEC.
Carmel	32.0	32.9	43.4	55.8	68.1	76.7	81.7	79.2	72.8	60.8	47.6	35.5
	24.5	24.7	34.6	46.4	57.7	66.9	71.4	69.2	63.0	51.1	39.6	28.7
	16.4	16.4	26.1	36.7	47.3	56.1	61.3	59.2	53.1	42.0	32.0	21.3
Bedford Hills	37.0	36.5	47.8	58.6	70.1	78.2	82.9	80.7	74.5	64.1	51.3	40.0
	27.9	27.1	37.5	47.5	58.6	66.9	72.2	70.1	63.7	53.1	41.7	31.2
	18.6	17.6	27.7	36.2	47.1	55.6	61.6	59.4	53.2	42.5	32.2	22.4
Bridgeport	37.2	36.9	47.0	57.9	69.4	77.7	82.9	80.9	75.3	64.5	51.6	39.7
	29.1	29.1	37.8	47.8	58.5	66.8	72.8	70.7	65.2	54.3	43.1	32.1
	21.0	21.3	28.6	37.7	47.6	55.9	62.7	60.5	55.1	44.1	34.6	24.5
New York	37.8	38.2	45.9	56.9	68.2	77.0	81.8	79.6	73.9	63.2	51.2	41.0
	30.9	31.0	38.5	48.8	59.8	68.8	73.9	72.4	66.5	55.9	44.2	34.3
	24.1	24.0	31.1	41.0	51.7	61.0	66.6	65.5	59.6	48.8	37.9	28.3

[*] Altitude of stations in feet: Carmel, 500; Bedford Hills, 425; Bridgeport, 140; New York, 314.

Over much of the year northwesterly winds prevail, but in the two warmest months southwesterly winds become dominant. Eastward from New York these southerly winds have a tendency to be felt earlier and for a longer time. At Bridgeport, in easternmost Fairfield, southwest winds predominate from May into October. The sea breeze is a usual and pleasant feature of the Connecticut coast during the warmest months of the year, but its influence is ordinarily limited to a narrow belt, 10 miles from the ocean, though occasionally it may reach 30 or 40 miles inland.[16]

Relative humidity is lowest in spring, 52 to 56 per cent, and is generally highest in early fall.[17] Near the coast, the humidity is related closely to the moist southerly winds prevailing in the summer.

The number of cloudy days is relatively low in southwestern Connecticut. Norwalk, in the least cloudy part, has 183 clear days annually,[18] New York about 108.[19]

WATER SUPPLY AND SEWAGE DISPOSAL[20]

The Westchester-Fairfield region consists mainly of crystalline rocks overlain by glacial deposits that, in Fairfield County especially, approach the structure of hardpan.[21] There are

[16] P. E. Church: A Geographical Study of New England Temperatures, *Geogr. Rev.*, Vol. 26. 1936, pp. 283–292; reference on p. 286.

[17] J. M. Kirk: The Weather and Climate of Connecticut, *Connecticut State Geol. and Nat. Hist. Survey Bull. No. 61*, 1939, p. 23.

[18] W. B. Liverance, Jr., and C. F. Brooks: Cloudiness and Sunshine in New England, *Bull. Amer. Meteorol. Soc.*, Vol. 24, 1943, pp. 263–274; reference on p. 273.

[19] R. DeC. Ward, C. F. Brooks, and A. J. Connor: The Climates of North America (Handbuch der Klimatologie, Vol. 2, Part J), Berlin, 1936, p. 245.

[20] Recommendations in line with the following have already been made by Malcolm Pirnie, consulting engineer, in reports dated January 21, 1946, covering two of the more northern sites under consideration for UN headquarters.

[21] H. S. Palmer: Ground Water in the Norwalk, Suffield, and Glastonbury Areas, Connecticut, *U. S. Geol. Survey Water-Supply Paper 470*, 1920; also H. E. Gregory and A. J. Ellis: Ground Water in the Hartford, Stamford, Salisbury, Willimantic and Saybrook Areas, Connecticut, *ibid., 374*, 1916.

numerous wells down to the crystalline rock, and in some places into this rock, but the amounts pumped are relatively small. A community of 50,000 people would require about 5,000,000 gallons of water daily. It is not likely that this amount could be developed from ground-water supplies. Also, in spite of the fact that in many locations impounding reservoirs could be constructed on one or another of numerous streams, the removal of such

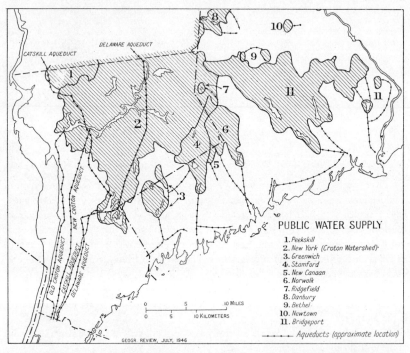

PUBLIC WATER SUPPLY

1. *Peekskill*
2. *New York (Croton Watershed)*
3. *Greenwich*
4. *Stamford*
5. *New Canaan*
6. *Norwalk*
7. *Ridgefield*
8. *Danbury*
9. *Bethel*
10. *Newtown*
11. *Bridgeport*

━━━ *Aqueducts (approximate location)*

GEOGR. REVIEW, JULY, 1946

FIG. 40—Principal public water supply watersheds and aqueducts '(including important supply mains in Connecticut) in Westchester and Fairfield Counties. Water is furnished by both municipal water departments and private water companies. (Based on manuscript map by Malcolm Pirnie and on a map, "Public Water Supplies of Connecticut," May, 1943, furnished through Warren J. Scott, Director of the Bureau of Sanitary Engineering, Department of Health, Hartford, Conn.)

surface waters would be likely to diminish existing supplies to existing reservoirs, which properly belong to the cities that built them.

Water supply would probably be most advantageously obtained from existing reservoirs of New York City's Croton system or from reservoirs of various Connecticut towns according to the location chosen. Fairly long pipe lines might be needed to meet requirements of particular sites, but the cost would be small as compared with the magnitude of other necessary expenditures.

Water from the existing reservoirs of the Croton system flows into New York City's water supply without filtration, but it has the advantage of fairly long storage before reaching the distribution systems of the city. However, if the UN should purchase its water supply from one of the Croton lakes, filtration would probably be necessary.

Any United Nations headquarters site in Westchester or Fairfield County would drain either into tributaries of the Croton Reservoir, which is part of New York City's water supply, or into streams draining into Long Island Sound that are being used for municipal water supply by various communities in Connecticut. Hence it would not be possible to discharge sewage, even after fairly complete treatment had been provided, into the Croton watershed or the watersheds of reservoirs belonging to Connecticut towns.

For a site not too far from the Hudson River, sewage might be pumped over the intervening ridge into the Hudson River basin, after primary treatment and the further treatment necessary to conform to the general program for preventing pollution of the Hudson River. For sites in the eastern part of the region, sewage might be pumped to a treatment plant or plants discharging into tributaries of the Norwalk River, which is not used for water supply. Complete treatment would probably be necessary to protect riparian owners. The terrain is so rugged in these areas, with outcrops of rock in many places, that the construction of sewage collection systems and pumping stations might entail considerable expenditure, though the cost would not be great in proportion to the total amount that would be required for establishing a headquarters.

The map (Fig. 40) shows the extensive area in northern Westchester occupied by New York City's Croton system watershed, and also watersheds now in use for Peekskill and the larger towns of Fairfield.

Relatively steep slopes and numerous brooks make drainage simple to lay out for almost any site that might be chosen.

LAND USE

Within the New York commuter area (see Fig. 41) as defined by the Regional Plan Association, 608 square miles or about one-fifth of the total land area is built up with commercial and residential structures, 207 square miles are devoted to parks, water-supply properties, and public institutions, and 83 square miles to semipublic uses—cemeteries, institutions, and other properties not likely to become available for development. After deduction of steep slopes, lakes, and swampland from remaining land "available," there are still nearly 1500 square miles suitable for expansion (see Fig. 42).[22]

In Westchester and the part of Fairfield within a 55-mile radius of downtown New York, total land area is slightly more than 600 square miles. In 1940, only 60.6 square miles were devoted to close residential development and 2 square miles to the principal industrial areas. Most of this, as Figure 43 shows, lay along Long Island Sound and in southern Westchester. There were 62.8 square miles devoted to parks, parkways, water supply, and other public purposes, and 36.2 to semipublic uses.[23] In Westchester County alone, 40 private golf clubs accounted (1936) for some 9 square miles of land use.[24]

Most of the remaining land, constituting 73 per cent of the area, is used in part for farms and for residential estates. According to the 1940 census, in Westchester 69.1 square miles were devoted to farming, and in Fairfield 213 square miles, including areas beyond the "commuter area."

---

[22] Land Suitable for Urban Expansion in the New York Metropolitan Region, *Regional Plan Assn. Bull. 66*, 1945, pp. 8–9.

[23] Urban Expansion: Fifteen Years of Development in the New York Region, *Regional Plan Assn. Bull. 63*, 1944, Table II (p. 5.)

[24] The Westchester County Planning Survey: A Report of Progress from June 1, 1934 to April 15, 1936, Westchester County Emergency Work Bureau, White Plains, 1936, p. 10.

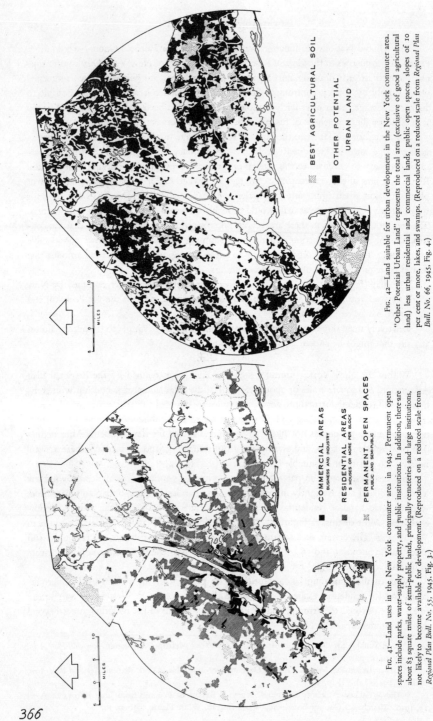

BEST AGRICULTURAL SOIL

OTHER POTENTIAL
URBAN LAND

FIG. 42—Land suitable for urban development in the New York commuter area. "Other Potential Urban Land" represents the total area (exclusive of good agricultural land) less urban residential and commercial lands, public open spaces, slopes of 10 per cent or more, lakes, and swamps. (Reproduced on a reduced scale from *Regional Plan Bull. No. 66*, 1945, Fig. 4.)

COMMERCIAL AREAS
BUSINESS AND INDUSTRY

RESIDENTIAL AREAS
5 HOUSES OR MORE PER BLOCK

PERMANENT OPEN SPACES
PUBLIC AND SEMI-PUBLIC

FIG. 41—Land uses in the New York commuter area in 1945. Permanent open spaces include parks, water-supply property, and public institutions. In addition, there are about 83 square miles of semi-public lands, principally cemeteries and large institutions, not likely to become available for development. (Reproduced on a reduced scale from *Regional Plan Bull. No. 55*, 1945, Fig. 3.)

FARMING AND PART-TIME FARMING[25]

Westchester County is forty-seventh in area of the 62 counties of New York State. It is fifty-fourth in number of farms, reporting 518 in the 1940 census; of the counties outside New York City, only Hamilton, Putnam, and Rockland reported fewer farms. Of the land area of the county of some 278,400 acres, 44,255 acres were in farms, an increase of 3222 acres over the farm acreage reported in 1930. Of this acreage, 13,530 acres were reported as used for crops in 1939, an increase of 2097 acres as compared with 1929. Of the farms reported, 132 were less than 10 acres, 49 were about the average size for the county, 85.4 acres, 140 were 100 acres or more, and 13 were 500 acres or more. In total value of farm products the county ranked forty-ninth in the state in 1939: $2,092,052 in a state total of $273,175,-038. This was an increase of $641,816 as compared with 1929, whereas for the whole state there was a decrease of $111,017,371. Of the 518 farms, only 9 were reported as yielding no farm produce in 1939. The products of greatest sales value were cultivated crops; the total of $1,136,059 was a marked increase over the total of only $149,318 in 1929. The largest item, $973,574, came from the sale of horticultural specialties, i.e. nursery products. Second in sales value were livestock and livestock products, totaling $809,737, which was, however, a considerable decrease from the total of $1,103,903 in 1929. Dairy products brought $504,479, and poultry and poultry products $218,315.

Of the 514 farms for which the census enumerators were able to obtain figures on production for 1939, 85 were reported as yielding produce valued at less than $250, as compared with only 15 in 1929. On 162 farms the produce was valued at $250 to $999, on 90 at $1000 to $2499, on 87 at $2500 to $5999, on 43 at $6000 to $9999, and on 30 at $10,000 to $19,999; on 17 the value amounted to $20,000 or more.

Fairfield County is fourth in area of the eight counties of Connecticut. It is fifth in number of farms, reporting 2772 in the 1940 census; Middlesex, Tolland, and Windham Counties reported fewer farms. Of the land area of the county of some 405,120 acres, 136,-422 acres were in farms, a decrease of 5982 acres from the farm acreage reported in 1930. Of this acreage, 36,716 acres were reported as used for crops in 1939, a decrease of 5215 acres as compared with 1929. Of the farms reported, 756 were less than 10 acres, 647 were about the average size for the county, 49.2 acres, 382 were 100 acres or more, and 13 were 500 acres or more. In total value of farm products the county ranked fifth in the state in 1939: $4,358,650 in a state total of $47,841,567. It may be worth noting that even in the agricultural state of Ohio in only 19 of its 88 counties was this figure exceeded in 1939, and to any appreciable degree in only 11. There was a decrease in total value of farm products of $215,952 as compared with 1929, but this is small in relation to a decrease of $5,167,045 for the whole state. Only 122 farms were reported as yielding no farm produce in 1939. Livestock products were of greatest sales value, $2,405,109, of which $1,675,380 came from dairy products, and $713,940 from poultry and poultry products. The total value of culti-

---

[25] For a detailed description of the agricultural value of Westchester soils see Cornelius Van Duyne and J. H. Bromley: Soil Survey of the White Plains Area, New York, *U. S. Dept. of Agric., Field Operations of the Bur. of Soils, 1919 (21st Rept.)*, 1925, pp. 563–606 (see also the accompanying soil map, Pl. 13, 1 : 62,500). In Fairfield County, detailed soils studies have been made only of the town of Wilton, but land-type maps indicating the general nature of the topography and the soils have been prepared for the entire county by the Connecticut Agricultural Experiment Station at New Haven (M. F. Morgan: The Soil Characteristics of Connecticut Land Types, *Connecticut Agric. Exper. Sta. Bull. 423*, 1939, Fig. 3 [p. 20] and maps 18–22).

SCALE : 1 : 250,000

WESTCHESTER - FAIRFIELD
LAND USE

Industrial

Commercial

Close residential

Permanent open area (parks, parkways, public water supply)

Golf course in use

Airport

Woodland and scrub

Lake and reservoir

41° 15'

73° 30'

369

vated crops sold or traded in 1939, including fruits, was $1,308,017, a marked increase over the total of $602,134 for 1929. Of this amount, horticultural specialties contributed $804,906.

Of the 2762 farms for which the census enumerators were able to obtain figures on production for 1939, 1159 were reported as yielding produce valued at less than $250, as compared with 162 in 1929. On 784 farms the produce was valued at $250 to $999, on 382 at $1000 to $2499, on 274 at $2500 to $5999, on 100 at $6000 to $9999, and on 43 at $10,000 to $19,999; on 20 the value amounted to $20,000 or more.

In spite of their relatively large agricultural production, farming in both counties is largely part-time, though to a smaller extent in Westchester than in Fairfield. Part-time farming has been a characteristic of agriculture in Connecticut since the early days when manufacturing was a matter of farmers with special skills producing in their homes or in small shops on their farms the articles required by the community. Many of the present industrial establishments of the state had their origin in such home industries. As the industries grew, they drew more and more on the farm population for both skilled and unskilled labor, and the farm population consequently became progressively less dependent on the farms for subsistence. Practically the whole state was thus affected; for factories and manufacturing shops made their appearance in almost every town and village. A period followed, beginning about 1870, when, as a result of the concentration of manufacturing at points on railroads or on tidewater, many village and small rural factories disappeared. Labor, too, became concentrated at these points; and not only did part-time farming decline, but the back-country farmers found that they were losing their local markets, largely because they were unable to move their produce as cheaply as farm products from the West could be brought in by rail and ships. However, with the development of motor transportation and surfaced highways the tide began to turn, and by 1920 farmers in almost every part of the state could once again work in the towns and villages and live on their farms. Townsmen, too, found that they could live in rural areas and continue to work in town. This new phase is considered to have got under way about 1917. Since 1924 it has been developing at a fairly constant rate, though there have been some periods of slackening.[26] Meanwhile the movement of New Yorkers into the more easily accessible parts of both Fairfield and Westchester Counties, as either full-time residents or summer commuters, has added its quota to the total of part-time farmers.

In Fairfield County, of heads of households on the 2772 farms in the 1940 census, 951, or 34.3 per cent, reported as having worked off their farms for some part of their income in 1939. Of these, 66 worked fewer than 50 days, 47 worked 50–99 days, and 838 worked 100 days or more; 881, or 31.8 per cent of the total, reported nonfarm work averaging 247 days each. In Westchester County, of 518 such heads of households, 108, or 20.8 per cent, reported as having worked off their farms for some part of their income. Of these, 11 worked fewer than 50 days, 9 worked 50–99 days, and 88 worked 100 days or more; 96, or 18.5 per cent of the total, reported nonfarm work averaging 226 days each.

INDUSTRY

The importance of manufacturing in both Fairfield and Westchester Counties is indicated by the 1940 census report, in which, in a list of 451 counties in the United States with

---

[26] See I. G. Davis and L. A. Salter, Jr.: Part-Time Farming in Connecticut: A Preliminary Survey, *Storrs Agric. Exper. Sta. Bull. 201, 1935.*

2500 wage earners or more employed in manufacturing establishments in 1939, Fairfield County ranks twenty-fourth and Westchester sixty-ninth. Fairfield is exceeded in Connecticut only by New Haven and Hartford Counties; Westchester ranks ninth in New York State.

In 1939, the last prewar year, out of a total of 2589 manufacturing and mechanical plants in the state of Connecticut, Fairfield County had 773, or 29.9 per cent, employing an average of 72,280 wage earners during the fiscal year 1938–1939, or 25.9 per cent of the average for the whole state. In the same year Westchester County had 523 plants, employing an average of 21,342 wage earners. However, since Fairfield's principal manufacturing centers, except Danbury, are along the coast and Westchester's are concentrated in the southern part of the county and in the cities and villages along the Hudson River, the greater part of both counties is essentially rural, with small, scattered industries in a country setting. Reminiscent of the early nineteenth century, when nearly every village in Connecticut had at least one manufacturing shop, is the fact that in 1939 even the rural towns of Bethel, New Canaan, and Newtown had a total of 28 plants, employing 933 persons. Bethel is a satellite of hat-making Danbury, and 10 of its 13 plants were devoted to hatmaking or the manufacture of various supplies for the hat industry; but the diversity of manufacturing in the other rural towns of the county is indicated by Newtown's 6 plants, with a total of 221 employees, whose products were paper boxes, fire hose, job-printing products, electrical molding insulation, millwork, and packaged teas and spices. Figures on industry in the rural villages of Westchester County in 1939 were not available for the compilation of this note, but reports for 1944 show, out of a total of 550 plants employing 53,324 persons, 95 plants, employing 12,397, scattered through the county in 32 villages, their products including all the major industry groups except automobiles and their equipment and rubber goods.

It is to be noted that, in spite of their wide distribution in the rural villages of both counties, none of the manufacturing plants listed in the directories for the two counties[27] are located within the originally inspected UN sites and that only the North Greenwich–North Stamford area is near enough to large industrial centers to be expected to furnish any considerable number of industrial employees.

In both counties manufacturing in the principal industrial centers is of almost endless variety; only Danbury, 46 of whose 72 plants in 1939 were devoted to the manufacture of hats or various hatmaker's supplies, is dominated by a single industry. In the chief manufacturing district of Fairfield County, the Bridgeport area, comprising Bridgeport, Shelton, Stratford, and Fairfield, the 9 plants with more than 1000 employees each in 1939 produced brass and copper materials and articles, electrical equipment and supplies, firearms and ammunition, cutlery, boring mills and turret lathes, silks and velvets, sewing machines and appliances, and airplanes. In Yonkers, Westchester's chief manufacturing center, with 15,-

---

[27] Directory of Connecticut Manufacturing and Mechanical Establishments, 1939, 1945, State of Connecticut, Dept. of Labor and Factory Inspection. The 1939 and 1945 directories were furnished, respectively, by Mr. Samuel Simonovitz, research associate, State Development Commission, and Mr. John C. Ready, deputy commissioner, Department of Labor. The Manufacturers Association of Connecticut also supplied a copy of the 1945 directory and other information.

Manufacturing Establishments & Employment by Major Industry Groups, Cities & Villages of Westchester County, 1944 (typewritten summary, supplied by Mr. William E. Zimmerman, New York State Department of Commerce). Also "The Master Table" for the New York metropolitan area, New York State Dept. of Commerce, [1944].

630 wage earners in manufacturing in 1944, the 3 plants in this employee category manu-factured insulated wire and cables, elevators and escalators, and carpets and rugs, and all the other major industry groups were represented except automobiles and equipment, leather and leather products, and rubber products.

The contribution by the two counties of materials for the prosecution of the war is indicated by the fact that in Fairfield County by 1945 the total number of plants had risen to 1082 and the number of employees for the year to 137,276, or nearly double the number in 1939, and in Westchester County by 1944 the number of plants had risen to 550 and the number of employees to 53,324, or more than double the number in 1939.

EDUCATION[28]

The insignificance of the county as an administrative unit in Connecticut as compared with New York is particularly well revealed by a comparison of the public-school systems of Fairfield and Westchester Counties. In Connecticut, as in all the other New England states, the town was originally a community, its center the town village. This organization still persists, even though many of the original town villages have become cities of consid-erable size. In Westchester County, on the other hand, as in all the other counties of New York State, the town as a community with a village center was the exception rather than the rule. Settlement was by families on dispersed farms rather than by communities; town boundaries were laid down without regard to village locations; and villages, to preserve the common interests of their populations, early sought separation from the rural popula-tion of the towns in which they were located, by means of incorporation.[29] The town and the incorporated village are by no means insignificant so far as local government is con-cerned, but many of the functions still retained by the New England town have in New York State become county functions.

For example, in Fairfield County maintenance of the public schools is a town function, and the school budget is recommended by the town Board of Finance and voted at the annual town meeting. In 13 of the most populous towns, supervision of all the public schools of the town, even where the original town village has grown into a large industrial center, is under a town superintendent of schools; the 10 rural towns are grouped together for supervision by state supervisors. In Westchester, on the other hand, there are 5 city schools and 16 village schools, all offering both elementary and high-school education, and each under its own superintendent, completely independent of town and county as to both super-vision and the voting and expenditure of school funds. The rural areas of Westchester are divided into two Supervisory Districts, each with its superintendent. The Supervisory Dis-tricts contain a certain number of consolidated or centralized districts. Fourteen of these maintain each a complete elementary and high school; the fine buildings housing these schools are an outstanding feature of the Westchester landscape. The remaining such dis-

[28] Information on the rural schools of Westchester County was supplied by Dr. Robert E. Bell and Mr. Harold E. Hollister, superintendents, respectively, of the First and Second School Districts of Westchester County. Mr. H. Morton Jeffords, superintendent of schools of the Town of Fairfield, supplied similar information for Fairfield County. Lists of schools with their registered attendance were also furnished by the Commissioners of Education of the two states.

[29] See C. R. Wasson and Dwight Sanderson: Relation of Community Areas to Town Government in the State of New York, *Cornell Univ. Agric. Exper. Sta. Bull. 555*, 1933, pp. 3-5.

tricts maintain either schools covering only the elementary and junior or middle high-school grades or schools covering only the elementary grades. The one-room, one-teacher school has almost disappeared in Westchester County. A few districts contract with their neighbors for the education of their children.

In Fairfield County also, the one-room school has almost disappeared. Fairfield County has continued its traditional town organization in the matter of school consolidation. When all the common-school districts in a town have been eliminated, the town boundary becomes the district boundary. Where a town has a high school in a city or village, pupils from the rural areas attend it on the same basis as the residents of the city or village. Eight of the towns of Fairfield County have no high school, and the town Board of Education arranges with a high school in a neighboring town for the accommodation of pupils and provides transportation and tuition for them, receiving a certain percentage of reimbursement from the state. In both counties bus service is provided for pupils living beyond reasonable walking distance of the schools they attend. In Westchester, bus service in each district, as well as all other school expenses, is financed by taxes levied directly for the purpose on the real property of the district. In Fairfield, as has been said, the schools do not have fiscal independence; school funds are only estimated by the Boards of Education.

Both counties have also numerous private schools (including parochial). Fairfield County, in addition to a large number of private elementary schools and kindergartens, has 26 schools offering high-school or college-preparatory education, as compared with 16 public schools in this category; Westchester has 23 private schools offering high-school or college-preparatory education, as compared with 36 public schools in this category. The attendance at these private secondary schools is small, however, as compared with that at the public high schools in both counties.

Institutions in the two counties offering education beyond the secondary school are the Sarah Lawrence College (for women only) at Bronxville, N. Y., the Danbury State Teachers College at Danbury, Conn., and two junior colleges in Westchester County—the Briarcliff Junior College at Briarcliff Manor and the Concordia Collegiate Institute at Bronxville. All of these are small: Sarah Lawrence had an enrollment for the year 1945–1946 of 301; the Danbury State Teachers College, 157; and the two junior colleges, a total of 271.

AN APPROACH TOWARD A RATIONAL
CLASSIFICATION OF CLIMATE

C. W. THORNTHWAITE

[With separate map, Pl. I, facing p. 94]

THE direction that the modern study of climate has taken has been dictated largely by the development of meteorological instruments, the establishment of meteorological observatories, and the collection of weather data. The catalogue of climatic elements consists of those that are customarily measured and usually includes temperature, precipitation, atmospheric humidity and pressure, and wind velocity. Increasingly, climatic studies have tended to become statistical analyses of the observations of individual elements. Because of this, climatology has been regarded in some quarters as nothing more than statistical meteorology.

THE ROLE OF EVAPORATION AND TRANSPIRATION

But the sum of the climatic elements that have been under observation does not equal climate. One element conspicuously missing from the list is evaporation. The combined evaporation from the soil surface and transpiration from plants, called "evapotranspiration," represents the transport of water from the earth back to the atmosphere, the reverse of precipitation. The rain gauge measures precipitation within acceptable limits of accuracy. We know reasonably well how rainfall varies from one place to another over the inhabited parts of the earth and also how it varies through the year and from one year to another. On the other hand, no instrument has yet been perfected to measure the water movement from the earth to the atmosphere, and consequently we know next to nothing about the distribution of evapotranspiration in space or time.

We cannot tell whether a climate is moist or dry by knowing the precipitation alone. We must know whether precipitation is greater or less than the water needed for evaporation and transpiration. Precipitation and evapotranspiration are equally important climatic factors. Since precipitation and evapotranspiration are due to different meteorological causes, they are not often the same either in amount or in distribution through the year. In some places more rain falls month after month than evaporates or than the vegetation uses. The surplus moves through the ground and over it to form

---

➤ DR. THORNTHWAITE, consulting climatologist, has spent the growing seasons of 1946 and 1947 in experiments "fitting crops to weather" (see p. 4).

streams and rivers and flows back to the sea. In other places, month after month, there is less water in the soil than the vegetation would use if it were available. There is no excess of precipitation and no runoff, except locally where the soil is impervious and cannot absorb the rain on the rare occasions when it falls. Consequently, there are no permanent rivers, and there is no drainage to the ocean. In still other areas the rainfall is deficient in one season and excessive in another, so that a period of drought is followed by one with runoff. The march of precipitation through the year almost never coincides with the changing demands for water.

Where precipitation is in excess of water need, the climate is moist. Where the water deficiency is large in comparison with the need, the climate is dry. Where precipitation and water need are equal or nearly equal, the climate is neither humid nor arid.

POTENTIAL EVAPOTRANSPIRATION AS A CLIMATIC FACTOR

The vegetation of the desert is sparse and uses little water because water is deficient. If more water were available, the vegetation would be less sparse and would use more water. There is a distinction, then, between the amount of water that actually transpires and evaporates and that which would transpire and evaporate if it were available. When water supply increases, as in a desert irrigation project, evapotranspiration rises to a maximum that depends only on the climate. This we may call "potential evapotranspiration," as distinct from actual evapotranspiration.

We know very little about either actual evapotranspiration or potential evapotranspiration. We shall be able to measure actual evapotranspiration as soon as existing methods are perfected. But to determine potential evapotranspiration is very difficult. Since it does not represent actual transfer of water to the atmosphere but rather the transfer that would be possible under ideal conditions of soil moisture and vegetation, it usually cannot be measured directly but must be determined experimentally. Like actual evapotranspiration, potential evapotranspiration is clearly a climatic element of great importance. By comparing it with precipitation we can obtain a rational definition of the moisture factor.

Precipitation is a strictly physical process, which meteorologists have investigated in much detail. Evapotranspiration is likewise a physical process, yet since it is subject to biological control, it must be studied by methods unfamiliar to the meteorologist. Information concerning evapotranspiration has come chiefly not from the meteorologist but from the biologist. For this reason it is necessary to make use of the literature and apply the methods of plant physiology. Nevertheless, evapotranspiration represents the return flow of water to the atmosphere and is thus an important meteorological process.

The only method so far developed that measures the actual evapotranspiration from a field or any other natural surface without disturbing the vegetation cover in any way is the so-called "vapor transfer" method. Water vapor when it enters the atmosphere from the ground or from plants is carried upward by the moving air. It is carried upward in small eddies or bodies of air that are replaced by drier eddies from above. Although we cannot see water vapor, we can measure it in the air. We find that when evaporation is taking place the amount of moisture is greatest in the air near the ground and decreases with distance above it. If we determine the rate at which the air near the ground is mixing with that above it and at the same time measure the difference in water-vapor content at the two levels, we can determine both the rate and the amount of evapotranspiration. Furthermore, we can determine equally well the amount of water condensed as dew.[1]

This method is not easy either to understand or to use. It is hard to use because it requires physical measurements more precise than are usually made. Furthermore, the coefficient of turbulent transfer of air is not a constant. It varies from time to time and from place to place. It even varies with height at a given time and place. In spite of these difficulties the method can be perfected and will answer many important questions for climatology and biology.[2]

Scientists have tried in various ways to determine the amount of water used by plants. One of the earliest attempts was to remove leaves or branches from a plant, let them dry for a brief time, and weigh them to see how much water they had lost. Another method is to place plants in sealed containers and measure the moisture that accumulates in the confined air. Experimenters have grown thousands of individual plants in pots, weighing them periodically to determine the evapotranspiration losses. These methods are highly artificial, and generalization from them sometimes gives fantastic

---

[1] See the note by John Leighly: New Occasions and New Duties for Climatology, *Geogr. Rev.*, Vol. 29, 1939, pp. 682–683.

[2] C. W. Thornthwaite and Benjamin Holzman: Measurement of Evaporation from Land and Water Surfaces, *U. S. Dept. of Agric. Tech. Bull. No. 817*, 1942; C. W. Thornthwaite: The Measurement of Evaporation and Transpiration from Natural Surfaces, *Proc. Hydrology Conference, State College, Pa., June 30–July 2, 1941 (Pennsylvania State College School of Engineering Tech. Bull. No. 27)*, 1942, pp. 185–197; idem: Atmospheric Turbulence and the Measurement of Evaporation, *Proc. Second Hydraulics Conference, June 1–4, 1942 (Univ. of Iowa Studies in Engineering, Bull. 27)*, Iowa City, 1943, pp. 280–288.

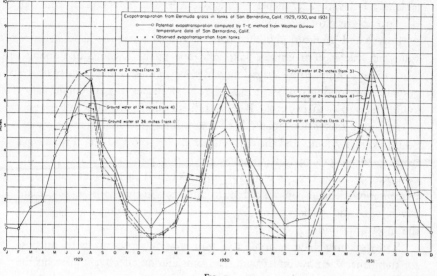

FIG. I

results. For example, in a German study transpiration from an oak wood-land was computed as being more than eight times the actual rainfall.[3]

There are other, less artificial methods of determining both water use and water need. In some irrigated areas rainfall, water applied by irrigation, and water outflow are all measured. The fraction of the water applied that does not run off is the evapotranspiration. Irrigation engineers have determined the evapotranspiration from plants growing in sunken tanks filled to ground level with soil in which water tables are maintained at different predetermined depths beneath the soil surface.[4] Lee found that the annual use of water by salt grass at Independence, Calif., ranged from 13.4 inches with the water table at 5 feet below the ground surface to 48.8 inches with it at 1.5 feet below. Debler reported a range in annual use of water by salt grass at Los Griegos, N. Mex., from 10.1 inches with the water table at 37 inches to 48.4 inches with it at 5 inches. Young and Blaney observed a range at Santa Ana, Calif., from 13.4 inches with free water 4 feet below the surface to 42.8 inches with it 1 foot below. Comparable figures for Bermuda grass at San Bernardino, Calif., were 28.19 inches with the water

---

[3] B. G. Ivanov: Evaporation under Natural Conditions: Methods of Study and Results Attained (Hydrometeorological Publications), Moscow, 1939. (Translated from the Russian by Headquarters, Army Air Forces Weather Division.)

[4] A. A. Young and H. F. Blaney: Use of Water by Native Vegetation, *California Dept. of Public Works, Division of Water Resources Bull. No. 50,* 1942.

table at 3 feet and 34.37 inches with it at 2 feet. The observations from San Bernardino are shown in Figure 1.

Lowry and Johnson[5] published data on annual water use in 12 irrigated valleys in the western United States and one in the Dominican Republic. Since water is supplied by irrigation, water use in these valleys approximates potential evapotranspiration. It ranges from 18 inches in a mountain valley in Colorado to 58 inches in the Barahona district in the Dominican Republic.

Although the various methods of determining potential evapotranspiration have many faults and the determinations are scattered and few, we get from them an idea of how much water is transpired and evaporated and how much would be if it were available. We find that the rate of evapotranspiration depends on four things: climate, soil-moisture supply, plant cover, and land management. Of these the first two prove to be by far the most important.

Some scientists have believed that transpiration serves no useful purpose for the plant. We now understand that transpiration effectively prevents the plant surfaces that are exposed to sunlight from being overheated. Most plants require sunlight for growth. The energy of the sun combines water and carbon dioxide in the leaves into food, which is later carried to all parts of the plant and used in growth. This process, which is called "photosynthesis," is most efficient when the leaf temperatures are between 85° and 90° F. But a leaf exposed to direct sunlight would quickly become much hotter if the energy of the sun were not disposed of in some way. The surface of dry ground may reach a temperature of 200° F.; temperatures higher than 160° F. have been measured one-fourth of an inch below the ground surface. The plant is admirably designed to dissipate heat, the leaves being like the fins of a radiator, and some of the excess heat is conducted into the adjacent air and carried away in turbulence bodies. In this way the air is heated. But some of the excess heat energy is utilized in transpiration, to change water from a liquid into a vapor. Most of the heat of evaporation must come from the plant. Thus, the greater the intensity of sunshine, the greater will be the tendency to overheating, and the larger will be the transpiration of a plant exposed to it, if water is available for the process. Transpiration is a heat regulator, preventing temperature excesses in both plant and air. Dew formation at night is the reverse of this process and tends to prevent low temperature extremes, since the heat released goes

---

[5] R. L. Lowry, Jr., and A. F. Johnson: Consumptive Use of Water for Agriculture, *Trans. Amer. Soc. of Civil Engineers*, Vol. 107, 1942, pp. 1243–1266 (Paper No. 2158); discussion, pp. 1267–1302.

mainly to the plant. Both transpiration and growth are related to temperature in the same way.

Atmospheric elements whose influence on transpiration has been studied include solar radiation, air temperature, wind, and atmospheric humidity. These factors are all interrelated. Although solar radiation is the basic factor, there seems to be a closer parallelism between air temperature and transpiration. The temperature of the transpiring part is most closely related to the rate of transpiration.

Transpiration and growth are both affected in the same way by variations in soil moisture. Both increase with increase of available water in the root zone of the soil, to an optimum. Above the optimum both are less, presumably because of poor aeration of the soil, which results in a lack of oxygen to supply the roots and an excess of carbon dioxide.[6] On the other hand, as water in the soil increases above the optimum for growth, direct evaporation from the soil surface also continues to increase.

We do not yet know how much we may increase or decrease transpiration by varying the type of plants or by modifying the plant cover. Since transpiration regulates leaf temperature, and since most plants reach their optimum growth at about the same temperature, we probably cannot change it very much except by reducing the density of the plant cover and thus wasting a part of the solar energy. If all the vegetation is removed from a field, there will be no transpiration. But as long as the root zone of the soil is well supplied with water, the amount of water transpired from a completely covered area will depend more on the amount of solar energy received by the surface and the resultant temperature than on the kind of plants.

Since potential evapotranspiration is an important climatic element, we need to know its distribution over the earth and how it varies through the year and from one year to another. Actual determinations are so few that it would be impossible to make a map of any area by means of them. At the present time the only alternative is to discover a relation between potential evapotranspiration and other climatic factors for which there are abundant data.

TEMPERATURE AND GROWTH

Many studies have been made of temperature and growth. Some investigators have measured the elongation of shoots, stems, and roots grow-

---

[6] A. J. Loustalot: Influence of Soil-Moisture Conditions on Apparent Photosynthesis and Transpiration of Pecan Leaves, *Journ. of Agric. Research*, Vol. 71, 1945, pp. 519–532; G. W. Schneider and N. F. Childers: Influence of Soil Moisture on Photosynthesis, Respiration and Transpiration of Apple Leaves, *Plant Physiology*, Vol. 16, 1941, pp. 565–583.

ing under various controlled temperatures. Others have determined increase in width of leaves and increase in dry weight of the plant. Rate of development of various insects under controlled temperature has been determined. There is always an optimum temperature for growth, a temperature at which the growth rate is highest. At lower or higher temperatures growth is slower. The temperature at which growth is most rapid seems to vary somewhat with the material under study and with the length of exposure but is always near 30° C. (86° F.). In his investigation of maize seedlings Lehenbauer[7] obtained most rapid growth for a 3-hour period at 29° C. and for 9–12 hours at 32° C. He says that for periods of 3 hours or longer the greatest rates of growth occur within the temperature range 29° to 32°. Wadley[8] found that the rate of development of the green bug was most rapid at 30° C. Similarly, there are minimum and maximum temperatures beyond which growth does not occur. These limits vary likewise, but the minimum is near 0° C. and the maximum somewhere above 40° C.

About half a century ago Van't Hoff[9] propounded the principle that the velocity of a chemical reaction doubles or trebles with each rise in temperature of 10° C. This is an exponential law of the form

$$v = ca^t, \tag{1}$$

in which a has the value 1.0718 when velocity, v, doubles with a 10° rise in temperature, and the value 1.1161 when v trebles. The Van't Hoff law has been applied by biologists to physiological processes. The customary procedure is to determine temperature coefficients from actual growth measurements. The temperature coefficient is the quotient of two growth rates that are separated from each other by a 10° interval of temperature, and by the Van't Hoff rule it is expected to range between 2 and 3. In reality, the coefficient varies much more widely. It exceeds 10.0 in the temperature range between 0° C. and 10° C. and falls steadily to values less than 1.0, above the optimum temperature at which growth and temperature are inversely related.

Lehenbauer[10] published the following table of temperature coefficients for 12-hour growth rates of shoots of maize seedlings, for various 10° ranges of temperature:

---

[7] P. A. Lehenbauer: Growth of Maize Seedlings in Relation to Temperature, *Physiological Researches,* Vol. 1, 1914, pp. 247–288.

[8] F. M. Wadley: Development-Temperature Correlation in the Green Bug, Toxoptera Graminum, *Journ. of Agric. Research,* Vol. 53, 1936, pp. 259–266.

[9] J. H. van't Hoff: Études de dynamique chimique, Amsterdam, 1884.

[10] *Op. cit.,* p. 281.

Temperature, °C.	12-22	13-23	15-25	18-28	20-30	21-31	22-32	25-35	32-42	33-43
Growth rate, 0.01 mm.	9-59	10-64	20-75	28-98	45-108	53-109	59-111	75-86	111-11	101-6
Coefficient	9.56	6.40	3.75	3.50	2.40	2.06	1.88	1.15	0.09	0.06

The temperature coefficient must have values of ∞ at the temperature minimum, 1.0 at the temperature optimum, and 0 at the temperature maximum. Only in the temperature range 20° to 30°, where the temperature coefficient is between 2 and 3, is the Van't Hoff law valid. Since the temperature coefficient drops continuously, the coefficient a in equation (1) must also drop. The Van't Hoff $a = 1.0718$ is valid at only one point on the curve and is no more significant than any other value of a. The fact that a drops steadily and falls below 1.00 when the optimum temperature is reached is far more significant than any average value of a (or of the temperature coefficient).

There is clearly some growth-inhibiting factor that is directly proportionate to temperature. It is only because of the accident that the temperatures which plants ordinarily experience under natural conditions are below the optimum, that growth is popularly assumed to vary directly with temperature. At temperatures above 30° C. the growth-inhibiting factor becomes greater than the growth-stimulating factor and the growth rate falls with rising temperature. Since the exponential equation $v = ca^t$ requires a continuously increasing growth rate with rising temperature, it does not truly express the relation between temperature and growth.

What the growth-inhibiting factor is, is uncertain. It may reasonably be the operation of water deficiency in the plant tissue. The amount of water in a plant is a balance between that absorbed by the roots and that transpired from the leaves. As the transpiration rate rises with increasing temperature, it will presently exceed the rate of water absorption. Then a suction pressure, or tension, develops in the plant, acting as a brake on transpiration and on growth. The moisture balance in the plant is upset, transpiration is reduced, and growth is retarded. A more satisfactory equation of growth, therefore, is the following:

$$v = a \frac{bce^{ct}}{(e^{ct} + b)^2},$$ (2)

in which a, b, and c are constants and e is the base of the Napierian system of logarithms. In this equation the numerator represents the growth-stimulating factor and the denominator the growth-inhibiting factor. The optimum temperature for growth is where numerator and denominator are equal.

When we fit the equation to a series of Lehenbauer's observations on the growth of maize seedlings, we have the following coefficients: $a = 1764.9$,

$b = 1118.8$, $c = .24$. The equation gives v as a percentage of the optimum growth rate. The Lehenbauer data and the growth curve derived from this equation are plotted in Figure 2. Some of the computed values of v are as follows:

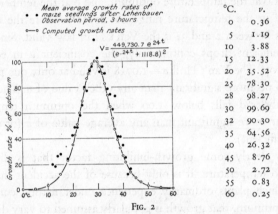

	°C.	v.
Mean average growth rates of maize seedlings after Lehenbauer Observation period, 3 hours	0	0.36
Computed growth rates	5	1.19
	10	3.88
$V = \dfrac{449{,}730.7\, e^{24t}}{(e^{.24t} + 1118.8)^2}$	15	12.33
	20	35.52
	25	78.30
	28	98.27
	30	99.69
	32	90.30
	35	64.56
	40	26.32
	45	8.76
	50	2.72
	55	0.83
	60	0.25

FIG. 2

DETERMINATION OF POTENTIAL EVAPOTRANSPIRATION

Unfortunately, there are no comparable controlled experiments on the relation of transpiration to temperature. The most reliable measurements of transpiration and evaporation together are for long periods of time. When only monthly or annual totals of evapotranspiration are available, the temperature relation cannot be determined precisely.

The determinations have shown that potential evapotranspiration is high in the southern part of the United States and low in the northern part and that it varies greatly from winter to summer. From observations like those of Figure 1, it has been found that when adjustments are made for variation in day length, there is a close relation between mean monthly temperature and potential evapotranspiration. Study of all available data has resulted in a formula that permits the computation of potential evapotranspiration of a place if its latitude is known and if temperature records are available. The formula is given, and its use described, in the appendix.

Figure 3 shows the distribution of average annual potential evapotranspiration in the United States. It is based on normals of some 3500 Weather Bureau stations, revised to 1930. The average annual water need in the United States ranges from less than 18 inches in the high mountains of the West to more than 60 inches in three isolated areas in the deserts of Arizona and southern California. It is less than 21 inches along the Canadian border of the eastern United States and more than 48 inches in Florida and southern

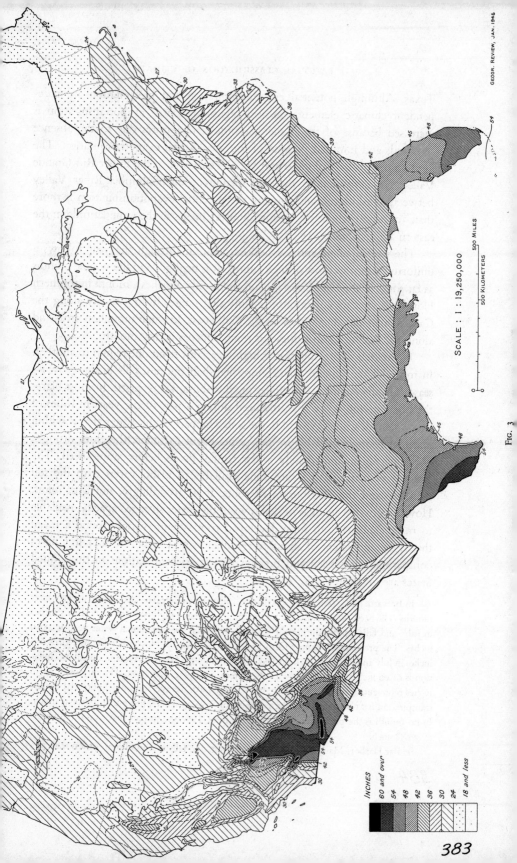

SCALE : 1 : 19,250,000

500 MILES

500 KILOMETERS

INCHES

60 and over
54
48
42
36
30
24
18 and less

FIG. 3

Texas. Although potential evapotranspiration and precipitation are independent climatic elements, in arid regions potential evapotranspiration is increased because of the higher daytime temperatures due to the absence of clouds and rain and because of the small actual evapotranspiration. The high values in the Colorado and Gila Deserts and in the lower Rio Grande Valley are examples. In the arid section of the Columbia River Valley between Washington and Oregon the potential evapotranspiration is more than 30 inches, whereas it is only about 21 inches in the same latitude in the eastern United States.

The march of potential evapotranspiration through the year follows a uniform pattern in most of the country. It is negligible in the winter months as far south as the Gulf Coastal Plain and is only 2 inches a month in southern Florida. It rises to a maximum in July that ranges from 5 inches along the Canadian border to 7 inches on the Gulf coast. In some mountain areas and along the Pacific coast it does not reach 5 inches in any month.

The march of precipitation is highly variable from one region to another. In much of the United States more than half the rain falls in the growing season. In the Pacific Coast States the distribution is reversed. In most places the precipitation is less than the need during a part of the year. In times of excess rainfall water is stored in the soil. The part of this water that is within reach of roots is used before the plants begin to suffer; therefore drought does not begin immediately when rainfall drops below water need. The amount of water in the root zone available to plants varies with the soil structure and the distribution of roots. It is, accordingly, not a constant. However, except in areas of shallow soil the water storage capacity available to mature plants with fully developed root systems varies around a mean that is the equivalent of about 10 centimeters or 4 inches of rainfall. Curves comparing water need and precipitation at selected stations in the United States are given in Figure 4.

In Brevard, N. C. (Fig. 4-A), less than half an inch of water is needed in each of the winter months. The need rises rapidly during the spring, reaches a high point of more than 5 inches in July, and falls rapidly during the autumn. The total average annual water need is 28.50 inches. The precipitation ranges from less than 3½ inches in November to more than 6½ inches in July and is greater than the need in every month. The total average annual precipitation is 61.06 inches, more than twice the potential evapotranspiration. The surplus of 32.56 inches represents runoff. In Salisbury, N. Y. (Fig. 4-B), the average annual potential evapotranspiration is 21.81 inches and the precipitation is 48.39 inches, more than twice as much. In no month is the precipitation less than the need. Here the surplus that runs off amounts to 26.58 inches.

In Bar Harbor, Maine (Fig. 4-C), the precipitation falls to a minimum of less than 3½

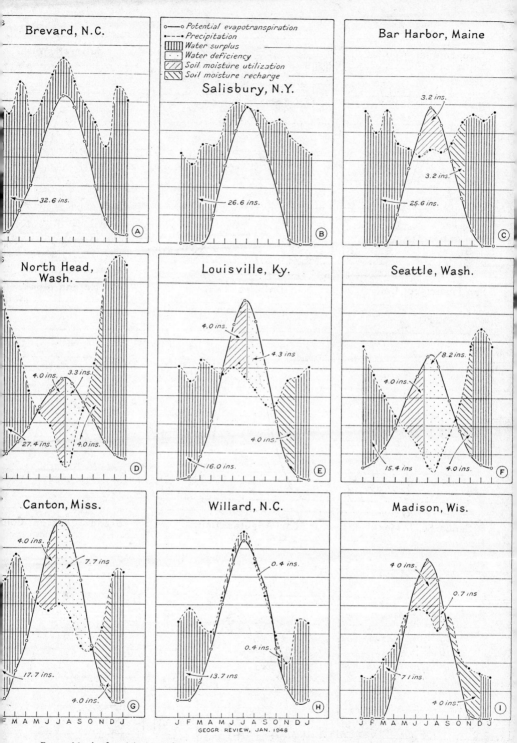

FIG. 4—March of precipitation and potential evapotranspiration at selected stations in the United States.

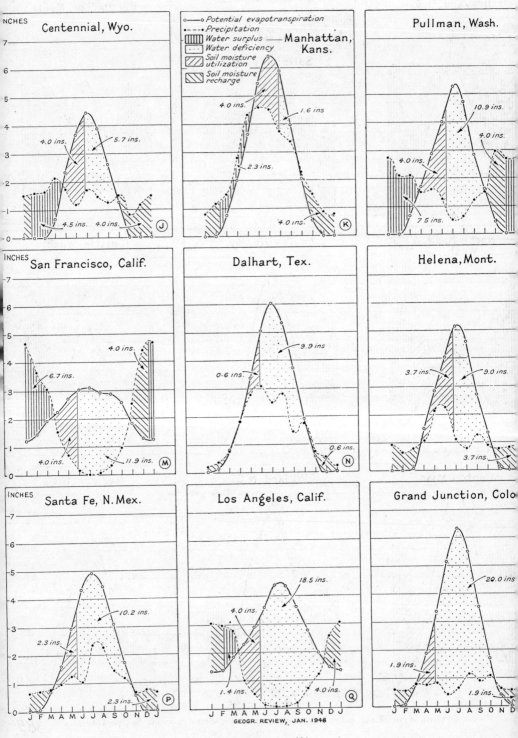

FIG. 4 (cont'd.)

GEOGR. REVIEW, JAN. 1948

inches in each of the 3 summer months, at exactly the time when potential evapotranspiration rises above 4 inches. Current rainfall is less than need, but the difference is made up from water in storage in the soil. In North Head, Wash. (Fig. 4-D), the precipitation exhibits marked seasonal variation: it is more than 7 inches a month in November, December, and January and less than 1 inch in July and August. Although water need is not large in any month, the July maximum being only 3.6 inches, it is in excess of rainfall during 5 months, from May through September. There is too much rain in winter and too little in summer. In late September, as the days grow cooler and shorter, water need falls below precipitation. For a while the rainfall not immediately needed goes to replace stored soil moisture that has been used up. From then on, the surplus water is lost so far as plant growth is concerned. It raises ground-water levels and produces surface and subsurface runoff. But it is of no benefit to plants and adds nothing to atmospheric moisture. In spring, as the days lengthen and become warmer, plant growth accelerates, and both transpiration and evaporation increase rapidly. By midspring water need exceeds precipitation. Thereafter, until midsummer, the excess demands for water are satisfied from the soil-moisture reserves. When these reserves are exhausted, the vegetation must rely solely on current rainfall. And current rainfall is not enough. Water use falls below water need; the plants suffer, and growth is retarded.

In Louisville, Ky. (Fig. 4-E), rainfall is fairly uniform through the year—between 3.5 and 4 inches a month except in autumn, when it falls below 3 inches. Since potential evapotranspiration is not uniform, however, there is a surplus of water in winter and a deficiency in summer, just as in North Head (Fig. 4-D) and Seattle (Fig. 4-F).

Although annual precipitation in Canton, Miss. (Fig. 4-G), is nearly 50 inches and summer rainfall averages 3.75 inches, the summer potential evapotranspiration is so large that there is a water deficiency of nearly 8.0 inches, almost the same as in Seattle.

In some places monthly precipitation and water need are nearly equal. For example, in Manhattan, Kans. (Fig. 4-K), winter rainfall is only a little greater than potential evapotranspiration and summer rainfall is only a little less. Water surplus and water deficiency are both small. In Madison, Wis. (Fig. 4-I), there is a maximum of rainfall in summer, but even so rainfall does not equal need; there is a small water deficiency in summer and a considerable water surplus in winter and spring. In Willard, N. C. (Fig. 4-H), potential evapotranspiration and precipitation are nearly the same in all the growing-season months. Rainfall is much greater than need in winter, however, and there is a water surplus of nearly 14 inches. In Dalhart, Tex. (Fig. 4-N), on the other hand, rainfall is equal to water need in winter but falls far short in summer, and there is a water deficiency of 10 inches.

In Grand Junction, Colo. (Fig. 4-R), rainfall is slight throughout the year. Water supply satisfies less than one-third of water need, and deficiency is very large. The climate is arid.

The curves of San Francisco, Calif. (Fig. 4-M), and Centennial, Wyo. (Fig. 4-J), show that in both places precipitation fails about equally to provide the water needed in June, July, and August. Water deficiencies, in inches, for June, July, and August are as follows: San Francisco 2.87, 3.07, 2.87; Centennial 2.48, 2.75, 2.44. But there is a vast difference in the relative aridity of the two places. Whereas July rainfall in Centennial provides about 1.5 inches of a needed 4.5 inches, in San Francisco there is no rain at all in July. In one place the water deficiency of July amounts to 62 per cent of the need, in the other to 100 per cent. The aridity of a place in a given period of time depends not on the numerical amount of the water deficiency but rather on the relation of this deficiency to the water need.

TABLE I—COMPARATIVE MOISTURE DATA OF SEATTLE, WASH., AND MANHATTAN, KANS.

In centimeters

ITEM	J	F	M	A	M	J	J	A	S	O	N	D	
					Seattle, Wash.								
Potential evap.	1.3	1.8	3.1	4.9	7.6	9.6	11.4	10.5	7.4	4.7	2.5	1.6	66
Precipitation	12.3	9.7	7.8	6.0	4.7	3.4	1.5	1.7	4.3	7.1	12.3	13.9	84
Storage change	0	0	0	0	-2.9	-6.2	-0.9	0	0	2.4	7.6	0	
Storage	10.0	10.0	10.0	10.0	7.1	0.9	0	0	0	2.4	10.0	10.0	
Actual evap.	1.3	1.8	3.1	4.9	7.6	9.6	2.4	1.7	4.3	4.7	2.5	1.6	45
Water deficiency	0	0	0	0	0	0	9.0	8.8	3.1	0	0	0	20
Water surplus	11.0	7.9	4.7	1.1	0	0	0	0	0	0	2.2	12.3	39
Runoff *	8.9	8.4	6.5	3.8	1.9	1.0	0.5	0.2	0.1	0.1	1.1	6.7	39
Moisture ratio	8.47	4.38	1.52	0.22	-.38	-.65	-.87	-.84	-.42	0.54	3.92	7.68	
					Manhattan, Kans.								
Potential evap.	0.0	0.0	1.9	5.1	9.3	13.9	16.4	15.0	10.1	5.2	1.4	0.0	78
Precipitation	2.0	3.0	3.8	7.1	11.1	11.7	11.5	9.5	8.6	5.8	3.8	2.2	80
Storage change	2.0	2.8	0	0	0	-2.2	-4.9	-2.9	0	0.6	2.4	2.2	
Storage	7.2	10.0	10.0	10.0	10.0	7.8	2.9	0	0	0.6	3.0	5.2	
Actual evap.	0.0	0.0	1.9	5.1	9.3	13.9	16.4	12.4	8.6	5.2	1.4	0.0	74
Water deficiency	0.0	0.0	0.0	0.0	0.0	0.0	0.0	2.6	1.5	0.0	0.0	0.0	4
Water surplus	0.0	0.2	1.9	2.0	1.7	0.0	0.0	0.0	0.0	0.0	0.0	0.0	5
Runoff *	0.0	0.1	1.0	1.5	1.6	0.8	0.4	0.2	0.1	0.1	0.0	0.0	5
Moisture ratio	∞	∞	1.00	0.39	0.19	-.16	-.30	-.37	-.15	0.11	1.71	∞	

*Assuming that 50 per cent of the water available for runoff in any month is held over until the following month. In watersheds of less than 100 square miles the percentage is probably smaller.

A moisture ratio that expresses the relative humidity or aridity of a month may be obtained by dividing the difference between precipitation and potential evapotranspiration by potential evapotranspiration,

$$\frac{p-e}{e} \quad \text{or} \quad \frac{p}{e} - 1. \tag{3}$$

Positive values of the ratio mean that the precipitation is excessive, negative values that it is deficient. A ratio of zero means that water supply is equal to water need.

WATER SURPLUS AND WATER DEFICIENCY

Numerical values of water surplus and water deficiency may be obtained as a simple bookkeeping procedure, precipitation being treated as income and potential evapotranspiration as outgo, and soil moisture as a reserve that may be drawn upon as long as it lasts. Sample computations for Seattle, Wash., and Manhattan, Kans., are given in Table I.

The distribution of average annual water deficiency in the eastern United States is shown in Figure 5. Deficiencies rise sharply to the west in the Great Plains States and are in excess of 10 inches in most of Texas. Deficiencies

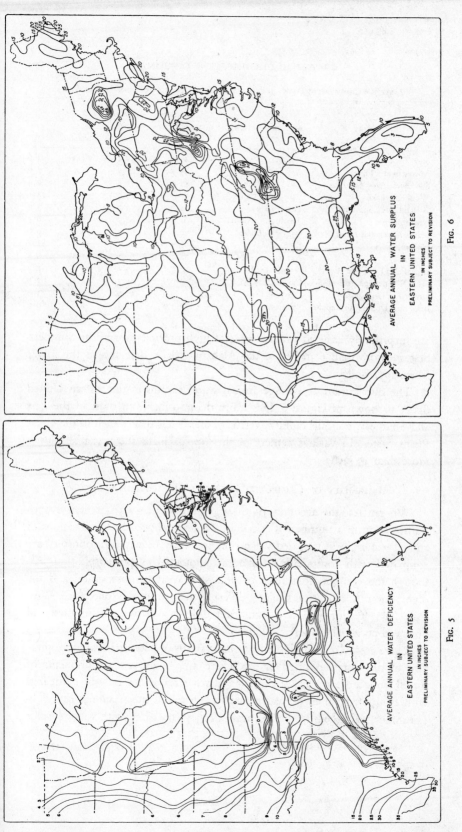

AVERAGE ANNUAL WATER SURPLUS
IN
EASTERN UNITED STATES
IN INCHES
PRELIMINARY SUBJECT TO REVISION

FIG. 6

AVERAGE ANNUAL WATER DEFICIENCY
IN
EASTERN UNITED STATES
IN INCHES
PRELIMINARY SUBJECT TO REVISION

FIG. 5

TABLE II—COMPARATIVE DATA ON IRRIGATED VALLEYS IN THE WESTERN UNITED STATES

VALLEY	WEATHER STATION	OBSERVED WATER USE cm.	POTENTIAL EVAPOTRANS. cm.	DIFF. cm.	DIFF. %
New Fork	Pinedale, Wyo.	46.6	45.4	−1.2	2.6
Michigan and Illinois	Walden, Colo.	45.7	46.9	1.2	2.6
Southwest Area, San Luis	San Luis, Colo.	53.0	51.8	−1.2	2.4
West Tule Lake	Tule Lake, Calif.	67.7	57.9	−9.8	14.5
Garland Div., Shoshone	Lovell, Wyo.	61.6	59.3	−2.3	3.7
North Platte	Torrington, Wyo.	60.4	60.7	0.3	0.5
Mason Creek and Boise	Caldwell, Idaho	66.1	66.5	0.4	0.6
Uncompahgre	Delta, Colo.	68.3	67.5	−0.8	1.2
Mesilla	Agr. College, N. M.	83.2	84.0	0.8	0.9
Greenfields Div., Sun River	Great Falls, Mont.	60.3	60.2	−0.1	0.2
Pecos River near Carlsbad	Carlsbad, N. M.	89.6	91.7	2.1	2.3
Lower Rio Grande	Del Rio, Tex.	115.8	117.0	1.2	1.0
Barahona, Dominican Repub.	Barahona	147.3	146.3	−1.0	0.7

are surprisingly large in various areas of high precipitation in the Southern States—more than 6 inches in the Alabama Black Belt and in the lower Mississippi Valley.

The distribution of average annual water surplus in the eastern United States is shown in Figure 6. It is more than 10 inches in most of the East and Southeast but falls rapidly westward and is less than 1 inch in the Great Plains States. In various centers in the Appalachians the water surplus is more than 35 inches.

RELIABILITY OF COMPUTED POTENTIAL EVAPOTRANSPIRATION

We can test the accuracy of the computed values of potential evapotranspiration in a number of ways. In Table II above the observations of annual water use in irrigated valleys published by Lowry and Johnson[11] are compared with computations of annual potential evapotranspiration. Although the computations refer to points of weather observation and the observations to irrigation projects differing in area, in only one place, West Tule Lake, Calif., is there a significant difference between computed and observed potential evapotranspiration.

There are no comparable direct observations of potential evapotranspiration in the eastern United States. There are, however, measurements of runoff from a great many streams for many years, which may be compared with computed values of water surplus. Observed mean annual runoff in 124 minor watersheds in the Tennessee Valley compared with water surplus

[11] Op. cit., pp. 1253 and 1301.

computed from data of temperature and precipitation at Weather Bureau stations[12] shows a close correspondence, especially noteworthy because the data of the Tennessee Valley Authority refer to areas ranging in size from a few square miles to nearly two thousand and are for a uniform period from 1920 to 1942, whereas the computations were made from averages of temperature and precipitation for periods of various lengths ending in 1930 and refer to the points of weather observation. Computed water surplus and measured runoff are equally close together in Ontario and Mexico, where potential evapotranspiration is respectively much smaller and much larger. The National Resources Board in its report of December 1, 1934, gives a map of average annual runoff in the United States, which may be compared with the map of water surplus, Figure 6. The correspondence is generally close, though there are discrepancies, some of which are due to admitted errors in the original runoff map.

From these and other tests it appears that the computed values of potential evapotranspiration are of the right order of magnitude throughout most of the United States. They are, nevertheless, only approximate. More exact determinations must await further study and the development of a more rational equation. Whether or not the formula can be used without modification to determine potential evapotranspiration in equatorial and polar regions is uncertain. This question also requires further study.

ESSENTIALS OF A CLIMATIC CLASSIFICATION

When the various climatic elements, such as temperature and precipitation, are plotted on maps, the values grade regularly except where gradients steepen on mountain slopes or along seacoasts. Nothing distinguishes any one value in the series from the others; hence divisions of the scales are arbitrary and frequently owe their origin to arithmetical or cartographical convenience. Divisions appearing on maps, selected perhaps to conform to a particular color scheme, gradually assume the role of climatic regions; for example, the 10-inch isohyet as the limit of agriculture.

Köppen made a significant advance in climatic classification when he undertook, first to identify the climatic regions and locate their boundaries from studies of the distribution of vegetation, and then to select numerical climatic values for the boundaries. Penck, De Martonne, and Thornthwaite employed the same method but used data of hydrology and soils to supple-

---

[12] See Figure 3 (p. 691) in H. G. Wilm, C. W. Thornthwaite, and others: Report of the Committee on Transpiration and Evaporation, 1943–44, *Amer. Geophys. Union Trans. of 1944*, Part 5, Washington, 1945, pp. 683–693.

ment those of vegetation in locating the boundaries of climatic regions. Although this method represents a step forward in that the climatic boundaries are not arbitrary, it is still empirical.

In order to achieve a rational quantitative classification of climate, definite and distinctive break points must be discovered in the climatic series themselves. No such break points exist in the data either of precipitation or of potential evapotranspiration. Both run in continuous series from very low values to very large ones. But when they are taken together, there are some distinctive points, and we have the beginnings of a rational classification.

The primary climatic factors relate to moisture and heat. We are interested in whether a climate is moist or dry and warm or cold. We also need to know whether there is seasonal variation—whether the climate is moist in one season and dry in another.

THE MOISTURE FACTOR

We cannot tell whether a climate is moist or dry by knowing precipitation alone; we must know whether precipitation is greater or less than potential evapotranspiration. Ignorance of the magnitude of water need has led to the development of a number of moisture indices, which attempt to evaluate the effectiveness of precipitation. It is recognized that water utilization or water loss, that is, evaporation and transpiration, must be related to precipitation somehow. Accordingly, a few of the indices make use of computed or measured values of evaporation usually from free water surfaces, lakes and reservoirs, or from evaporation pans.

In 1905 Transeau[13] produced an index of precipitation effectiveness, by using the quotient of total annual measured precipitation and annual evaporation as computed by Russell[14] for a year for about 150 stations, and made a map of the precipitation-evaporation ratio in the eastern United States. In 1933 Isozaki[15] computed ratios for 99 stations in Japan, using average annual precipitation and annual evaporation from pans, and made a moisture map of the Japanese Empire. Trumble,[16] making use of measurements of evaporation from pans in South Australia, derived an empirical equation relating

[13] E. N. Transeau: Forest Centers of Eastern America, *Amer. Naturalist*, Vol. 39, 1905, pp. 875–889.
[14] Thomas Russell: Depth of Evaporation in the United States, *Monthly Weather Rev.*, Vol. 16, 1888, pp. 235–239.
[15] Masaru Isozaki: Thornthwaite's New Classification of Climate and Its Application to the Climate of Japan, *Journ. of Geogr.*, Tokyo Geographical Society, Vol. 45, 1933, pp. 234–245 (in Japanese).
[16] H. C. Trumble: The Climatic Control of Agriculture in South Australia, *Trans. and Proc. Royal Soc. of South Australia*, Vol. 61, 1937, pp. 41–62; *idem:* Climatic Factors in Relation to the Agricultural Regions of Southern Australia, *Trans. Royal Soc. of South Australia*, Vol. 63, 1939, pp. 36–43.

monthly evaporation to vapor-pressure deficit, which he computed from temperature values. He determined empirically that water need of a month exceeds water supply when computed evaporation is more than three times precipitation. His map of southern Australia shows the number of months of the year when precipitation is less than water need. Wilson[17] produced a moisture index by dividing evaporation from a Livingston porous cup atmometer by annual precipitation and made a moisture map of Ohio.

Numerous investigators, recognizing that temperature is the major control of evaporation, have substituted temperature for evaporation in their moisture indices. The Lang rain factor, $I = P/T$, indicates that the effectiveness varies directly with precipitation and inversely with temperature. De Martonne's index of aridity, $I = P/(T + 10)$, is a slight refinement of Lang's. Köppen's three formulae for delimiting the dry climates, $I = 8P/(5T + 120)$, $I = 2P/(T + 33)$, and $I = P/(T + 7)$, presented in 1918, 1923, and 1928 respectively, are similar to those of Lang and De Martonne. All use annual values of precipitation and temperature given in the metric system.

In 1931 Thornthwaite[18] utilized evaporation data from the continental United States and derived an empirical equation by which the precipitation-evaporation ratio could be determined from monthly values of precipitation and temperature. He used this moisture index in making a climatic map of North America and a later one of the earth.[19]

In 1936 Ångström[20] suggested a modification of De Martonne's index of aridity. He found that the index of aridity was proportionate to duration of precipitation, which was in turn directly proportionate to amount of precipitation and inversely proportionate to an exponential function of temperature. His humidity coefficient is $I = P/(1.07^t)$, in which the denominator of the fraction doubles with each rise of 10° C. in temperature, in accordance with Van't Hoff's law. Ångström published maps of northwestern Europe showing the humidity coefficient in January and July. In 1939 Church and Gueffroy[21] used the Ångström formula to make similar maps of the United States. In 1946 Setzer[22] utilized Van't Hoff's law in the

[17] J. D. Wilson and J. R. Savage: An Evaporation Survey of Ohio, *Ohio Agric. Exper. Sta. Bull.* 564, 1936.

[18] C. W. Thornthwaite: The Climates of North America According to a New Classification, *Geogr. Rev.*, Vol. 21, 1931, pp. 633–655.

[19] *Idem:* The Climates of the Earth, *Geogr. Rev.*, Vol. 23, 1933, pp. 433–440.

[20] Anders Ångström: A Coefficient of Humidity of General Applicability, *Geografiska Annaler,* Vol. 18, 1936, pp. 245–254.

[21] P. E. Church and E. M. Gueffroy: A New Coefficient of Humidity and Its Application to the United States, *Geogr. Rev.*, Vol. 29, 1939, pp. 665–667.

[22] José Setzer: A New Formula for Precipitation Effectiveness, *Geogr. Rev.*, Vol. 36, 1946, pp. 247–263.

development of a moisture index. Although developed independently, Setzer's index is identical with Ångström's. Setzer published a map of the moisture index in the state of São Paulo, Brazil.

Ångström[23] has ably explained what the investigator wishes to accomplish with moisture indices:

Especially with geographical, geological, or biological problems in view, [one has] tried to express the humidity or aridity of a climate through some kind of coefficient which is expected to be a measure on conditions of humidity not in the simple physical sense, but involving an indication of the climatic tendency to a surplus or deficiency of water with consequences upon the structure of the ground, the existence of rivers, floods, lakes or deserts etc. It is evident that the humidity of the soil is hereby a prime factor, and as this element is more seldom directly measured it seems justified to try to replace it by some kind of coefficient deduced from the current meteorological data.

A Moisture Index

It is now apparent that the actual evaporation and transpiration from the soil is not what must be compared with precipitation in order to obtain a moisture index, but, rather, the potential evapotranspiration. Where precipitation is exactly the same as potential evapotranspiration all the time and water is available just as needed, there is neither water deficiency nor water excess, and the climate is neither moist nor dry. As water deficiency becomes larger with respect to potential evapotranspiration, the climate becomes arid; as water surplus becomes larger, the climate becomes more humid. Where there is a water surplus and no water deficiency, the relation between water surplus and water need constitutes an index of humidity. Similarly, where there is a water deficiency and no surplus, the ratio between water deficiency and water need constitutes an index of aridity. Expressed as percentages these two indices are:

$$I_h = \frac{100s}{n} \quad \text{and} \quad I_a = \frac{100d}{n}, \qquad (4)$$

where I_h and I_a are indices of humidity and aridity respectively, s is water surplus, d is water deficiency, and n is water need. The ultimate in the scale of aridity is where there is no precipitation and the water deficiency is consequently equal to the water need, making I_a equal to 100 per cent. As precipitation and potential evapotranspiration are independent of each other, the index of humidity does not reach a limit where water surplus equals water need, that is, where precipitation is twice potential evapotranspiration, but continues above 100 per cent.

Since water surplus and water deficiency occur at different seasons in

[23] Op. cit., p. 245.

most places, both must enter into a moisture index, the one affecting it positively, the other negatively. Although a water surplus in one season cannot prevent a deficiency in another except as moisture may be stored in the soil, to a certain extent one may compensate for the other. Water surplus means seasonal additions to subsoil moisture and ground water. Deeply rooted perennials may make partial use of subsoil moisture and thus minimize the effect of drought. Transpiration proceeds, but at reduced rates. For this reason, a surplus of only 6 inches in one season will counteract a deficiency of 10 inches in another. Thus in an over-all moisture index the humidity index has more weight than the aridity index: the latter has only six-tenths the value of the former. The moisture index is:

$$I_m = I_h - .6I_a \quad \text{or} \quad I_m = \frac{100s - 60d}{n}. \tag{5}$$

Moist climates have positive values of I_m; dry climates have negative values. Figure 7 shows how climatic types are separated in terms of the moisture index, I_m, and makes clear how they are related to water surplus and water deficiency. The various climatic types together with their limits are as follows:

Climatic Type		Moisture Index
A	Perhumid	100 and above
B_4	Humid	80 to 100
B_3	Humid	60 to 80
B_2	Humid	40 to 60
B_1	Humid	20 to 40
C_2	Moist subhumid	0 to 20
C_1	Dry subhumid	−20 to 0
D	Semiarid	−40 to −20
E	Arid	−60 to −40

The index values −60, 0, and 100 are entirely rational limits of moisture regions. That the others are also may be seen in the nomograms of Figure 7. These definitions of moisture regions appear to be in final form. Further work is needed to improve the means for determining potential evapotranspiration, moisture surplus, and moisture deficiency. This may lead to revision of the location of the moisture regions but will not change the definition of them.

These climatic types are the same, and have the same meaning, as those proposed in an earlier climatic classification.[24] However, whereas the limits in the previous classification were determined empirically by study of vegetation, soils, drainage patterns, and so on, these limits are rational and

---

[24] Thornthwaite, The Climates of North America (*op. cit.*).

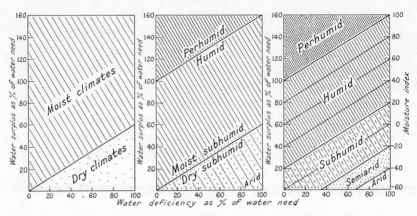

FIG. 7—Delineation of moisture regions on basis of water surplus and water deficiency.

are established solely in terms of the relation between potential evapotranspiration and precipitation. It is possible to convert the present moisture
index, I, to the old $P-E$ index by means of the following equation:

$$P-E = .8I + 48. \tag{6}$$

The distribution of the moisture regions of the United States is shown
in Plate I A. The moist climates of the East and the dry climates of the
West are separated by moisture index o, in a line that extends from western
Minnesota southward to the Gulf of Mexico. This is a very important line,
since it separates regions of prevailing water surplus from those of water
deficiency. Although dry climates predominate in the western United
States, there is a belt of moist climates along the Pacific coast as far south
as the San Francisco peninsula. Moist climates appear also as islands in the
western mountains.

Perhumid climates are not extensive in the United States. They occur
along the coasts of Washington, Oregon, and northern California and on
the western slopes of the Cascades and the Sierras. There is a single small
island in the high Rockies of Colorado, and other islands on high elevations
in the Appalachians. A narrow belt along the Maine coast is perhumid.
Humid climates are most extensive in the East, but they occur adjacent to
perhumid climates on the Pacific coast and on high areas elsewhere in the
West. Subhumid climates are most extensive in the Middle West, wide
belts of moist subhumid and dry subhumid extending from the Canadian
border in Minnesota and North Dakota to the Gulf coast of Texas. Much
of the Florida peninsula is moist subhumid. Smaller subhumid areas occur
in the West, mostly as belts along the lower mountain slopes. The Great

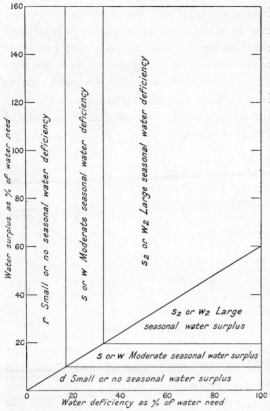

FIG. 8—Nomogram to determine seasonal regime of moisture.

Plains and much of the intermountain region are semiarid. Arid climate is most extensive in the Southwest. There are, however, small arid areas in Washington, Oregon, Idaho, Montana, Wyoming, Utah, and Colorado. Most of the San Joaquin Valley of California is arid.

SEASONAL VARIATION OF EFFECTIVE MOISTURE

It is important to know whether a place is continuously wet or continuously dry, or whether it is wet in one season and dry in another. The moisture index can indicate how humid or how arid a climate is, but it cannot at the same time distinguish climates with seasonal moisture variation from those without it. In the moist climates, if there is a dry season, we need to know how dry it is; in the dry climates, how wet the wet season is if one occurs. In moist climates water deficiency may be large, moderate, small, or nonexistent. In dry climates the same is true of water surplus (see Fig. 8).

By definition, a large water deficiency or surplus is an amount sufficient to make the climate one grade drier or moister than it would be otherwise. For example, in San Francisco the water surplus of 6.68 inches (24.6 per cent of the water need) makes the climate less dry, changing it from semiarid (D) to dry subhumid (C₁). Los Angeles, with a somewhat larger water deficiency and a smaller winter surplus, remains semiarid (D). A moderate water surplus or deficiency will, by definition, change the climate one-half grade.

The symbols s and s₂ indicate respectively moderate and large seasonal variation of moisture, with the drier season occurring in summer; w and w_2 are used similarly where the drier season occurs in winter. Where water need and precipitation march through the year approximately parallel to each other, there will be little or no seasonal variation of moisture. Here the symbols r and d are used, the first to designate the areas with little or no water deficiency in moist climates, and the second little or no water surplus in dry climates. The climatic subdivisions are defined in terms of the humidity and aridity indices as follows:

Moist Climates (A, B, C_2)	Aridity Index
r little or no water deficiency	0 – 16.7
s moderate summer water deficiency	16.7 – 33.3
w moderate winter water deficiency	16.7 – 33.3
s_2 large summer water deficiency	33.3+
w_2 large winter water deficiency	33.3+

Dry Climates (C_1, D, E)	Humidity Index
d little or no water surplus	0 – 10
s moderate winter water surplus	10 – 20
w moderate summer water surplus	10 – 20
s_2 large winter water surplus	20+
w_2 large summer water surplus	20+

The symbols s, s_2, w, and w_2 have the same meaning in both moist and dry climates in spite of the fact that they are defined differently. They refer to the season when rainfall is most deficient.

The winter dry, w and w_2, types do not occur in the United States. In fact, these types are much less widely distributed over the earth than would be deduced from a study of the seasonal march of precipitation. Water need is naturally larger in summer than in winter; and in many areas of maximum summer rainfall, water need and precipitation are essentially together through the year, and there is neither summer water surplus nor winter water deficiency. For example, in Nanking, China, the average precipitation of the three summer months is 55.0 centimeters and of the winter months only 12.0; but since water need varies even more widely between winter and summer, the climate is not of the w type. The water surplus occurs in late winter and spring, not in summer.

In Figure 9 representative stations are grouped according to whether the seasonal range of effective moisture is small, moderate, or large. Those in which precipitation most nearly parallels potential evapotranspiration and both water surplus and water deficiency are small are Ames, Iowa (C_2r), Alexandria, Minn. (C_2r), and Grafton, N. Dak. (C_1d).

The distribution in the United States of the climatic subtypes based on

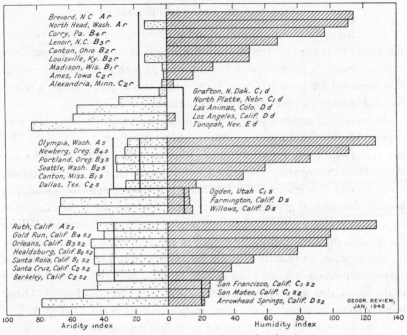

FIG. 9—Seasonal regime of moisture at selected stations.

seasonal variation of effective moisture is shown in Plate I B. Types r and d, representing small seasonal variation, are most extensive. Types s and s_2 prevail in the Pacific-coast region, where precipitation comes mainly in winter; s_2 does not occur except where the march of precipitation is opposite to that of water need and for this reason has its most extensive development in California. Type s may occur as well in regions of prevailing summer rain if summer water need sufficiently exceeds it. There are several areas of s climate in the southern United States and a few isolated stations in the Northeast. Canton, Miss. (B_1s), and Dallas, Tex. (C_2s), are examples. A large s area extends from eastern Texas and central Oklahoma eastward into Arkansas and Louisiana. A smaller area occupies the lower Mississippi Valley, and another crosses Alabama from Georgia to Mississippi along the well-known Black Belt.

The existence of the s type in the southeastern United States is surprising. Summer rainfall is fairly large, and it is not generally realized that water need is larger. Summer drought is serious in much of the eastern United States, even in the r type climates. In the s type summer drought is chronic. Supplementary irrigation becomes an important need.   *399*

An Index of Thermal Efficiency

Potential evapotranspiration is an index of thermal efficiency. It possesses the virtue of being an expression of day length as well as of temperature. It is not merely a growth index but expresses growth in terms of the water that is needed for growth. Given in the same units as precipitation it relates thermal efficiency to precipitation effectiveness.

In equatorial regions, where mean monthly temperature does not vary appreciably through the year, a mean annual temperature of 23° C. (73.4° F.) is a reasonable boundary between megathermal and mesothermal climates. Away from the equator, where there is a seasonal variation of temperature, mean annual temperature at the boundary is lower, 21.5° C. (70.7° F.), because the reduced growth and water need of winter are more than offset by an accelerated growth and an increased water need of summer. Where the mean temperature of every month is 23°, and if the station is directly on the equator, so that there is no variation in day length, the potential evapotranspiration is 114.0 centimeters (44.88 inches). This may be taken as the index that separates megathermal and mesothermal climates. Other boundaries in the series are in a descending geometric progression (p. 82).

Climatic regions based on temperature efficiency are analogous to those derived from the moisture index and are designated by similar symbols. Microthermal (C′) and mesothermal (B′) climates are subdivided like the subhumid (C) and humid (B) climates.[25] The distribution of the thermal regions in the United States is shown in Plate I C. Mesothermal (B′) climates are most extensive. Microthermal (C′) climates occur along most of the Canadian border and extend southward along the Rocky Mountains in a continuous belt to southern New Mexico. There are three areas of megathermal (A′) climate: southern Florida, southern Texas, and the arid parts of southern California and southwestern Arizona. Only small isolated areas of tundra (D′) occur, in the high Sierras of California, the northern Rockies of Wyoming and Montana, and the central Rockies of Colorado. There are no instrumental records of frost (E′) climate in the United States, and it does not appear on the map.

The megathermal (A′) climates of the United States are different from those of equatorial regions. Summer days are longer and hotter, and winter days are shorter and colder. Temperature and day length work together

---

[25] Although the symbols are the same as those used in the original classification, the climatic limits differ considerably from the old ones. Consequently, the symbols have different meanings. For example, in the original scheme tundra was E′ and frost climate F′. Mesothermal climates are more extensive than previously shown.

400

to bring about seasonal variations in potential evapotranspiration or temperature efficiency. The difference is illustrated in Figure 10-A. Whereas at Belém, Brazil, the range is only from 10.3 to 13.1 centimeters, at Barahona, Dominican Republic, it is from 8.2 to 16.2 centimeters, and at Miami, Fla., from 5.2 to 17.8 centimeters. At the mesothermal border the mean tem-

TE INDEX		CLIMATIC TYPE	
cm.	in.		
		E'	Frost
14.2	5.61		
		D'	Tundra
28.5	11.22		
		C'_1	
42.7	16.83		Microthermal
		C'_2	
57.0	22.44		
		B'_1	
71.2	28.05		
		B'_2	
85.5	33.66		Mesothermal
		B'_3	
99.7	39.27		
		B'_4	
114.0	44.88		
		A'	Megathermal

perature of the coldest month is as low as 50° F. in some stations. Freezing temperatures may occur almost annually, whereas in equatorial stations frosts are entirely unknown. For this reason certain plants popularly associated with tropical climates do not grow in the megathermal climates of the United States. However, plant growth continues, although at reduced rates, throughout the winter.

The mesothermal (B') climates occupy a wide range of latitudes in the eastern and central United States. Summer temperatures fall off slowly from south to north: the mean July temperature in the lower Rio Grande Valley of Texas is 85° F., and it is above 70° F. in the Yellowstone Valley of Montana. Day length, on the other hand, increases from south to north—about 14 hours in southern Texas and 16 hours in northern Montana. Consequently, average July potential evapotranspiration decreases slowly: it is about 18 centimeters in southern Texas and 15 centimeters in Montana. The fact that winter temperatures and day length both decrease from south to north has less influence because potential evapotranspiration is small even on the southern margin of the climatic zone. However, the growing season becomes shorter, and the northern edge of the zone, where annual potential evapotranspiration is only 50 per cent of the maximum for the climatic type, is reached near the Canadian border. The four subdivisions of the

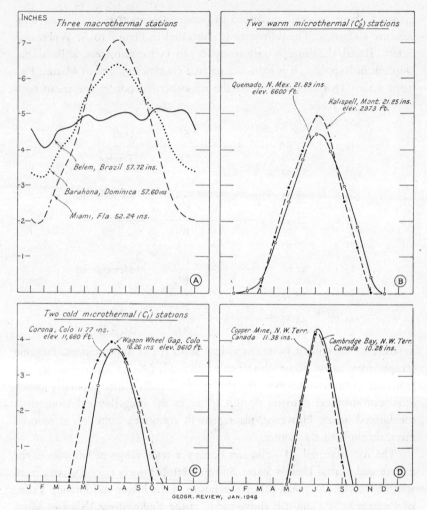

INCHES
Three macrothermal stations

Two warm microthermal (C′₂) stations

Quemado, N. Mex. 21.89 ins.
elev. 6600 ft.

Kalispell, Mont. 21.85 ins.
elev. 2973 ft.

Belem, Brazil 57.72 ins.

Barahona, Dominica 57.60 ins.

Miami, Fla. 52.24 ins.

Ⓐ

Ⓑ

Two cold microthermal (C′₁) stations

Corona, Colo 11.77 ins.
elev. 11,660 ft.

Wagon Wheel Gap, Colo
16.26 ins elev. 9610 ft.

Copper Mine, N. W. Terr.
Canada 11.38 ins.

Cambridge Bay, N. W. Terr.
Canada 10.28 ins.

Ⓒ

Ⓓ

J F M A M J J A S O N D J   J F M A M J J A S O N D J
GEOGR. REVIEW, JAN. 1948

Fɪɢ. 10—March of potential evaporation. For *macrothermal* read *megathermal* (a preferable form suggested by Mr. A. B. Hoen).

mesothermal climates appear to have real validity, but since no appropriate names for them have been found, they are identified only by subscripts 1 to 4 following symbol B′.

Microthermal (C′) climates extend continuously from the Canadian border in Montana to within 200 miles of the Mexican border in New Mexico. They are at high elevations in the southern part of their range and descend to lower elevations in the north. Quemado, N. Mex., and Kalispell Mont., have the same annual potential evapotranspiration and are both warn microthermal (C'_2); the first is 6600 feet above sea level, the second only 2973 feet. Figure 10-B shows the march of potential evapotranspiration in these two stations. Spring and summer temperatures are considerably lower in Kalispell. The growing season is shorter, but since summer days are longer, higher rates of water use and more rapid growth compensate for shorter time of plant activity.

The colder type of microthermal climates (C'_1) is not areally important in the United States.[26] The two most extensive areas are in Wyoming and Colorado, though smaller areas are found in several western states. Wagon Wheel Gap, Colo., is near the warm limit of the type, and Corona, Colo., is near the cold limit (Fig. 10-C). Although the temperatures of the warmest months are low (Corona mean July temperature, 48.8° F.; Wagon Wheel Gap, 56.2° F.), the potential evapotranspiration is surprisingly large, nearly 10 centimeters (4 inches). Annual precipitation is in excess of water need in both places, but summer rainfall is less than summer potential evapotranspiration. At Wagon Wheel Gap summer water deficiency amounts to 2.2 inches. Short growing season and low summer temperature do not prevent droughts.

No currently reporting Weather Bureau station in the United States has tundra (D') climate. However, it undoubtedly occurs in various isolated high areas, mostly in the West. The summit of Mt. Washington, in New Hampshire, has an annual water need of 12.9 inches, which places it on the tundra margin. Figure 10-D shows the march of potential evapotranspiration in two stations in the far north of Canada. Both are very near the microthermal-tundra boundary; Coppermine is just above the line, and Cambridge Bay just below. Although the mean temperature of July, the warmest month, is only about 50° F. in both places, the water need is astonishingly high, being above 10 centimeters (4 inches). Average annual potential evapotranspiration exceeds precipitation in both places, and summer drought is a characteristic feature of the climate. In southern and eastern Greenland, on the other hand, precipitation greatly exceeds evapotranspiration, and there is a large water surplus, a part of which nourishes the ice-cap, and a part of which runs off in summer.

In the climate of perpetual frost (E') temperatures need not remain continuously below the freezing point. Although frost effectively prevents vegetation growth, and thus transpiration, nevertheless some water passes into the atmosphere by evaporation or sublimation. At the outer limit of the frost climate potential evapotranspiration is 14.2 centimeters (5.61

---

[26] This type is equivalent to taiga (D') in the previous classification.

inches). It is evident that even in the frost climate moisture differentiation is important, because if precipitation exceeds potential evapotranspiration, ice will accumulate and a glacier will develop. On the other hand, if precipitation is less than this critical value, ice accumulation is impossible. It is not certain that true frost (E') climate exists anywhere in the United States. A snow line or mountain glacier does not necessarily indicate a frost climate.

Summer Concentration of Thermal Efficiency

At the equator, where day length is the same throughout the year and where temperature is also uniform, seasonal variation of potential evapotranspiration will be small. With no variation no season can be called summer, and the potential evapotranspiration of any consecutive three months will constitute 25 per cent of the annual total. On the other hand, in the Polar Regions, where the growing season is entirely within the three summer months, the potential evapotranspiration of these months will constitute 100 per cent of the total. Between these extremes, as potential evapotranspiration falls from that characteristic of megathermal (A') climates to that of frost (E') climates, the part that is concentrated in summer gradually rises from 25 per cent to 100 per cent. This rise results from an increasing length of midsummer days, and an increase in the length of winter, with increase in latitude.

The astronomical motions of the earth tend to produce a certain fixed relation between the summer index of thermal efficiency and the annual index. This relation has been approximately determined from a series of stations in the interior low plains of North America. The summer concentration appears to be inversely proportionate to the logarithm of the annual index. The relation is described by the equation

$$s = 157.76 - 66.44 \log E, \tag{7}$$

in which s is summer concentration in percentages and E is potential evapotranspiration in inches.

But there are a number of meteorological situations in which the relation is modified or altered and is, in consequence, abnormal. On small oceanic islands and seacoasts dominated by onshore winds in middle and high latitudes summer temperatures are less warm, and winter temperatures less cold, than elsewhere in these latitudes. The summer concentration of thermal efficiency is lower than it should be for the latitude. In mountains there is a more or less uniform reduction of temperature throughout the year. Annual and summer thermal-efficiency indices are both reduced, but not in the same proportion. Here, too, the summer concentration of thermal

404

Table III—Comparative Moisture Data of Selected Stations

In inches

Station	Water need	Summer need %	Precipitation	Water surplus	Water def.	Surplus % of need	Def. % of need	Moisture index	Climatic type
A. Brevard, N. C.	28.50	51.1	61.06	32.56	0.00	114.2	0.	114.2	$A\ B'_2rb'_4$
B. Salisbury, N. Y.	21.80	67.2	48.39	26.58	0.00	121.8	0.	121.8	$A\ C'_2rb'_1$
C. Bar Harbor, Maine	22.32	59.1	47.09	25.55	0.00	114.5	0.	114.5	$A\ C'_2rb'_2$
D. North Head, Wash.	24.72	41.1	48.86	27.40	3.27	110.8	13.2	102.9	$A\ B'_1ra'$
E. Louisville, Ky.	31.77	55.5	43.47	15.95	4.28	50.2	13.5	42.2	$B_2B'_2rb'_3$
F. Seattle, Wash.	26.14	46.4	33.35	15.43	8.23	59.0	31.5	40.2	$B_2B'_1sa'$
G. Canton, Miss.	38.70	50.6	49.10	17.68	7.68	45.6	19.8	33.8	$B_1B'_3sb'_4$
H. Willard, N. C.	35.35	49.7	49.05	13.70	0.00	38.8	0.	38.8	$B_1B'_3rb'_4$
I. Madison, Wis.	25.12	61.4	31.54	7.09	0.67	28.2	2.7	26.6	$B_1B'_1rb'_2$
J. Centennial, Wyo.	18.86	63.7	17.68	4.49	5.67	23.8	30.1	5.7	$C_2C'_2sb'_1$
K. Manhattan, Kans.	30.83	57.8	31.50	2.28	1.61	7.4	5.2	4.3	$C_2B'_2rb'_2$
L. Pullman, Wash.	24.13	58.1	20.71	7.48	10.91	31.0	45.3	3.9	$C_2B'_1s_2b'_2$
M. San Francisco, Calif.	27.09	33.3	21.88	6.68	11.89	24.6	43.8	-1.7	$C_1B'_1s_2a'$
N. Dalhart, Tex.	29.02	56.9	19.09	0.00	9.92	0.	34.2	-20.5	$D\ B'_2db'_2$
O. Helena, Mont.	22.32	48.1	13.31	0.00	9.01	0.	40.4	-24.2	$D\ C'_2db'_4$
P. Santa Fe, N. Mex.	24.41	56.1	14.21	0.00	10.19	0.	41.7	-25.1	$D\ B'_1db'_3$
Q. Los Angeles, Calif.	32.01	38.7	14.96	1.42	18.47	4.4	57.7	-30.2	$D\ B'_2da'$
R. Grand Junction, Colo	28.74	59.2	8.70	0.00	20.04	0.	69.9	-41.8	$E\ B'_2db'_2$
S. Fresno, Calif	36.22	52.8	9.17	0.00	27.04	0.	74.7	-44.8	$E\ B'_3db'_3$
T. Tonopah, Nev.	25.43	58.7	4.84	0.00	21.38	0.	84.0	-50.4	$E\ B'_1db'_2$

efficiency is abnormally low. On the other hand, in some regions the normal seasonal march of temperature is exaggerated. Summer temperatures are increased by advection of hot tropical air, and winter temperatures are lowered by advection of cold polar air. In these regions the summer concentration is abnormally high.

POTENTIAL EVAPOTRANSPIRATION		TEMPERATURE-EFFICIENCY TYPE	SUMMER CONCENTRATION	SUMMER CONCENTRATION
Ins.	Cms.		Percentage	Type
		A′		a′
44.88	114.0		48.0	
		B′4		b′4
39.27	99.7		51.9	
		B′3		b′3
33.66	85.5		56.3	
		B′2		b′2
28.05	71.2		61.6	
		B′1		b′1
22.44	57.0		68.0	
		C′2		c′2
16.83	42.7		76.3	
		C′1		c′1
11.22	28.5		88.0	
		D′		d′
5.61	14.2			
		E′		

The extent to which the summer-concentration percentage fails to meet the above requirements is a measure of its abnormality. San Francisco, for example, has a potential evapotranspiration of 27.09 inches and a summer concentration of 33.3 per cent. Thus summer concentration is that of full megathermal (a′) climate, though the temperature-efficiency type is actually only first mesothermal (B′1). San Francisco is an example of a so-called "marine" climate.

Summer concentration of thermal efficiency in the United States is shown in Plate I D. The displacement of the various zones from the comparable ones of thermal efficiency (Pl. I C) is a measure of oceanity or continentality.

The abnormality of the summer-concentration percentage deserves special study, but it will be more profitable on a world basis than for the United States alone.

ELEMENTS OF THE CLASSIFICATION

Four symbols used together give a complete description of a climate. The necessary data for classifying the stations in Figure 4 are presented in Table III. Water need, in the first column, is, of course, potential evapotranspiration. The second column gives the percentage that summer potential evapotranspiration is of the annual total. The column labeled "Surplus as percentage of need" gives the humidity index, and that labeled "Deficiency as percentage of need" the index of aridity. The moisture index is obtained by subtracting six-tenths of the latter from the former.

The various subdivisions of mesothermal, microthermal, and humid climatic types do not have individual names but can be referred to only by symbol. Thus we can say first, second, third, or fourth mesothermal. Brevard, N. C. (AB$'_2$rb$'_4$), is perhumid, second mesothermal, with no season of water deficiency, and a temperature-efficiency regime normal to fourth mesothermal. San Francisco, Calif. (C$_I$B$'_I$s$_2$a$'$), is dry subhumid, first mesothermal, with large winter water surplus, and a temperature-efficiency regime normal to megathermal.

Superficially the present system is similar to its predecessor[27] in that the same factors are employed; namely a moisture factor, a heat factor, and the seasonal variation of the two. Actually, the two systems are fundamentally different. In the earlier classification, climatic types were identified, and boundaries were located, empirically, through study of the distribution of vegetation, soils, drainage features, and so on. In the present classification, climates are defined rationally, and boundaries are determined by the data.

The difference may be illustrated by the change in point of view respecting vegetation. The earlier study adopted Köppen's position that the plant is a meteorological instrument which integrates the various factors of climate and which, with experience, can be "read" like a thermometer or a rain gauge. In the present study, vegetation is regarded as a physical mechanism by means of which water is transported from the soil to the atmosphere; it is the machinery of evaporation as the cloud is the machinery of precipitation.

Climatic boundaries are determined rationally by comparing precipitation and evapotranspiration. The subdivisions of the older classification were justly criticized as being vegetation regions climatically determined. The present climatic regions are not open to this criticism, since they come from a study of the climatic data themselves and not from a study of vegetation.

This classification can be improved. A first step will be to develop better means of determining potential evapotranspiration. Additional observations are needed, particularly in the tropics and in high latitudes. With new data available, the present formula can be revised, or perhaps a new and more rational formula can be devised. A truly rational method of delimiting the temperature-efficiency regions has not yet been developed. A relation be-

---

[27] Thornthwaite, The Climates of North America (op. cit.).

tween the heat factor and the moisture factor may exist that will provide the rational basis. So far it has not been discovered.

There is an encouraging prospect that this climatic classification which is developed independently of other geographical factors such as vegetation, soils, and land use, may provide the key to their geographical distribution.

Soil-forming processes are related to water surpluses and water deficiencies; so are hydrological regimes and drainage patterns. The problem of the origin of the prairies may come near solution in an analysis of annual frequency of water deficiency and water surplus. Furthermore, much can be learned regarding soil productivity and best land use through a study of magnitude and frequency of water deficiency. Finally, we have a better understanding than ever before of the qualities of a climate when we are able to compare the potential evapotranspiration through the year with the precipitation.

APPENDIX I

THE DETERMINATION OF POTENTIAL EVAPOTRANSPIRATION

The relation between mean monthly temperature and potential evapotranspiration adjusted to a standard month of 30 days, each having 12 hours of possible sunshine, in four selected areas is shown in Figure 11. In each area the relationship within the range of temperature involved is well expressed by an equation of the form

$$e = ct^a, \tag{8}$$

in which e is monthly evapotranspiration in centimeters and t is mean monthly temperature in °C. From these observations it is seen that there is no simple relationship between monthly evapotranspiration and monthly temperature. The coefficients c and a vary from one place to another. Thus an equation having coefficients derived from observations made in a warm climate does not yield correct values of potential evapotranspiration for an area having a cold climate, and vice versa. In Figure 12 the lines showing the relationship between temperature and evapotranspiration in several areas tend to converge where potential evapotranspiration is 13.5 centimeters and temperature is 26.5° C. At lower temperatures there is increasing divergence in potential evapotranspiration.

In a general equation constants c and a must be allowed to vary with a factor that is small in cold climates and large in hot climates. Mean annual temperature is not satisfactory because in some places it is affected by below-freezing temperatures. A special equation was developed for the purpose. A monthly index is obtained from the equation $i = (t/5)^{1.514}$. Summation of the 12 monthly values gives an appropriate heat index, I. While this index varies from 0 to 160, the exponent a in the above equation varies from 0 to 4.25. The relation between the two is closely approximated by the expression

$$a = 0.0000006751 I^3 - 0.0000771 I^2 + 0.01792 I + 0.49239. \tag{9}$$

408

Climatic type

A   Perhumid
B₄ Humid
B₃ Humid
B₂ Humid
B₁ Humid
C₂ Moist subhumid
C₁ Dry subhumid
D   Semiarid
E   Arid

Moisture index = $\dfrac{\text{humid} - \text{arid}}{\text{need}}$

The coefficient c in equation (8) above varies inversely with I. From these relations a general equation for potential evapotranspiration was obtained. It is

$$e = 1.6 \left(10t/I\right)^a, \tag{10}$$

in which a has the value given in equation (9).

The formula gives unadjusted rates of potential evapotranspiration. Since the number of

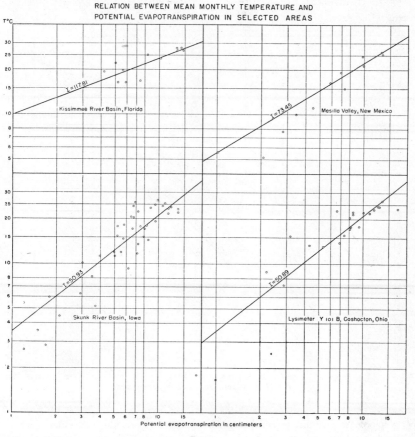

RELATION BETWEEN MEAN MONTHLY TEMPERATURE AND
POTENTIAL EVAPOTRANSPIRATION IN SELECTED AREAS

FIG. II

days in a month ranges from 28 to 31 (nearly 11 per cent) and the number of hours in the day between sunrise and sunset, when evapotranspiration principally takes place, varies with the season and with latitude, it becomes necessary to reduce or increase the unadjusted rates by a factor that varies with the month and with latitude.

This mathematical development is far from satisfactory. It is empirical, and the general equation does not accord with the newly developed law of growth. Furthermore, the equation is completely lacking in mathematical elegance. It is very complicated and without nomograms and tables as computing aids would be quite unworkable. The chief obstacle at present to the development of a rational equation is the lack of understanding of why potential evapotranspiration corresponding to a given temperature is not the same everywhere. Not until this matter is understood will a rational method be possible.

In spite of the lack of a theoretical foundation, this method makes it possible to arrive at values of potential evapotranspiration that are approximately correct and that give an entirely new approach to the problems of climatic classification.

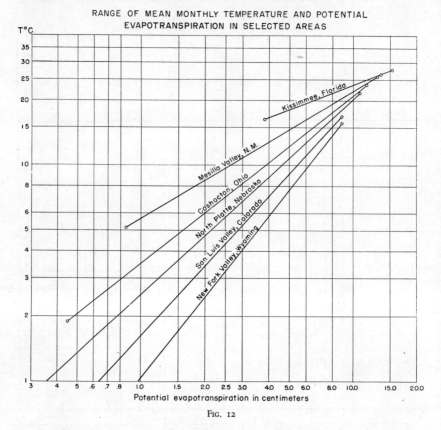

RANGE OF MEAN MONTHLY TEMPERATURE AND POTENTIAL EVAPOTRANSPIRATION IN SELECTED AREAS

Fig. 12

In order to determine potential evapotranspiration, mean monthly values of temperature must be available, and the latitude of the station must be known. Three steps are involved in the computation, and all three are accomplished by means of a nomogram and tables.

The first step is to obtain the heat index, I. Table IV gives monthly values of i corresponding to monthly mean temperatures. Summation of the 12 monthly values gives the index, I.

The next step is to determine unadjusted values of potential evapotranspiration from the nomogram in Figure 13.[28] Since there is a linear relation between the logarithm of temperature and the logarithm of unadjusted potential evapotranspiration, straight lines on the nomogram define the relationship. All lines pass through the point of convergence at

---

[28] A table has been prepared for this step, but it is too long to publish here. It will be placed on file at the American Geographical Society.

410

TABLE IV

T°C	.0	.1	.2	.3	.4	.5	.6	.7	.8	.9
0			.01	.01	.02	.03	.04	.05	.06	.07
1	.09	.10	.12	.13	.15	.16	.18	.20	.21	.23
2	.25	.27	.29	.31	.33	.35	.37	.39	.42	.44
3	.46	.48	.51	.53	.56	.58	.61	.63	.66	.69
4	.71	.74	.77	.80	.82	.85	.88	.91	.94	.97
5	1.00	1.03	1.06	1.09	1.12	1.16	1.19	1.22	1.25	1.29
6	1.32	1.35	1.39	1.42	1.45	1.49	1.52	1.56	1.59	1.63
7	1.66	1.70	1.74	1.77	1.81	1.85	1.89	1.92	1.96	2.00
8	2.04	2.08	2.12	2.15	2.19	2.23	2.27	2.31	2.35	2.39
9	2.44	2.48	2.52	2.56	2.60	2.64	2.69	2.73	2.77	2.81
10	2.86	2.90	2.94	2.99	3.03	3.08	3.12	3.16	3.21	3.25
11	3.30	3.34	3.39	3.44	3.48	3.53	3.58	3.62	3.67	3.72
12	3.76	3.81	3.86	3.91	3.96	4.00	4.05	4.10	4.15	4.20
13	4.25	4.30	4.35	4.40	4.45	4.50	4.55	4.60	4.65	4.70
14	4.75	4.81	4.86	4.91	4.96	5.01	5.07	5.12	5.17	5.22
15	5.28	5.33	5.38	5.44	5.49	5.55	5.60	5.65	5.71	5.76
16	5.82	5.87	5.93	5.98	6.04	6.10	6.15	6.21	6.26	6.32
17	6.38	6.44	6.49	6.55	6.61	6.66	6.72	6.78	6.84	6.90
18	6.95	7.01	7.07	7.13	7.19	7.25	7.31	7.37	7.43	7.49
19	7.55	7.61	7.67	7.73	7 79	7.85	7.91	7.97	8.03	8.10
20	8.16	8.22	8.28	8.34	8.41	8.47	8.53	8.59	8.66	8.72
21	8.78	8.85	8.91	8.97	9.04	9.10	9.17	9.23	9.29	9.36
22	9.42	9.49	9.55	9.62	9.68	9.75	9.82	9.88	9.95	10.01
23	10.08	10.15	10.21	10.28	10.35	10.41	10.48	10.55	10.62	10.68
24	10.75	10.82	10.89	10.95	11.02	11.09	11.16	11.23	11.30	11.37
25	11.44	11.50	11.57	11.64	11.71	11.78	11.85	11.92	11.99	12.06
26	12.13	12.21	12.28	12.35	12.42	12.49	12.56	12.63	12.70	12.78
27	12.85	12.92	12.99	13.07	13.14	13.21	13.28	13.36	13.43	13.50
28	13.58	13.65	13.72	13.80	13.87	13.94	14.02	14.09	14.17	14.24
29	14.32	14.39	14.47	14.54	14.62	14.69	14.77	14.84	14.92	14.99
30	15.07	15.15	15.22	15.30	15.38	15.45	15.53	15.61	15.68	15.76
31	15.84	15.92	15.99	16.07	16.15	16.23	16.30	16.38	16.46	16.54
32	16.62	16.70	16.78	16.85	16.93	17.01	17.09	17.17	17.25	17.33
33	17.41	17.49	17.57	17.65	17.73	17.81	17.89	17.97	18.05	18.13
34	18.22	18.30	18.38	18.46	18.54	18.62	18.70	18.79	18.87	18.95
35	19.03	19.11	19.20	19.28	19.36	19.45	19.53	19.61	19.69	19.78
36	19.86	19.95	20.03	20.11	20.20	20.28	20.36	20.45	20.53	20.62
37	20.70	20.79	20.87	20.96	21.04	21.13	21.21	21.30	21.38	21.47
38	21.56	21.64	21.73	21.81	21.90	21.99	22.07	22.16	22.25	22.33
39	22.42	22.51	22.59	22.68	22.77	22.86	22.95	23.03	23.12	23.21
40	23.30									

$t = 26.5°$ C. and $PE = 13.5$ cm. The slope of the line is determined by the heat index of the station. For example, the heat index of Brevard, N. C., is 56.0, and the line ruled on the nomogram represents the relationship between potential evapotranspiration and temperature at that place. At a mean temperature of 10° C. (50° F.) the unadjusted potential evapotranspiration is 3.6 centimeters.[29] Knowing the index (I) of the station, one sets a straightedge in

[29] For accurate computation it is desirable to make a nomogram on a larger scale on logarithm paper that is commercially available. Keuffel and Esser No. 359-112L (logarithmic, 2 x 3 cycles) is satisfactory. The point of convergence and the heat-index scale are easily added. A transparent rule may be used.

TABLE V—MEAN POSSIBLE DURATION OF SUNLIGHT IN THE NORTHERN AND SOUTHERN HEMISPHERES EXPRESSED IN UNITS OF 30 DAYS OF 12 HOURS EACH

N. Lat.	J	F	M	A	M	J	J	A	S	O	N	D
0	1.04	.94	1.04	1.01	1.04	1.01	1.04	1.04	1.01	1.04	1.01	1.04
5	1.02	.93	1.03	1.02	1.06	1.03	1.06	1.05	1.01	1.03	.99	1.02
10	1.00	.91	1.03	1.03	1.08	1.06	1.08	1.07	1.02	1.02	.98	.99
15	.97	.91	1.03	1.04	1.11	1.08	1.12	1.08	1.02	1.01	.95	.97
20	.95	.90	1.03	1.05	1.13	1.11	1.14	1.11	1.02	1.00	.93	.94
25	.93	.89	1.03	1.06	1.15	1.14	1.17	1.12	1.02	.99	.91	.91
26	.92	.88	1.03	1.06	1.15	1.15	1.17	1.12	1.02	.99	.91	.91
27	.92	.88	1.03	1.07	1.16	1.15	1.18	1.13	1.02	.99	.90	.90
28	.91	.88	1.03	1.07	1.16	1.16	1.18	1.13	1.02	.98	.90	.90
29	.91	.87	1.03	1.07	1.17	1.16	1.19	1.13	1.03	.98	.90	.89
30	.90	.87	1.03	1.08	1.18	1.17	1.20	1.14	1.03	.98	.89	.88
31	.90	.87	1.03	1.08	1.18	1.18	1.20	1.14	1.03	.98	.89	.88
32	.89	.36	1.03	1.08	1.19	1.19	1.21	1.15	1.03	.98	.88	.87
33	.88	.86	1.03	1.09	1.19	1.20	1.22	1.15	1.03	.97	.88	.86
34	.88	.85	1.03	1.09	1.20	1.20	1.22	1.16	1.03	.97	.87	.86
35	.87	.85	1.03	1.09	1.21	1.21	1.23	1.16	1.03	.97	.86	.85
36	.87	.85	1.03	1.10	1.21	1.22	1.24	1.16	1.03	.97	.86	.84
37	.86	.84	1.03	1.10	1.22	1.23	1.25	1.17	1.03	.97	.85	.83
38	.85	.84	1.03	1.10	1.23	1.24	1.25	1.17	1.04	.96	.84	.83
39	.85	.84	1.03	1.11	1.23	1.24	1.26	1.18	1.04	.96	.84	.82
40	.84	.83	1.03	1.11	1.24	1.25	1.27	1.18	1.04	.96	.83	.81
41	.83	.83	1.03	1.11	1.25	1.26	1.27	1.19	1.04	.96	.82	.80
42	.82	.83	1.03	1.12	1.26	1.27	1.28	1.19	1.04	.95	.82	.79
43	.81	.82	1.02	1.12	1.26	1.28	1.29	1.20	1.04	.95	.81	.77
44	.81	.82	1.02	1.13	1.27	1.29	1.30	1.20	1.04	.95	.80	.76
45	.80	.81	1.02	1.13	1.28	1.29	1.31	1.21	1.04	.94	.79	.75
46	.79	.81	1.02	1.13	1.29	1.31	1.32	1.22	1.04	.94	.79	.74
47	.77	.80	1.02	1.14	1.30	1.32	1.33	1.22	1.04	.93	.78	.73
48	.76	.80	1.02	1.14	1.31	1.33	1.34	1.23	1.05	.93	.77	.72
49	.75	.79	1.02	1.14	1.32	1.34	1.35	1.24	1.05	.93	.76	.71
50	.74	.78	1.02	1.15	1.33	1.36	1.37	1.25	1.06	.92	.76	.70
S. Lat.												
5	1.06	.95	1.04	1.00	1.02	.99	1.02	1.03	1.00	1.05	1.03	1.06
10	1.08	.97	1.05	.99	1.01	.96	1.00	1.01	1.00	1.06	1.05	1.10
15	1.12	.98	1.05	.98	.98	.94	.97	1.00	1.00	1.07	1.07	1.12
20	1.14	1.00	1.05	.97	.96	.91	.95	.99	1.00	1.08	1.09	1.15
25	1.17	1.01	1.05	.96	.94	.88	.93	.98	1.00	1.10	1.11	1.18
30	1.20	1.03	1.06	.95	.92	.85	.90	.96	1.00	1.12	1.14	1.21
35	1.23	1.04	1.06	.94	.89	.82	.87	.94	1.00	1.13	1.17	1.25
40	1.27	1.06	1.07	.93	.86	.78	.84	.92	1.00	1.15	1.20	1.29
42	1.28	1.07	1.07	.92	.85	.76	.82	.92	1.00	1.16	1.22	1.31
44	1.30	1.08	1.07	.92	.83	.74	.81	.91	.99	1.17	1.23	1.33
46	1.32	1.10	1.07	.91	.82	.72	.79	.90	.99	1.17	1.25	1.35
48	1.34	1.11	1.08	.90	.80	.70	.76	.89	.99	1.18	1.27	1.37
50	1.37	1.12	1.08	.89	.77	.67	.74	.88	.99	1.19	1.29	1.41

the appropriate position on the nomogram and reads potential evapotranspiration corresponding to the given mean temperature of the month. The nomogram is used only when tempera-

412

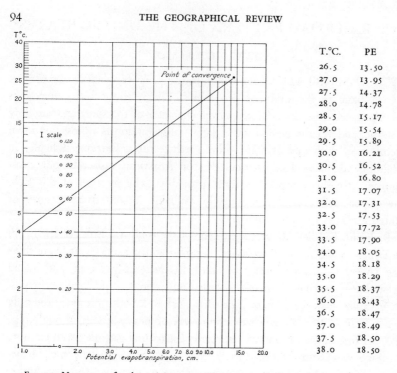

T.°C.	PE
26.5	13.50
27.0	13.95
27.5	14.37
28.0	14.78
28.5	15.17
29.0	15.54
29.5	15.89
30.0	16.21
30.5	16.52
31.0	16.80
31.5	17.07
32.0	17.31
32.5	17.53
33.0	17.72
33.5	17.90
34.0	18.05
34.5	18.18
35.0	18.29
35.5	18.37
36.0	18.43
36.5	18.47
37.0	18.49
37.5	18.50
38.0	18.50

FIG. 13—Nomogram for determining potential evapotranspiration and table for use at higher temperatures.

ture is 26.5° C. or less. (The accompanying table gives potential evapotranspiration corresponding to the higher temperatures). Twelve values are obtained for the 12 months. These are unadjusted values for months of 30 days of 12 hours each.

Finally, these values of potential evapotranspiration are adjusted for day and month length. Table V gives correction factors by which the unadjusted potential evapotranspiration of each month must be multiplied. The corrections must be the appropriate ones for the latitude of the station. The correction factor for 50° N. latitude will be used for all stations farther north. The same limitation applies in the Southern Hemisphere. Potential evapotranspiration is in centimeters. Summation of the 12 monthly values gives annual potential evapotranspiration in centimeters. The computations for Brevard, N. C., follow:

	J	F	M	A	M	J	J	A	S	O	N	D	Y
t.°C.	0.9	1.1	4.7	9.2	13.3	17.3	18.8	18.4	16.1	10.3	4.7	1.2	9.7
I	0.07	0.10	0.91	2.52	4.40	6.55	7.43	7.19	5.87	2.99	0.91	0.12	39.06
Unadj. PE	0.2	0.4	2.0	4.2	6.3	8.4	9.2	9.0	7.2	4.7	1.9	0.4	
Adj. PE	0.2	0.3	2.1	4.6	7.6	10.2	11.4	10.4	7.4	4.6	1.6	0.3	60.7

413

THE RAILROAD PATTERN OF THE UNITED STATES*

EDWARD L. ULLMAN

TRANSPORTATION is a true measure of space relations and as such is basic to the study of geography. The relations and connections between areas are reflected in the character of transport and the flow of traffic, and yet the geography of land transportation is almost unknown as compared with that of many other earth features. Extreme difficulty in obtaining adequate data, particularly for American railroads, our most important freight transport medium, probably explains most of this lack. This paper will present some newly available quantitative measures of United States rail facilities and traffic.

Railroads handled about 50 per cent of the total ton-miles of freight in the United States in 1939, coastwise shipping 26 per cent, Great Lakes shipping 10 per cent, pipe lines 7 per cent, highways 6 per cent, and inland waterways 2 per cent.[1] Railroads handled only about 10 per cent of the passenger-miles, however. Coastal and Great Lakes shipping provided the only serious competition to railroads as movers of heavy goods, though pipe lines, because of their economy, especially for natural gas, may well be more formidable rivals in the near future. Railroads, then, are the principal medium through which location factors operate, to influence the distribution of heavy industry and other basic economic activities.

TRACKAGE: MULTIPLE AND SINGLE

Conventional railroad maps either put all railroads in one category or classify them subjectively as main lines, secondary lines, and lines "not shown," a classification that might be acceptable if the lines were put in the proper categories, but they seldom are. There is probably as much difference between the poorest and best railroads as between the poorest automobile road and a superhighway. The heaviest-used 10 per cent of United States railroad mileage carries 50 per cent of the total ton-miles, the lightest-used 10 per cent less than half of 1 per cent; and their construction varies accordingly.[2]

Nevertheless, some general conclusions can be drawn from an over-all

---

* The author thanks the Milton Fund of Harvard University for financial support in the preparation of this article.

[1] Board of Investigation and Research: The National Traffic Pattern, *79th Congr., 1st Sess.*, Senate Doc. No. 83, 1945, p. 22, Table 2.

[2] Data from H. H. Copeland and Sons.

➤ DR. ULLMAN is assistant professor of regional planning, Harvard University.

map of United States railroads (Fig. 1). Density of lines is greatest in the northeastern quarter of the country; the Appalachian, Ozark, and Rocky Mountains show up as barriers; but the most noticeable change in pattern occurs in the level Great Plains at about the 100th meridian, the approximate boundary between humid and semiarid climate and between cropland and grazing land.

The principal long stretches of four-track lines are the Pennsylvania Railroad from Pittsburgh to New York and the New York Central from Cleveland to Albany (Fig. 2). Three-track lines add some mileage, mostly in the same area but extending out slightly farther. The westernmost extension of triple track is Aurora, Ill., the southernmost Washington, D. C., and even these points are not connected continuously with the other three- and four-track lines. Small in extent though the multiple-track sections are, they are almost unique, few other regions have any three- and four-track sections except a few short lines (one of the longer stretches is a 72-mile segment from London to Kettering, England; another, about 40 miles, from Brussels to Antwerp). Their presence in the United States reflects the concentration of enormous streams of traffic produced by the world's most highly developed continental region enjoying free trade. In other words, this is the railroad facility corresponding to American mass production for a large home market. Specifically, the three- and four-track sections are related also to topógraphy, as will be explained later.

The inclusion of two-track lines adds tracks particularly in the Northeast (Fig. 1) but also brings in two transcontinental lines, the Union Pacific and the Santa Fe, and main lines to the south—the Atlantic Coast Line, the Southern and the Illinois Central, and the coal-carrying roads of the Pocahontas region. Note the almost complete absence in Texas, probably explained by a combination of (1) movement through pipe lines of the principal commodity, oil; (2) the level terrain, which permits many alternative routes; and (3) the relatively recent development of the area at a time when competing transportation and improved methods of operating single-track lines were available.

In contrast with three- and four-track lines, the United States has a much smaller percentage of double track than most European countries.[3] In northwestern Europe double track is the rule. In the United States it is still the exception in most areas, for the following reasons:

---

[3] In France about half the lines are two track or more in comparison with about one-eighth in the United States (cf. Maurice Pardé: Les chemins de fer des États-Unis," *Annales de Géographie*, Vol. 56, 1947, pp. 274–294, ref. on p. 275; see note in this issue of the *Geogr. Rev.*). In England the proportion of double track is even higher.

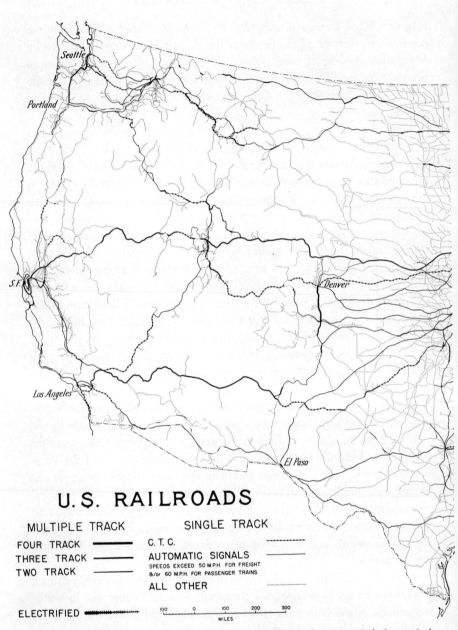

U.S. RAILROADS

MULTIPLE TRACK	SINGLE TRACK

MULTIPLE TRACK

FOUR TRACK ▬▬▬

THREE TRACK ▬▬▬

TWO TRACK ▬▬▬

SINGLE TRACK

C. T. C. ··············

AUTOMATIC SIGNALS ▬▬▬
SPEEDS EXCEED 50 M.P.H. FOR FREIGHT
&/or 60 M.P.H. FOR PASSENGER TRAINS

ALL OTHER ············

ELECTRIFIED ▬▬▬▬

```
100   0   100   200   300
        MILES
```

FIG. 1—Railroads of the United States. The lines are classified from most important to least important in the six categories shown. The categories chosen are the best quantitative indicators obtainable from present data.

416

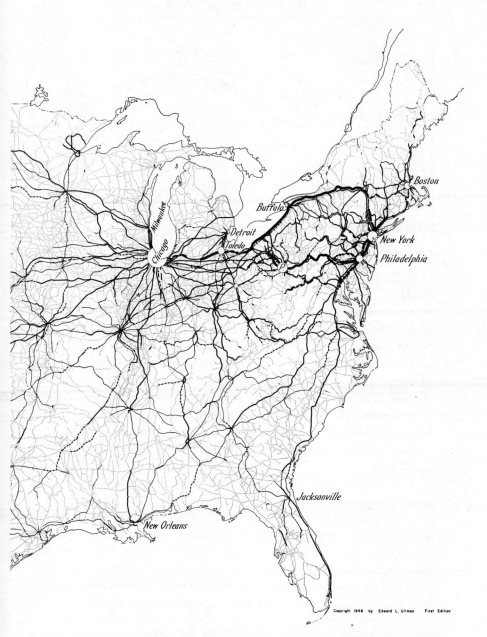

Copyright 1948 by Edward L. Ullman   First Edition

A two-color map about three times the size of Figure 1 with additional place names and railroad identifying initials is planned for sale at about $1.00 a copy, with discounts for quantities. Write Edward L. Ullman, Geographic Institute, 2 Divinity Avenue, Cambridge 38, Mass."

417

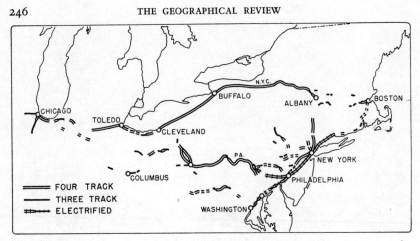

FIG. 2—Location of 3- and 4-track lines in the United States. All lines in this category, save a few short terminal stretches, are in the northeastern quarter of the country.

1. Many sections are less intensively developed than northwestern Europe.

2. The number of trains is smaller on many important railroads because of the relatively lighter passenger traffic and the much greater capacity of freight trains.

3. More alternative routes are available in most sections, mainly because of competition between privately owned roads, in contrast with state or regional monopolies in Europe.

4. Because of the preponderance of single track, operating methods have been adjusted to this condition, and single-track capacity has been increased, spectacularly so in recent years as a result of the improvement of signaling.

Between the single-track railroads of the United States differences are great, though quantitative measures of these differences are difficult to obtain. Type of ballast, roadbed, or weight of rail might be used, but the government does not report such figures, and it would be impracticable to obtain them from the individual roads. One possibility remains—signaling data. On this basis single-track roads can be divided into three categories, from highest to lowest capacity: lines with centralized traffic control (CTC), lines with automatic signals, and lines without automatic signals.

CENTRALIZED TRAFFIC CONTROL

Centralized traffic control is a recent development peculiar to the United States, which, in addition to other advantages, increases the capacity of

Fig. 3—Characteristic location of Centralized Traffic Control (CTC) at end of double track. Note the signs indicating end of double track and beginning of CTC. and the bridge and rough country in background where road changes to single track. On the Southern Pacific Railroad's overland route between Ogden and San Francisco at a point between Vista and Massie, Nevada. (Courtesy Union Switch and Signal Co.)

single-track lines so much that it is used as a cheap substitute for the addition of second track.[4] Estimates indicate that CTC increases capacity as much as 50 to 80 per cent. One of its characteristic locations is as a link between sections of double track (Fig. 3).

In the United States much CTC is in operation in the West (Fig. 1), because this is the region where traffic has increased most in recent years. Most heavy-traffic lines in the Northeast were already multiple-track, but some double-track lines have had CTC installed in place of a third track, as on the Boston and Maine, the Rock Island, and sections of the Norfolk and Western and the Chesapeake and Ohio.

In addition to increasing capacity, CTC makes for faster operation and improves the competitive position of some routes, such as the new, roundabout transcontinental via Denver composed of the Burlington, Rio Grande, and Western Pacific Railroads. It is also peculiarly suited to desert areas, where it is difficult to maintain train-order operators, as on the Union Pacific in southern Nevada.

AUTOMATIC BLOCK SIGNALS

Lines with automatic block signals round out the picture of main lines in the United States, though some main lines on which trains operate at

---

[4] "Principles and Economics of Signaling," in "American Railway Signaling, Principles, and Practice," Association of American Railroads, Signal Section, New York, 1946. (Chap. 3); ref. on p. 58.

419

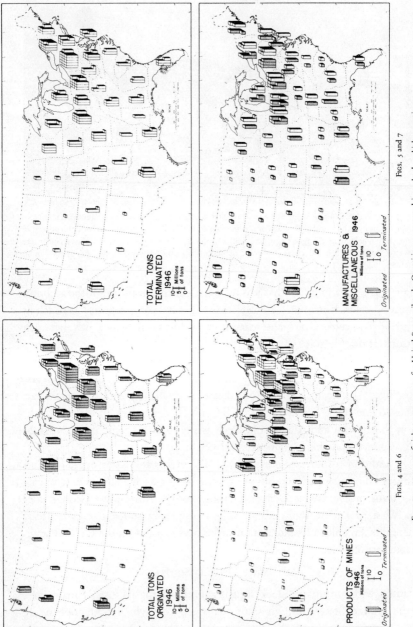

FIGS. 4 and 6

FIGS. 5 and 7

FIGURES 4 TO 10 are freight tonnage maps for United States railroads. Quantities are reported in carloads, which comprise 95 per cent of traffic; New England states are combined; so are Maryland, Delaware, and the District of Columbia. (Base is Goode Base Map No. 10, copyright 1937. Courtesy of University of Chicago Press.)

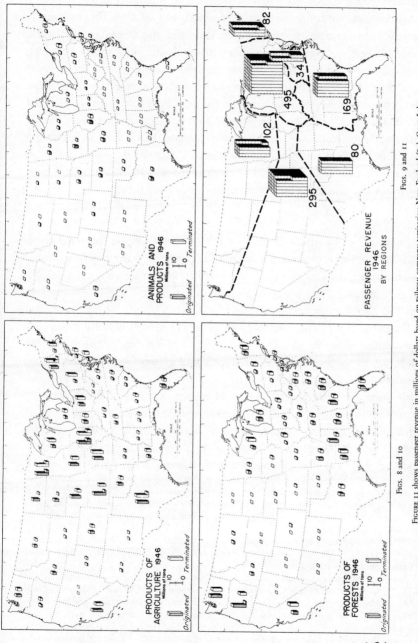

ANIMALS AND
PRODUCTS 1946

Millions of tons

10
Originated   0 Terminated

PRODUCTS OF
AGRICULTURE 1946

Millions of tons

10
Originated   0 Terminated

PRODUCTS OF
FORESTS 1946

Millions of tons

10
Originated   0 Terminated

PASSENGER REVENUE
1946
BY REGIONS

82

34

495

169

102

80

295

FIGS. 9 and 11

FIGS. 8 and 10

FIGURE 11 shows passenger revenue in millions of dollars based on railway company territories: New England (82), Great Lakes
and Central Eastern (combined, 495), Pocahontas (34), Southern (160), Southwestern (80), Central Western (295), and Northwestern
(102). (Base same as Figs. 4–10.)

421

relatively high speeds do not have automatic signals. Automatic block signals are installed to increase capacity, speed, and safety and consequently are good quantitative indicators of the character and importance of track. The trackage map (Fig. 1) shows lines with automatic block signals on which passenger trains operate at more than 60 miles an hour or freight trains at more than 50 miles an hour, because complete data were available for these lines only. Even this information was reported in usable form for the first time in 1948, as a result of an Interstate Commerce Commission safety order.[5] This eliminates some slower track with signals, particularly in mountain areas, though not as much as one might expect. It is therefore a combination measure, though most lines with automatic block signals are so well built that trains can operate at relatively high speeds over them.

TRAFFIC-PRODUCING AREAS

Inasmuch as no traffic-flow map for railroads can be compiled from available statistics comparable to maps of highway or waterway flow, traffic data must be provided in other forms—maps of tonnage by states (origin and termination) and passenger revenue by regions and textual descriptions of traffic on the most important lines.[6]

Study of the production maps (Figs. 4–11) reveals a fairly close correspondence with the trackage map (Fig. 1). The industrial Northeast stands out as the pre-eminent traffic-producing area for both freight and passengers, and the arid West and much of the Southeast show up as light-traffic areas. The Pocahontas region of eastern Kentucky, West Virginia, and contiguous Virginia originates enormous quantities of coal (Fig. 6) and thus resembles the neighboring industrial belt in heavy-traffic characteristics, though, as might be expected, it is not a heavy passenger-traffic producer (Fig. 11). The Pocahontas region has a freight revenue of 325

---

[5] Map showing automatic-signal locations was compiled from point-to-point tables in ICC 29543, "Appliances, Methods, and Systems Intended to Promote Safety of Railroad Operation," returns to ICC questionnaire forms RR-1, 2, 3, 4, 5, and 6, Interstate Commerce Commission, Washington, D. C., 1947. Unpublished records.

[6] H. H. Copeland and Sons have prepared, at great expense, confidential traffic-flow maps for United States railroads. They will not permit these maps to be reproduced, but they have kindly allowed me to use them for research and teaching.

The source of the tonnage maps is the Interstate Commerce Commission's *Statement No. M-550* (SCS), "Tons of Revenue Freight Originated and Tons Terminated in Carloads by Classes of Commodities and by Geographic Areas," calendar year 1946. This has appeared annually since 1940.

The source of the passenger statistics is *Statistics of Railways in the United States, 1946*, Interstate Commerce Commission, Washington, 1948, which covers only the railroad regions. Statistics by states are not available except for a two-week test period in 1933, in the Federal Coordinator of Transportation's "Passenger Traffic Report," 1934, Appendix 2. Freight statistics by stations and trade areas were also published in the "Freight Traffic Report," 1935, Appendix 3, but they give a misleading picture.

million dollars and a passenger revenue of only 34 million, in contrast with New England's 176-million-dollar freight revenue and 83-million-dollar passenger revenue, a ratio of freight to passenger revenue of almost 10 to 1 for the Pocahontas region and about 2 to 1 for New England.[7]

Products of mines made up more than one-half of the freight tonnage originated by United States railroads in 1946, and in years past the proportion was even higher. Coal is by far the most important single commodity. In 1939 it accounted for more than one-third of the total tons carried and provided more than one-fifth of the total freight revenue.[8]

Some features of the mineral traffic in addition to the heavy movement in the coal areas are: (1) the large tonnage originating in Minnesota, representing principally iron ore from the Mesabi range and reflected on the trackage map by the short double-track lines from the Mesabi to the north shore of Lake Superior, where transshipment is made to lake steamers; (2) the large net imports in the nonmining, industrial areas such as New England and New Jersey; and (3) the rather surprisingly large traffic in Florida, two-thirds of which is phosphate rock hauled a few miles from the vicinity of Bartow, America's chief producer of phosphate, principally to Tampa for transshipment by boat.

Maps showing the other major commodity groups tell their own story (Figs. 7–10). The products-of-agriculture map (Fig. 8) is illustrative of the relations between production geography and transportation. The general eastward movement of agricultural products into the populous industrial belt is readily inferred: the important originating areas are the Corn Belt and the Spring Wheat and Winter Wheat Belts of Mid-America; the disproportionately heavy terminating areas are New England and the Middle Atlantic States. Some apparent anomalies may be noted. For example, Iowa, the leading agricultural state, does not originate as much tonnage as its poorer neighbors Minnesota, Nebraska, and Kansas. This is quite logical, however, because Iowa, in contrast with a cash-grain state such as Kansas, feeds its corn to hogs on the farm and thus ships out a lighter-weight but higher-value finished product.

MAIN ROUTES[9]

Two broad zones of movement stand out in the American railroad traffic

---

[7] *Statistics of Railways in the United States, 1946 (op. cit.)*, Table 158, p. 179.

[8] Board of Investigation and Research: Economics of Coal Traffic Flow, *79th Congr., 1st Sess., Senate Doc. No. 82*, 1945, p. 11, Table 8.

[9] Data for this section have been obtained from a study of Copeland traffic-density charts, railroad passenger timetables, and other sources.

pattern: first, and most important, the west-east movement across the industrial belt; second, the somewhat parallel movement from the Pocahontas and eastern Kentucky coal fields to the northwest and east. Density of traffic on these sets of lines is so heavy that they stand out even more sharply than on the trackage maps. A third major set of lines might be added by including the eastern ends of the transcontinental lines crossing Minnesota, Iowa, and Missouri. Density on these lines, however, is far lighter than on the other two sets.

By far the heaviest traffic in America is on the Pennsylvania from Pittsburgh to New York. The next heaviest, but much less important for freight, is on the New York Central through the Mohawk corridor (Fig. 2). This route divides in the vicinity of Albany, freight density being higher across the Berkshires toward Boston on the Boston and Maine and the Boston and Albany than south along the Hudson to New York City. New York City, however, stands out as the focus of eastern seaboard traffic, because of the heavy freight flows on the Lackawanna, the Erie, the Lehigh Valley, and the Reading-Jersey Central as well as on the Pennsylvania.

The water-level route of the New York Central along the Hudson and Mohawk is a great advantage and enables the road to compete with the Pennsylvania, even though the Central's distance from New York to Chicago is 961 miles, as compared with the Pennsylvania's 908 miles.[10] Although the New York Central is an important route, it is minor in comparison with the combined flows to New York over the other roads from the West and has less than half the freight density of the Pennsylvania alone, which climbs over the mountains.[11] This difference in density is reflected in facilities. Although both lines are four-track, all four tracks of the Pennsylvania are main tracks, whereas on the New York Central only two are built to highest speed standards. Weight of rail on the Pennsylvania is 152 pounds a yard, on the New York Central 127 pounds. Both lines have automatic train-stop or cab signals that make signal changes more quickly visible and thus tend to speed operation and raise capacity. The Pennsylvania, however, has recently installed carrier radio communication on all passenger trains between Harrisburg and Pittsburgh and on all freight trains for a good part

---

[10] Distances via the freight cutoffs on both lines are slightly shorter (the Trenton cutoff north of Philadelphia on the Pennsylvania, and the Castleton cutoff south of Albany on the New York Central).

[11] In number of passenger trains the New York Central seems to be slightly ahead, with 34 scheduled trains in one direction along the Mohawk, as compared with 28 for the Pennsylvania across the Alleghenies. Additional sections are also run on each line. The heaviest passenger density in the United States, outside suburban areas, is on the Pennsylvania between Philadelphia and New York and on the New Haven between New York and New Haven, followed by the Pennsylvania's line to Washington.

of this stretch, which further speeds operations and raises capacity.[12] Also, from Harrisburg to New York the Pennsylvania is electrified—a third capacity-raising factor. Statements such as "The Pennsylvania route is scarcely second in importance to the New York Central" no longer have a place in geography textbooks.

Southward across the great east-west trunks, such as the Pennsylvania and the Baltimore and Ohio, the percentage of coal handled increases until a peak of 75 per cent or more is reached on such roads as the Chesapeake and Ohio, the Norfolk and Western, and the Virginian. About two-thirds of the coal moves west and one-third east;[13] of the westbound, much is ultimately destined for transshipment from Lake Erie ports, primarily Toledo;[14] the eastbound goes principally to Hampton Roads for transshipment northward by boat up the Atlantic coast, to provide eastern New England with coal.

Space does not permit individual notice of the remaining main lines, but they can be readily picked out from the trackage maps. Mention should be made, however, of the Louisville and Nashville's coal line from the southeastern Kentucky coal fields to Cincinnati, which has traffic comparable with that of all but the heaviest-density lines just mentioned and a heavier freight density than any other line outside the climax area except the short Mesabi iron-ore roads. Other heavy-density stretches are the Illinois Central from the Illinois coal fields northward, the Santa Fe in eastern Kansas, and the Union Pacific between Omaha and Salt Lake City. The Union Pacific has the heaviest freight density (for any considerable distance) of the transcontinental lines, with greatest concentration across Wyoming, primarily bridge traffic funneled across the Continental Divide but also some local coal.

The heaviest Canadian freight density[15] is between Winnipeg and Port Arthur – Fort William, principally wheat from the Prairie Provinces headed for Lake shipment and export. Examination of Canadian traffic-density charts shows that little crosses the United States border. The main Canadian flows are strikingly east-west and remain within Canada.

---

[12] "Train Communications on Pennsylvania," *Railway Age*, Vol. 123, 1947, pp. 516–520.

[13] On the Norfolk and Western in recent years 68 per cent was westbound (E. A. Grubb: Coal Supports the Norfolk and Western, *Trains*, Vol. 8, No. 1, 1947, p. 14).

[14] A. G. Ballert: The Coal Trade of the Great Lakes and the Port of Toledo, *Geogr. Rev.*, Vol. 38, 1948, pp. 194–205.

[15] In contrast with the United States, Canadian traffic density has been mapped in published form, in "Report of the Royal Commission to Inquire into Railways and Transportation in Canada, 1931–32," Ottawa, 1932. The effort to keep western Canadian traffic in Canada has been pointed out by S. B. Jones in "The Forty-Ninth Parallel in the Great Plains, *Journ. of Geogr.*, Vol. 31, 1932, pp. 357–368, and "The Cordilleran Section of the Canada–United States Borderland," *Geogr. Journ.*, Vol. 89, 1937, pp. 439–450.

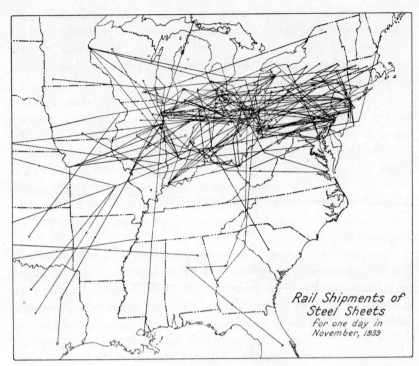

FIG. 12—One-day shipments of steel sheets in November, 1939. This map is representative of cross-hauling. Elimination of the basing point system will drastically reduce crosshauling.

SOME TRAFFIC CHARACTERISTICS

Four features characterizing traffic flows on United States railroads should be noted.

1. The routes just described are composed of a series of overlapping long, medium, and short hauls. The average length of freight haul in 1946 was 224 miles, with a range from 170 miles in the eastern district to 303 miles in the western district; the average passenger journey exclusive of commutation was 130 miles (including commutation 82 miles), with a range from the eastern district to the western of 76 miles to 307 miles exclusive of commutation (51 to 205 including commutation).[16]

2. Direction of freight movement is often unbalanced; in general, it is heavy toward the industrial belt and light outbound, with a normal ratio of about 2 to 1 eastbound over westbound on transcontinentals and as much as 3 to 1 or higher in New England.

3. Although the all-important movement of most bulky freight involves

---

[16] *Statistics of Railways in the United States, 1946 (op. cit.)*, p. 38. Table 44.

426

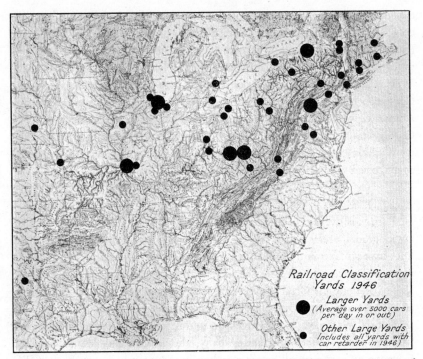

FIG. 13—Location of principal freight classification yards in the United States, 1946. Location of larger yards based on Freight Terminal Survey of Association of American Railroads, 1946; other large yards from same source plus all yards with car retarders (indicative of the larger and busier yards), as reported by Union Switch and Signal Company and General Railway Signal Company. (Base reproduced from Erwin Raisz: Map of Landforms of the United States, 1939.)

relatively little crosshauling, higher-value freight may show considerable crosshauling (Fig. 12). The recent Supreme Court decision abolishing the basing-point system for cement and the voluntary action of the steel industry in abolishing basing points for steel may eliminate much crosshauling in these commodities, but brand names, national advertising, and other factors apparently will maintain crosshauling in higher-priced goods.

4. Goods do not always move by the shortest or even easiest route between terminals. The Federal Coordinator of Transportation estimated that in 1934 the average freight car moved above 11 per cent farther than if it had used a direct line in common use.[17] Studies of special commodities by the Board of Investigation and Research in 1939 indicated an average circuity of almost 20 per cent.[18] Competition between railroads is the primary

[17] Freight Traffic Report (op. cit.), Vol. I, p. 77.
[18] The National Traffic Pattern (op. cit.), p. 47.

explanation, but valid reasons exist for some circuity, such as avoidance of congested terminals. In a few cases a longer route even has cheaper rates (justified on the grounds of necessarily slower service) such as the so-called differential routes via Canadian lines from New England to the Middle West. Passenger traffic has less circuity because loss of time means more. Geographers, however, will find it to their advantage to know that there are alternative routes they can take, especially for longer trips, such as from Chicago to New York via Hamilton, Ont., Buffalo, Pittsburgh, Cincinnati, or Washington, D. C., all for the same fare. Don't, however, trust a local agent to sell you a circuitous ticket on short notice!

RELATION OF RAILROADS TO TOPOGRAPHY AND PRODUCTION

Railroads are extraordinarily sensitive to grades. Many routes try to avoid grades greater than 0.5 of 1 per cent. Most transcontinental main lines have a maximum grade of 2.2. per cent across mountains. Valley alignments on a national scale are discernible in many places, as along the Mohawk Valley or along the Great Valley. One effect of grades is to cause railroads to add extra tracks, even though cost of construction is high, in order to enable the return of pusher locomotives or to run passenger trains round slow freights, as on the Boston and Albany, the Boston and Maine, and the Lackawanna, or to install better signaling in mountains—for example, CTC on the Union Pacific across the Blue Mountains of Oregon. Most important, however, are the reduction in number of through routes and the channelizing of traffic, which necessitates extra tracks in the constrictions, as on the Baltimore and Ohio across the eastern Appalachians.

The funneling of traffic through mountains places most large classification yards at points where rail lines fan out on leaving the barrier zone (Fig. 13); such points are generally not close to large cities. In addition, of course, most of the large yards are in the heavy-density area, the northeastern quarter of the country.

Sensitive though railroads are to grades, the predominant locating factor seems to be traffic. The heaviest-traveled route in the United States, the Pennsylvania, climbs the mountains to connect the east and west sides of the all-important manufacturing belt. Railroad facilities generally are most numerous in high-production areas; the coal in the Appalachians, for example, acts as a powerful magnet drawing railroads to these mountains. Although relief strongly affects the local or site alignments of major American railroads, production and traffic appear as more important determinants of their regional arrangement and location.

428

RECENT INDUSTRIAL DEVELOPMENT
IN THE GULF SOUTH

JAMES J. PARSONS

THE physical growth of America's industrial plant in the past decade has perhaps nowhere been more spectacular than in the Gulf South. Unsurpassed accessibility to petroleum, natural gas, and key chemical raw materials is here combined with low power costs, tidewater shipping facilities, a mild climate, and a growing regional and export market. Each of these factors, together with a boundless enthusiasm for regional promotion, has contributed to a proliferation of industrial plants on the coastal plains and in the piny woods that is remolding the face of the landscape in much of Texas and Louisiana.

Unlike the Pacific Coast States, where also industrial expansion has been greatly accelerated in recent years, neither Texas nor Louisiana has received any mass influx of population. In fact, between 1940 and 1947, the period of maximum population displacement in the United States, there was an estimated net out-migration of 140,000 persons from Texas and 119,000 from Louisiana.[1] The total population of the two states, estimated by the Bureau of the Census at 9,806,000 in 1948, has increased 22 per cent since 1930, a rate only 3 per cent above that for the nation and one that is due wholly to natural increase.

EXTENT AND CHARACTER OF INDUSTRIAL GROWTH

The bulk of the manufacturing employment is concentrated in a few metropolitan areas. More than half of Texas' 242,000 production workers reported in the 1947 Census of Manufactures were in four of the 254 counties: Harris (Houston), Dallas, Tarrant (Fort Worth), and Jefferson (Beaumont–Port Arthur). In Louisiana, where 50,000 of the 110,000 wage earners were in the New Orleans Metropolitan District and East Baton Rouge Parish, the concentration is partly camouflaged by the highly dispersed lumbering and pulp and paper industries, which together accounted for more than one-third of the state total.

---

[1] "Estimates of the Population of the United States, by Regions, Divisions, and States: July 1, 1940 to 1947," *Current Population Repts.: Population Estimates*, Ser. P-25, No. 12, U. S. Bureau of the Census, Aug. 9, 1948.

▶ MR. PARSONS is instructor in geography at the University of California, Berkeley. He contributed "California Manufacturing" to the April, 1949, number of the *Geographical Review*.

429

Here, as elsewhere, the rural farm population, in part displaced by the increased mechanization of agriculture, has been drawn in large numbers to the urban centers. There are few cities in the Gulf South that cannot boast a doubled population in the past 30 years or less. Oil-rich Houston, bell-wether of the Gulf Coast cities and leading industrial metropolis of the South, has witnessed a metropolitan (Harris County) population growth from 63,000 in 1900 to an estimated 780,000 in 1949. The city is the center of the oil and gas industry and one of the most important deep-water ports in the country. In tangible form its growth is evidenced by modern skyscrapers, endless new bungalow subdivisions, factories and warehouses along the Ship Channel and the five trunk-line railroads that radiate from the center of the city. Unlike most older cities, Houston has not piled up a "vertical popula-tion." Both in its sprawling physical structure and in its ebullient confidence in its own destiny it resembles Los Angeles more than any other city in the country.

In contrast, New Orleans (estimated metropolitan district population 666,000) and Dallas (estimated Dallas County population 545,000) are financial and wholesaling centers, where industrial expansion has been largely confined to the food, apparel, and other consumers' goods industries.

Between 1929 and 1947, comparable years of capacity peacetime produc-tion, factory jobs in Texas and Louisiana increased 60 per cent. Yet neither state qualifies even remotely as "industrialized," their combined wage-earner density (percentage of the total population engaged in manufacturing) being 3.3 per cent in 1947, as compared with 7.9 per cent for the nation. Together they contained an estimated 6.7 per cent of the total population yet accounted for only 2.7 per cent of the nation's factory pay roll (in dollars), 3.0 per cent of its production workers, and 3.2 per cent of all "value added by manu-facture." Although gains have been registered in each of these categories, the economy is still exploitative, based primarily on oil and cotton.

Nevertheless, the recent growth of the physical industrial plant in Texas and Louisiana has been impressive. The vast facilities built to meet wartime emergencies have nearly all been converted to peacetime production, and private capital has financed a huge postwar building program. The petro-leum refining and chemical industries, with their peculiarly high ratio of capital investment to labor force, can probably be credited with more than 90 per cent of all new development. The chemical industry, in particular, has experienced a striking growth: the number of production workers in Texas and Louisiana rose from 10,700 in 1939 to 27,400 in 1947. Capital has come in equal measure from the government (especially for synthetic rubber) and from established eastern concerns, several of which have concentrated a large part of their postwar expansion along the Gulf Coast. Labor has been supplied almost entirely from the local market at wage rates prevailing in the Northeast, but modern technological advances, especially automatic instrument control, have meant relatively few jobs in relation to investment. The largest

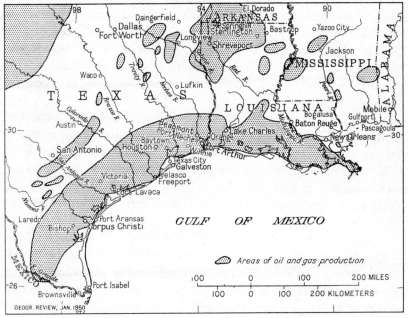

FIG. 1—The Gulf South, showing generalized areas of oil and gas production.

chemical plant in the region, Dow's twin installation at the mouth of the Brazos River in Texas, is manned by only 3100 employees, though it represents an investment of more than 165 million dollars.

Virtually all the new plants are removed from existing built-up areas, where land has been cheap, taxes lower, and waste disposal problems at the minimum. The grimy, congested factory district of the older manufacturing centers is not a part of the industrial landscape developing on the Gulf Coast. Larger plants commonly stand in the center of vast tracts of company-owned land. In some places, such as Lake Charles, La., and Borger, Tex., much of the working population lives in new model communities, usually government-built and often several miles from the parent city. The population within a 15-mile radius of Borger, a synthetic rubber, carbon black, and petroleum refining center in the Texas Panhandle, has increased since 1940 from 15,000 to an estimated 45,000. The growth of the Freeport-Velasco area, site of the Dow Chemical Company, has been fully as spectacular.

The extreme sensitivity of the chemical industry to availability of raw materials accounts for the larger part of the industrial development, especially in the Gulf port cities. Synthetic organics, made from ethylene, propylene, and butylene derived from petroleum and natural gas, are the most important group of chemicals produced. Seventy-five chemical companies are said to have built plants on the Gulf Coast since 1940, half of them since the end of the war. Investment in chemical plant facilities here between 1940 and 1947 represented 26 per cent of the national investment in such facilities,[2] in a period when the chemical industry was nearly doubling its productive capacity.

Government financing of war plants between 1939 and 1945 in the West South Central States (Louisiana, Texas, Oklahoma, and Arkansas) was nearly five times their share of "value added" in 1939.[3] Texas led all the states in the dollar value of industrial construction contracts awarded in both 1946 and 1947, according to trade estimates. In 1948, although ranking second to California, it contributed 12.8 per cent to the country's industrial building.[4]

PORT DEVELOPMENT

Development of deep-water shipping facilities was a necessary preliminary to much of the Gulf Coast's new industrial activity. Outshipments of wheat, cotton, crude oil, refinery products, sulphur, and phosphate rock still constitute the main part of the Gulf ports' commerce, but manufactured products are moving increasingly to both foreign and eastern markets. Completion of the 80-million-dollar, 1100-mile Intracoastal Waterway in

---

[2] *Chemical and Engineering News*, Vol. 25, 1947, p. 79.

[3] A. J. Wright: Recent Changes in the Concentration of Manufacturing, *Annals Assn. of Amer. Geogrs.*, Vol. 35, 1945, pp. 144–166; reference on p. 161.

[4] An analysis of industrial construction contracts announced in the *Engineering News-Record* from July, 1945, through December, 1948 (released in processed form by the Territorial Information Department, 140 South Dearborn St., Chicago, Ill.), shows a total investment of 323 million dollars in Texas, as compared with 191 million in California, 169 million in Ohio, 147 million in Pennsylvania, and 118 million in Illinois. Among leading industrial areas, Houston ranks first with 110 million dollars of new projects, as compared with New York–Newark–Jersey City, 88 million; Pittsburgh, 79; Chicago, 79; Detroit, 76; Cleveland, 75; Philadelphia-Camden, 56; Los Angeles, 55; and San Francisco–Oakland, 48. Omitted from these calculations are contracts valued at less than $100,000 and those carried out by the industrial concern itself.

For chemical plants alone, for the longer period 1939-1947, combined government and private investment (in millions of dollars) within the Gulf South was distributed as follows: Sabine-Neches industrial area, 166; Freeport-Velasco, 163; Houston, 144; Baton Rouge, 113; Lake Charles, 49; Borger, 49; Corpus Christi, 45. Magnesium facilities are included in these figures (computed from a list of plants in *Chemical Industries*, Vol. 60, 1947, pp. 404–406, and other sources).

mid-1949 has given Brownsville and the lower Rio Grande Valley a direct barge link with the Mississippi River system. Feeder canals connect to eleven inland Texas towns in addition to those served by the six deep waterways between the Mississippi and the Rio Grande: Calcasieu (Lake Charles), Sabine-Neches (Port Arthur, Beaumont, Orange), Galveston-Texas City-Houston, Freeport, Port Aransas-Corpus Christi, and Brazos Island (Port Isabel-Brownsville). Dallas and Fort Worth, 300 miles inland, expect to be linked eventually to the Intracoastal by canalization of the Trinity River, as does Shreveport on the Red River.

As American industry increasingly reaches across the seas for its raw materials,[5] the Gulf ports should be in a more and more favorable position to supply the westward-moving American market. In the past, imports have been significant only at New Orleans and Mobile, but recently coffee, jute, newsprint, and bananas have been moving into Houston in growing quantities. South American ores and petroleum may one day become major imports here, depending in part on the long-term policy for conservation of domestic resources adopted by industry and government.

The new stature of the Gulf ports is indicated by the fact that in a recent year eight of them—Houston, New Orleans, Beaumont, Port Arthur, Texas City, Port Aransas, Lake Charles, and Corpus Christi—were among the country's fourteen leading deep-water ports in tonnage. Except for Houston and New Orleans, petroleum products, destined primarily for domestic markets, constituted all but an insignificant part of the total. In 1948 the Gulf ports handled between 20 and 25 per cent of the water-borne foreign commerce of the country, measured either by value or by weight, and a considerably larger percentage of shipments on Army and Navy chartered vessels. New Orleans still ranks an easy first among them in foreign trade, with Houston and Galveston competing for second place and Mobile fourth.

Everywhere in the Gulf South port development has depended more on community push and drive than on natural advantages. Texas alone has 13 deep-water ports that are largely man-made, the most important of which owe their existence to the Houston Ship Channel and the Sabine-Neches Waterway. The former is a 58-mile-long artificial channel, 34 feet deep, which links Houston with Galveston Bay and the Gulf of Mexico. Regular sailings from the Port of Houston began in 1915, with the completion of the dredging of Buffalo Bayou. In 1948 the port handled more than 40 million tons (of which 5½ million was foreign trade), a new Gulf port record. It has

[5] Jean Gottmann: Changements de structure dans la géographie humaine des États-Unis, *Annales de Géogr.*, Vol. 57, 1948, pp. 131–145 and 219–226.

remained basically a raw-materials port, with more than 80 per cent of its cargo petroleum products and much of the rest cotton. Galveston, a "dry cargo" port, ships principally cotton, wheat, and sulphur. Since the destruction of the Texas City port facilities in 1947, considerable Bolivian tin concentrate has moved across Galveston's wharves.

FIG. 2—Turning basin of the Houston Ship Channel, looking east. The channel is lined with industrial plants for much of the 26 miles from the turning basin to Galveston Bay. (Courtesy of the Houston Port and Traffic Bureau.)

The Sabine-Neches Waterway links Beaumont, Orange, Port Arthur, and Port Neches to the Gulf by 61 miles of channel dredged into the soft organic muck of the coastal plain. Collectively the Sabine-Neches ports outrank Houston in tonnage handled, owing chiefly to heavy shipments of petroleum products. At Port Arthur, one of the Gulf Coast's youngest, most rapidly growing, and most interesting cities, two of the largest oil refineries in the country stand side by side, employing 11,000 persons and drawing oil by pipe line from East and West Texas, Oklahoma, Kansas, and Louisiana.[6]

An aggressive campaign to win the interior trade once securely in the hands of eastern ports has permitted New Orleans to challenge Baltimore for the title of "America's Second Port" in terms of value of cargo handled, in the same way that Houston has moved into contention for second place on the basis of tonnage. Baton Rouge, 220 miles from the mouth of the Missis-

[6] J. W. Newton: The Sabine-Neches Area of Texas: An Industrial Survey, Texas Geogr. Mag., Vol. 13, 1949, pp. 5–10.

sippi, at the head of navigation for ocean-going vessels, ships the bulk of the petroleum products from its great refinery upstream by barge to the interior of the continent. Bauxite from the Guianas is imported for the new Kaiser alumina plant. Bauxite also moves in significant quantities to Mobile, where an Aluminum Company of America plant has been operating since 1939, and to Gulfport, Miss., a government stock-piling depot.

PETROLEUM

Petroleum and natural gas are the basis for the Gulf Coast's rapid urban and industrial growth. Since the Spindletop field came in south of Beaumont in 1901, crude-oil production in Texas alone has amounted to one-third of the all-time production of the United States and 21 per cent of world production. In 1947, Texas produced 44 per cent of the country's crude oil and contained 55 per cent of its proved reserves. Louisiana and Mississippi, with 10 per cent of the reserves, have become major producing states. Since 1941, Louisiana's new coastal fields have pushed it ahead of Oklahoma and Illinois to rank third, behind Texas and California.

Although changing standards of recovery and conservation, together with new developments offshore on the so-called "tidelands," have raised proved Gulf Coast petroleum reserves to new highs, the area is nonetheless living on accumulated capital rather than on the interest of its natural wealth. Vastly increased domestic requirements for crude petroleum (now close to six million barrels a day) will hasten the time when resort must be had to import, shale, or synthetic sources. Soaring exploration and recovery costs may even price Gulf Coast oil out of some of its markets long before exhaustion threatens. Recently, for example, comparison of the costs of many synthetic organic chemicals when produced from petroleum and from coal (via acetylene) has become increasingly favorable to coal.[7] This trend, if continued, may have serious implications for the burgeoning petrochemical industry.

Petroleum refining has tended in recent years to be located nearer to market centers than to producing areas, apparently because markets are more assured and constant than crude-oil supplies.[8] On the Gulf Coast, however, this tendency has been less pronounced than elsewhere. In 1947 refinery runs in Texas and Louisiana represented 68 per cent of crude-oil production in the two states (as compared with 74 per cent in 1940), in part owing to cheap

---

[7] H. W. Zabel: What's Ahead for Petrochemicals? *Chemical Industries*, Vol. 62, 1948, pp. 390–393.

[8] On this general subject see "Petroleum Transportation," *Industry Rept.: Domestic Transportation*, U. S. Dept. of Commerce, Office of Domestic Commerce, Jan.–Mar., 1949.

water transportation available to domestic markets, in part to the mild winters, which cut refinery construction costs by the elimination of much costly weatherproofing, pipe insulation, and roofing.

Thirty-four per cent of the country's petroleum refining capacity is in Texas and Louisiana (totaling 2,076,950 barrels of crude oil daily). Most of the refineries are clustered in four principal districts: Houston–Texas City (802,000 barrels), Beaumont–Port Arthur (705,000), Baton Rouge (235,000), and Lake Charles (131,000). Corpus Christi (88,000 barrels) and New Orleans (75,000) are secondary centers. Of the twelve largest refineries in the country, six are on the Gulf Coast, including the two largest, at Baton Rouge and at Baytown on the Houston Ship Channel.

This large refining capacity has been a powerful attraction to the segment of the chemical industry concerned with the synthesizing of organic molecules. Formerly wasted refinery gases, together with natural gas, provide the starting point for a vast array of synthetic organic chemicals, which in turn are the building blocks for many industrial alcohols, solvents, plastics, explosives, detergents, synthetic rubbers, and synthetic fibers as well as vital raw materials for 100-octane gasoline.[9] Indeed, the manufacture of high-octane gasoline is itself a complex chemical operation. The high degree of versatility inherent in synthetic organic chemicals ("synthetic" in the sense that they do not occur in nature but are products of chemical synthesis and conversion) leaves room for much fruitful industrial research. Moreover, isomeric modifications in the paraffin, olefin, and acetylene groups are said to give the aliphatic hydrocarbons of petroleum a wider range of industrial possibilities than the aromatic hydrocarbons of coal tar.[10]

NATURAL GAS AS A RAW MATERIAL

The increased industrial use of natural gas, both as an industrial raw material and as a clean, cheap, and convenient fuel, has been of particular significance to the Gulf South.[11] There is much confusion regarding reserves, but in B.T.U. (British thermal unit) equivalents natural-gas reserves probably exceed petroleum reserves. It has been authoritatively predicted that "the time will come when the products of natural gas and its contained liquids will be more important than the production of oil" in Texas.[12]

---

[9] An exhaustive series of articles by E. H. Johnson on the industrial development of Texas, especially the chemical industry, appeared in the *Texas Business Review* between 1943 and 1945 (Bureau of Business Research, College of Business Administration, University of Texas, Austin).

[10] Gustav Egloff, quoted in the *Texas Business Review*, Vol. 18, No. 12, 1945, p. 12.

[11] K. W. Johnson: The Natural Gas Industry of the Southwest and Its Significance to Industrial Development, *Monthly Business Rev.*, Federal Reserve Bank of Dallas, Vol. 34, 1949, pp. 33–41.

[12] E. L. DeGolyer in the *Dallas Morning News*, May 22, 1949.

Within the past 10 years natural gas has become an important source of premium gasoline. At nearly 200 cycling and natural-gasoline plants in Texas and Louisiana condensate or distillate is separated from both casing-head and gas-well gas, and the residue, or dry gas, is compressed and either returned to the reservoir or marketed to pipe lines. Economic considerations have been largely the reason for the effective conservation measures for casing-head gas carried out in recent years. In 1948 the Texas Railroad Commission began imposing disciplinary shutdowns on some Gulf Coast fields where flaring of casing-head gas continued. Some sentiment has even been expressed against the further export of Texas and Louisiana gas by pipe lines to domestic and industrial markets in the North, East, and West. The lower house of the Texas Legislature passed a resolution in the spring of 1949 directing the State Railroad Commission actively to oppose any additional interstate pipe lines that would export gas from Texas, indicating that the state should keep its gas at home as an inducement to industry.

Competitive bidding by pipe-line companies has forced the field price of natural gas from two cents a thousand cubic feet to as much as 10 cents within less than 10 years. The price of butane and propane, in increasing demand as domestic fuels, has also risen enormously. Further, the desire of the oil companies to produce maximum amounts of hydrocarbon fuels from existing crude supplies is making refinery gases, another favorite industrial raw material, less and less available. Only the extremely high rate of obsolescence allowed for in the petrochemical industry has made huge capital outlays justifiable where exhaustion of low-cost raw materials lies within the foreseeable future.

Natural Gas as a Fuel

As a cheap fuel natural gas has attracted a growing smelting and refining industry to the Gulf Coast. The best-known plant is the government-owned Tin Processing Corporation smelter at Texas City, still operated in part by Dutch technical personnel, which handles tin concentrates from Bolivia and, in small amounts, from Southeast Asia. The 1948 output of this, the only major tin smelter in the Western Hemisphere, was 23 per cent of world production (exclusive of the U.S.S.R.).[13] Natural gas is also used by the electrolytic zinc plant opened in 1942 at Corpus Christi, the zinc smelters at Amarillo and Dumas in the Panhandle, and the antimony smelter at Laredo.

Most significant is the Port Comfort plant of the Aluminum Company of America that is rising from the wastelands across Lavaca Bay from Port Lavaca, Tex. Here alumina delivered by barge from Mobile will be reduced

---

[13] *Yearbook Amer. Bur. of Metal Statistics 1948*, New York, 1949, p. 100.

to pig aluminum by electrochemical processes. The electricity will be generated by natural gas from wells under Matagorda Bay, the first peacetime use by Alcoa of power other than water power for aluminum reduction except for a brief period in the earliest days of the industry. The scheduled annual output of 57,000 tons will represent about 9 per cent of the nation's aluminum ingot production.

Glass manufacture, often attracted by cheap gas, has been established significantly only at Wichita Falls and Waco, Tex., and at Shreveport, La. Glass sands for these plants are brought from Arkansas and Missouri.

ALKALIES AND CHLORINE

Earliest developments in the Gulf Coast chemical industry were in alkali and chlorine production.[14] Attracted by an almost unlimited supply of brine from the coastal salt domes, lime from shell deposits, and abundant gas and oil for fuel, the Southern Alkali Corporation completed the pioneer soda ash–caustic soda plant at Corpus Christi in the fall of 1934. By the following year similar plants were in operation at Lake Charles and Baton Rouge. These at first employed the ammonia soda process, but later installations provided for the electrolysis of brine to produce both chlorine and caustic. Greatly increased demand led to expansion of these facilities during the war and postwar years, and new plants were opened at Freeport and Houston. Most recently a government-built magnesium plant has been converted into a second electrolytic caustic soda–chlorine unit at Lake Charles, and the company also leases a unit from the government at Pine Bluff, Ark. Today the Gulf Coast produces one-fifth of the nation's electrolytic caustic soda–chlorine output; the Dow Chemical Company at Freeport-Velasco is the leading producer. Oil refineries, chemical plants, and paper mills provide the largest market for these products. Most of the chlorine produced at the new 14-million-dollar Diamond Alkali plant at Houston is delivered to a single customer, by a 10,300-foot pipe line under the Ship Channel.

SYNTHETIC RUBBER

The war gave the synthetic organic chemicals industry of the Gulf Coast its initial boost with the development, almost overnight, of a giant synthetic-rubber program using natural gas and the lighter fractions from refinery runs as basic raw materials. More than half of the nation's war-built synthetic-rubber capacity is represented by the butadiene, styrene, copolymer (GR-S,

---

[14] W. H. Shearon, Jr.: Chlorine and Alkali Production in the Southwest, *Chemical and Engineering News*, Vol. 26, 1948, pp. 3474–3475.

i.e. Government Rubber–Styrene), and butyl (GR-I, i.e. Government Rubber–Isobutylene) rubber plants of Texas and Louisiana. Although most of the plants in other sections have shut down, the Gulf Coast plants have continued to operate close to capacity since the war. Synthetic rubber's competitive position with respect to natural rubber appears to be favorable. Consumption of synthetic rubber in the United States in 1948 was 442,000 tons (of which 345,000 tons was GR-S), which was well above the 215,000-ton minimum set by Congress and constituted about 40 per cent of total primary rubber consumption.

Butadiene, the principal raw material of GR-S rubber, is produced at Baton Rouge, Lake Charles, Port Neches, Baytown, and Houston from refinery gases supplied in large volume by new processes in cracking, especially catalytic cracking. The largest of the plants, at Port Neches, uses butane from five near-by refineries, removing the butadiene and returning the residue gas for use as fuel. At the synthetic-rubber center of Borger the butane is derived from natural gas. Adjacent to each of these oil-company-operated butadiene units stand copolymer plants, leased from the government by established rubber companies. At Baton Rouge and Baytown there is also production of butyl rubber for inner tubes, another product of refinery gases. The other raw material for GR-S rubber is styrene, made at Velasco and at Texas City from natural gas obtained from near-by cycling plants. By weight the finished product is one part styrene and three parts butadiene. A considerable part of the surplus postwar styrene output has gone into plastics.

OTHER SYNTHETIC ORGANIC CHEMICALS

The stimulus of war brought other petrochemical industries to the Gulf Coast. Natural gas is the raw material, together with air and water, for the manufacture of anhydrous ammonia for fertilizers at government-built explosives plants now operated by private industry at Lake Charles and Sterlington, La., at El Dorado, Ark., and near Dumas in the Texas Panhandle. These four plants, built during the war, received half of the government's investment in such units to provide the fixed nitrogen required for explosives. Plans for a plant, financed by private capital, in Yazoo City, Miss., were announced in 1949.

The Houston area, with its 27 chemical plants along the banks of the Ship Channel, is heralded by some as the future chemical capital of the world. In addition to alkalies and chlorine, its products include synthetic glycerin, sodium silicate, industrial alcohols, insecticides, plastic resins, sulphuric acid, ammonium sulphate, and ammonium phosphate, the last using Florida phosphate rock.

439

The industrial boom town of Texas City, some 40 miles to the southeast on Galveston Bay, has seen its population increase from 3500 in 1930 to a swollen 27,000 (1949), although half of its 6000 factory workers live in Galveston and other neighboring communities. Here the Monsanto Chemical Company has completely rebuilt its large styrene plant, destroyed by a port explosion in April, 1947, which resulted in the death of more than 500 persons and property damage of 50 million dollars. The even larger Carbide and Carbon Chemicals plant near by produces a long list of synthetic organics from hydrocarbons supplied in part by Texas City's oil refineries.

Refinery wastes also provide the raw materials for the new 22-million-dollar Jefferson Chemical Company plant at Port Neches, which makes ethylene oxide, ethylene glycol, and other glycols for the manufacture of cellophane, plastics, detergents, and brake fluids. A second major chemical plant announced for Port Neches will employ intermediates obtained from Jefferson, which, like many other Gulf Coast chemical companies, is jointly owned and operated by a national chemical concern and a major oil company.

One of the more spectacular postwar developments in synthetic hydrocarbons is the new Sabine River Works of the Du Pont Ammonia Division near Orange, Tex., for the manufacture of nylon salts, methanol for antifreeze, and formaldehyde and polythene for plastics. The nylon salts solution is shipped to yarn plants in Delaware, Virginia, and Tennessee. About 60 million cubic feet of natural gas is used daily in the plant, obtained from a huge new gas-processing establishment at Winnie, 40 miles to the southwest, where methanol, formaldehyde, and acetaldehyde are also produced. Du Pont has a second nylon salts plant under construction on a 1700-acre tract at Victoria, Tex., which will also use natural gas.

Ground was broken for the first of Dow's two major Texas plants in 1940 at the mouth of the Brazos River. The primary magnesium extracted from sea water here, together with bromine, probably accounted for more than 75 per cent of world production of this metal in 1948. Chemicals produced in important quantities include caustic soda, chlorine, hydrochloric acid, vinyl chloride for plastics, glycols, chlorinated solvents, and ethylene dibromide, the last used entirely in the manufacture of antiknock leaded gasolines. In locating here the company considered such factors as adaptability of the site to huge sea-water intake pumps (300 million gallons is pumped daily from a depth of 30 feet), waste disposal, and the availability of brine, mud shell, natural gas, transportation facilities, and large amounts of cheap land. To secure future supplies of gas for both power and process uses, the company controls nearly 100,000 acres of oil and gas leases through a subsidiary.

Twenty-eight miles southwest of Corpus Christi, near Bishop, the

Fig. 3—The Esso Company's Baton Rouge refinery and butadiene plant on the Mississippi River. Extensive new housing develop-
in the background. (Courtesy of the Esso Standard Oil Company.)

Fig. 4—E. I. du Pont de Nemours and Company's Sabine River works near Orange, Tex. (Courtesy of the Orange
Chamber of Commerce.)

441

Celanese Corporation is using 200,000 gallons of butane and propane a day
to produce acetic acid and acetone for its manufacture of cellulose acetate
yarn and plastics. Methanol, formaldehyde, and other industrial chemicals
are also sold to outside consumers; production both of acetic acid and of
formaldehyde at Bishop in 1947 exceeded production for the entire country
in 1939. The plant ships 350 to 400 tank cars of organic chemicals a month.
In addition to butane and propane, the company uses some 40 million cubic
feet of dry natural gas daily for driving compressors. The plant was originally
designed for butadiene production, but the war ended before it got into
operation. It stands surrounded by fields of grain sorghum in the midst of
some of the world's largest natural-gas reserves. On the south it is bounded
by the vast King Ranch; the fact that one of the directors of Celanese is
related by marriage to the Kleburg family, which controls the 1,250,000-
acre ranch, may have been a factor in selection of the site.

The new industrial activity extends along the Texas Gulf Coast all the
way to the Mexican frontier. At Brownsville both natural gasoline and
oxygenated aliphatic chemicals are to be produced at the Carthage Hydrocol
plant scheduled for completion by the end of 1949. The plant will use an
improved Fischer-Tropsch process to take synthetic gasoline, Diesel oil, and
industrial alcohols from the more than seven trillion cubic feet of proved
natural-gas reserves in the lower Rio Grande Valley. This plant, which is
financed by an 18½-million-dollar RFC loan, and the other two major
chemical plants under construction near by are said to represent a total new
industrial investment in this area of more than 50 million dollars.

Nowhere is industrial interrelationship better illustrated than at Baton
Rouge, where the huge, 40-year-old Esso Standard refinery north of the city
has recently gathered about it a brood of lesser manufacturers, each dependent
on one of the others either for raw materials or for market. Alkali and
chlorine production finds its principal market in the refinery and the alumina
plant. Other chemical plants supply sulphuric acid, hydrofluoric acid, and
industrial alcohol. The Ethyl Corporation's tetraethyl lead production, three
times that of the nation's only other such establishment, at Deepwater, N. J.,
furnishes antiknock compounds for gasoline. The company also produces
here hydrochloric acid, metallic sodium, chlorine, and sodium sulphate
(salt cake), together with ethylene dibromide and ethylene dichloride, which
constitute more than one-third of the weight of tetraethyl lead compounds.

SULPHUR

The superabundance of sulphur on the Gulf Coast has not been a particular attraction to industry. Sulphuric acid, the chief end product of sulphur,

is almost always manufactured close to the market. However, as a result of increased lead prices, plans were announced in 1949 for the establishment of a large titanium oxide plant on the Mississippi River near New Orleans to make white paint pigment from imported Indian ilmenite. The choice of location is explained by the immense quantities of sulphuric acid used in the process and the proximity of Louisiana's Grande Ecaille sulphur mines.

Some Nonchemical Industries

Industrial utilization of second-growth southern pine and hardwood has increased with the decrease of reserves of virgin saw timber. Sulphate-process pulp production began in the South in 1911 at Orange, Tex. Important kraft-paper centers in the Gulf South are located at Bastrop, Springhill, and Bogalusa, La., Pascagoula, Miss., and Mobile, Ala. The pioneer newsprint mill in the South, which opened at Lufkin, Tex., in 1940, remains the only one, though a second is scheduled for completion in 1950 at Childersburg, in central Alabama. At Houston both food-container stock and high-grade coated white paper are produced from bleached sulphate pulp in a large new plant on the Ship Channel.

Texas, since the war, has had its own iron and steel industry. The 60-million-dollar Sheffield plant on the Houston Ship Channel, in part government financed, has one blast furnace and seven open hearths and employs some 3500 persons. Most of its output is marketed in Texas and Louisiana; the oil-field-equipment producers in Houston are an important outlet. Another government-built blast furnace recently purchased by Texas capital at Daingerfield, in the East Texas piny woods, is to be supplemented by steel-making facilities in the near future. East Texas hematite ores and Oklahoma coking coals supply the raw materials for both plants. Some Mexican ore has been received at Houston.

Although Texas and Louisiana together produce one-quarter of the nation's cotton, they are both net importers of cotton textiles. The apparel industry is of importance in Dallas, which has become the South's style center for women's wear, and also in San Antonio and many smaller centers where low-wage, nonunion labor is still available.

Of particular significance to the agricultural economy of the region is the new Corn Products Refining Company plant at Corpus Christi, which is producing dextrose sugars, starches, and protein feed from 600 million bushels of dwarf grain sorghum a year.

A meat-packing industry at Fort Worth, shipbuilding at Mobile, fruit and vegetable canning in the Rio Grande Valley, and the refining of both domestic and imported sugar cane and molasses at New Orleans are other localized industries in the Gulf South. Three of New Orleans' largest industrial plants produce building materials. At Dallas there is an automobile assembly plant where each car carries a windshield sticker "Made in Texas by Texans" as it leaves the assembly line; at Longview, Tex., there is a large new earth-moving-equipment plant.

The Gulf Coast, 1000 miles closer, by way of the Panama Canal, to the Galápagos–Central America fishing grounds than California ports, is well located for the development of a tuna-canning industry, and plans have been announced for canneries at Houston and at Pascagoula. Outfitting of tuna boats is said to be cheaper than at San Diego or San Pedro.

THE AIRCRAFT INDUSTRY

Geographical dispersion of strategic industrial plants is being increasingly dictated by both economic and military considerations. As compared with the more vulnerable Atlantic and Pacific coastal cities, the Gulf South is in a favored position. During the war Texas and Louisiana received important new aircraft manufacturing industries. The huge Higgins and Consolidated Vultee facilities at New Orleans have since been converted to other types of production, but in Texas the two major establishments have continued in operation as aircraft plants.

The more important of these, and the largest industrial employer in the South, is the giant government-owned Consolidated Vultee plant a few miles northwest of Fort Worth. In mid-1949 it was employing 14,000 persons in three shifts. Production began in 1942, just one year after ground was broken, and by November, 1943, employment had reached a peak of 30,600. The choice of location was related in part to the company's plans for the future manufacture of flying boats, which might be test-flown from an adjacent lake, in part to the existence of a military airfield of a length adequate for B-29's. Labor was recruited almost entirely from Texans, though key men were brought from Consolidated's San Diego plant and some thousand new employees were sent to California for training with the understanding that they would return to the Fort Worth plant.

The former North American bomber assembly plant at Grand Prairie, midway between Fort Worth and Dallas, is occupied by two aircraft companies. The larger, Chance Vought, moved its entire establishment here from Stratford, Conn., in 1948–1949, including 1300 Connecticut employees, with their families and belongings. The rest of the company's 5600 employees are Texans. This unprecedented move from the congested Connecticut coast

444

to the Texas plains required 1006 freight cars and was undoubtedly dictated, in part at least, by strategic considerations.

INDUSTRIAL PROMOTION

Promotional activity by local and state agencies, utility companies, and organized industrial districts has been intense in the Gulf South and has probably influenced the location of many new concerns, particularly in the consumers' goods industries. A bond issue approved by Fort Worth voters made possible the purchase of the 1450 acres of land required for the Consolidated aircraft plant. One popular device has been the nonprofit industrial foundation that builds plants to industry's specifications and then rents them on low-cost, long-term leases. Mississippi counties and municipalities are empowered to raise funds through special bond issues for this purpose under the widely publicized "Balance Agriculture with Industry" Act of 1944. Louisiana, with a somewhat unsavory political reputation and an unfavorable tax structure as compared with neighboring Texas, has offered 10-year exemptions from both state and local ad valorem taxes on all new industrial establishments. Between December, 1945, and July, 1949, such exemptions were granted on 381 million dollars' worth of new facilities, which, according to the State Department of Commerce and Industry, should eventually provide 31,686 new jobs.

The economy of the Gulf Coast is still largely oriented to the production of raw materials and staple, heavy-tonnage chemical and petroleum products. Substantial expansion of the regional market, both in numbers and in buying power, would seem imperative before either Texas or Louisiana can take its place alongside the manufacturing states of the North and East. Yet the Gulf South's resource base and its location with respect to world markets and trade routes are much superior to those of California, for example. Overdraft has caused an alarming drop in certain East Texas water tables, but conservation measures and utilization of surface runoff should provide relief at not too great a cost. Although the menace of destructive hurricanes and tidal waves along the low coastal margins is real, improved forecasting techniques in recent years help to discount the danger.

The future of the region lies with the oil and gas reserves, with the geophysicists, the wildcatters, the reservoir engineers, and the recovery technologists. The longer the subsurface deposits of hydrocarbons can be made to last, the closer the cities of the Gulf Coast should be able to approach to their cherished "industrial destiny." Without this resource base their whole economic structure must almost inevitably crumble.

445

CLIMATE AND ZONAL DIVISIONS OF THE BOREAL FOREST FORMATION IN EASTERN CANADA*

F. KENNETH HARE

THE boreal forest formation is the great belt of coniferous forest stretching across the subarctic latitudes of Eurasia and North America. Perhaps because of its inaccessibility and unsuitability for permanent rural settlement, the boreal forest has been little studied by geographers in North America, though Russian and Scandinavian workers have devoted much time to it. The phytogeographer and the ecologist have been concerned primarily with the southern part of the formation, which is the main home of the lumbering industries of Canada, Scandinavia, and the U.S.S.R. The greater part of the formation, beyond the limit of merchantable trees, has received scant attention.

The idea that the boreal forest consists of an endless repetition of muskeg and forest, with little difference from one place to another, is a popular delusion. In both Eurasia and eastern North America the formation resolves itself naturally into three or four zonal divisions, each with its characteristic type of cover and each standing in a definite and predictable relationship to climate. This paper is devoted to a study of these zonal divisions in Canada east of the Ontario-Manitoba boundary, and particularly in the great Labrador-Ungava peninsula, where the author himself has worked.

Labrador-Ungava offers many advantages to the student of the zonal structure of the boreal forest. The peninsula is essentially a tilted peneplain, relatively low in latitude 58° (near the Arctic tree line) but rising southward to a general level approaching 3000 feet some 50 to 100 miles north of the St. Lawrence. Toward the river it falls in a spectacular and highly complex escarpment, the Laurentide scarp, which has yet to appear on most contour maps of North America. The southward rise of altitude has the effect of offsetting to some extent the normal southward rise of temperature. The thermally controlled zonal divisions of the boreal forest are hence widened and can be studied over much greater distances than in Russia or Finland.

*The author wishes to express his gratitude to Dr. Ilmari Hustich, pioneer of forest studies in Labrador, to Dr. Pierre Dansereau of the department of botany, University of Michigan, and to Mr. Harry Lash of the department of geography, McGill University, for advice and assistance in the preparation of this paper.

➤ DR. HARE, formerly a research climatologist with the British Meteorological Office, is now chairman of the department of geography at McGill University, Montreal.

446

The same is true on a smaller scale between Hudson Bay and Lake Superior.

A further advantage springs from the fact that the entire eastern half of the Canadian boreal forest has an abundant precipitation. Control of growth by temperature, well known to be the usual climatic control of natural vegetation in high latitudes, is thus manifested in full measure. Drought effects such as those reported by Marie Sanderson in western Canada are unknown.[1]

The boreal forest formation in eastern Canada, as elsewhere, is bounded on the north by the tundra. On the south, it passes into a mixed forest formation, the Great Lakes–St. Lawrence Forest of Halliday[2] or the Lake Forest of Weaver and Clements.[3] A similar mixed forest borders the Russian boreal forest west of the Urals. As with the zonal divisions of the boreal forest itself, both the southern and northern limits are readily determinable in climatological terms.

COMPOSITION

The chief associations of the formation are dominated by white spruce (*Picea glauca*), black spruce (*P. mariana*), larch or tamarack (*Larix laricina*), and balsam fir (*Abies balsamea*). The jack pine (*Pinus banksiana*)is also an important element in the western half of the region. Tree lines of these species are given in Figure 1, but a discussion of their climatic relations is not attempted in this paper.

The black spruce, white spruce, and tamarack have almost identical northern tree lines, and all three range throughout the formation in North America, though the tamarack is rare in Alaska. Their relative abundance, however, varies greatly. In Labrador-Ungava, black spruce is overwhelmingly the most common. In northern and central districts it occurs either alone or in association with tamarack; in the south and southeast black spruce–balsam fir is the principal association.

Balsam fir and jack pine have northern tree lines for which no exact climatic equivalent can be found. The jack pine, for example, has made little progress into Labrador-Ungava, in spite of apparently favorable climate.

Associated with the dominant coniferous species is a small group of hardwoods having a widespread distribution in the boreal forest in both

---

[1] Marie Sanderson: Drought in the Canadian Northwest, *Geogr. Rev.*, Vol. 38, 1948, pp. 289–299.

[2] W. E. D. Halliday: A Forest Classification for Canada, *Dominion Forest Service Bull. 89*, Ottawa, 1937.

[3] J. E. Weaver and F. E. Clements: Plant Ecology, 2nd edit., New York and London, 1938. pp. 496–500.

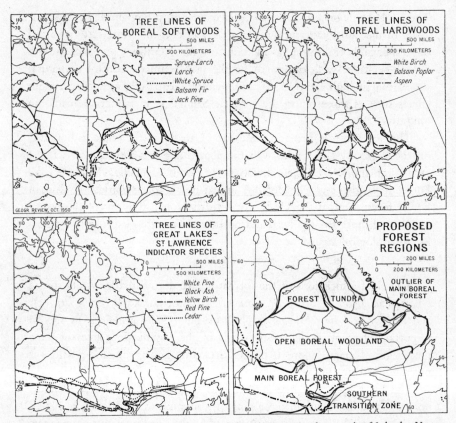

FIG. 1—Tree lines of boreal softwoods. Note absence of the jack pine from much of Labrador-Ungava. The two spruces and the larch have coincident tree lines in most places.

FIG. 2—Tree lines of boreal hardwoods. Note limited extent of aspen in Labrador-Ungava.

FIG. 3—Tree lines of species typical of the Great Lakes–St. Lawrence mixed forest formation. Two species, the cedar and the black ash, invade the main boreal forest.

FIG. 4—Proposed zonal divisions of the boreal forest in Labrador-Ungava. The term "region" is applicable because the map was originally drawn to establish natural regions in the peninsula; "zonal division" is a better term as applied to the boreal forest as a whole. The classification closely follows that of Hustich, but the terminology and the position of boundaries are revised. "Southern transition zone" refers to the ecotone between the boreal and Great Lakes–St. Lawrence forests.

North America and Eurasia, though the actual species differ between the two land masses. The North American representatives are the white birch (*Betula papyrifera*), balsam poplar (*Populus balsamifera*), aspen (*Populus tremuloides*), and certain alders (*Alnus* spp.). None of these trees form part of the climax, but all are important elements in the successions. Their tree lines are shown in Figure 2.

Birch and aspen attain their greatest significance in areas recently burned.

448

Huge areas of birch-aspen associes[4] extend today over the fire-devastated parts of Labrador-Ungava and northern Ontario. Beneath the pale-green foliage of the hardwoods, spruce, larch, and fir seedlings grow rapidly, and in a few decades the climax coniferous association is re-established. Figure 5 shows the succession on the flood-plain bluffs of the Hamilton River in Labrador. White birch and aspen also occur as individual relict trees in the coniferous associations (Fig. 8), though aspen does not appear in northern Labrador-Ungava.

Balsam poplar occurs widely throughout the region, though it is always local in distribution. The alders are found almost exclusively along water-courses and lake shores, forming impenetrable thickets through which landings can hardly be forced.

Along the southern margins of the formation the boreal forest is invaded by isolated individuals or groves of species proper to the Great Lakes–St. Lawrence mixed forest formation. Among the softwoods, these include the white cedar or arbor vitae (*Thuja occidentalis*), white pine (*Pinus strobus*, a dominant species of the mixed forest), and red pine (*P. resinosa*). The hard-woods include black ash (*Fraxinus nigra*), yellow birch (*Betula lutea*), and bigtooth aspen (*Populus grandidentata*). The cedar and black ash invade the boreal forest deeply, but the others penetrate only a short distance. Tree lines of most of these species are shown in Figure 3. At the southern limit of the boreal forest, white and red pines and sugar maple become dominants.

Forest Types

The boreal forest formation is not readily divisible into associations, as is the deciduous forest. Partly because of the small number of species, partly because the region has been heavily glaciated and hence suffers from deranged drainage and highly variable soils, the forest exhibits structural types rather than fixed associations. These types differ as to the spacing of trees, the layering of the vegetation, and the nature of the ground cover. Many of them are definitely not "climax" and probably represent succes-sional stages that must soon give way to a higher form of forest. The prin-ciples of succession in the boreal forest are, however, too vaguely understood to allow a genetic classification. Accordingly the forest types are ranked as equals in the following discussion, regardless of their status.

The classification of forest types used here is based on a study by the

---

[4] An "associes" is the successional equivalent of "association." The birch-aspen communities of the boreal forest are short-lived, yielding place to the coniferous forest that is climax in the formation; hence the use of "associes" rather than associations.

FIG. 5—Birch-aspen associes on old burn, flood-plain bluff of the Hamilton River. The birch-aspen community serve as a cover beneath which the black spruce climax is regenerating.

450

Fig. 6—Close-forest stand of black spruce near Alexander Lake, in the Lake Melville Basin, growing on rough ground moraine. Note the close spacing of the trees and the deep shade of the floor. This is the most common forest type of the main boreal forest.

Fig. 7—Interior view of the close-forest shown in Figure 6. Young spruces, feather mosses, and a few small herbs cover the deeply shaded floor.

451

Fɪɢ. 8—Lichen-woodland—characteristic forest type of the open boreal woodland—on the sand plain of the Hamilton River delta. Black spruce is the only conifer, its "candelabrum" shape due to a special form of lateral branching. Relict white birch on right. Rich and unbroken *Cladonia* lichen floor.

Fɪɢ. 9—Another view of the lichen-woodland forest on the sand plains. Dwarf birch occurs as a shrub here, and the dominant spruces are widely spaced.

452   621

Finnish ecologist Hustich.[5] He has studied both the Labrador and the Scandinavian-Finnish boreal forest, and his classification for the Labrador-Ungava region can be cross-referred to both the Russian taiga and the forests of western Canada as studied by Raup.[6] Hustich's detailed subdivisions are not considered here, and new English terms are suggested for the main types. These are three in number:

1. The *close-forest* type ("Moist Series" of Hustich) is a continuous stand of closely spaced trees, in Labrador-Ungava usually a black spruce–balsam fir association. Such stands occur on well-drained land with a water-retentive soil and hence with abundant but not excessive moisture. The ground vegetation is rich in mosses, especially feather mosses, and there are some characteristic small herbs such as bunchberry (*Cornus canadensis*) and wood sorrel (*Oxalis montana*). Figures 6 and 7 show the exterior and interior of a typical specimen area, in this case a solid stand of black spruce.

2. The *lichen-woodland* type ("Dry Series" of Hustich) consists of open stands of trees with a thick and beautiful floor of lichens. Black and white spruce, tamarack, and jack pine all occur in such woodland, though the spruces are overwhelmingly the dominants. The lichen floor consists of a layer several inches thick of the pale-gray, purple, orange, or green fruiting bodies of *Cladonia,* the genus to which the so-called "reindeer mosses" belong. The trees are from 2 to 25 yards apart. Black spruce tends to assume a beautiful "candelabrum" form in the lichen-woodlands. This type occurs only on drier sites in the south but is widespread in central and northern districts. Various subtypes of lichen-woodland probably cover more than 60 per cent of the Labrador-Ungava plateau and are widespread throughout the formation in North America and Eurasia. Figures 8 and 9 show representative aspects of this type, though they do scant justice to its beauty. The term "woodland" is used to suggest the wide spacing of the trees.

3. The *muskeg* type ("Wet Series" of Hustich) occurs on badly drained ground and is variable in appearance. Black spruce and, to a smaller extent, tamarack are the typical trees. Both are slow-growing and slow-reproducing, appearing like gaunt sticks often largely devoid of branches or green leaves. The wet ground is covered by sphagnum mosses and certain shrubs, of which Labrador tea (*Ledum groenlandicum*), leatherleaf (*Chamaedaphne calyculata*), and a heath (*Kalmia angustifolia*) are representative.

---

[5] Ilmari Hustich: On the Forest Geography of the Labrador Peninsula: A Preliminary Synthesis, *Acta Geographica*, Vol. 10, No. 2, 1949; reference on pp. 36–42.

[6] H. M. Raup: Phytogeographic Studies in the Athabaska-Great Slave Lake Region, II, *Journ. Arnold Arboretum*, Vol. 27, 1946, pp. 1–85.

These clear-cut forest types occur throughout the formation in eastern Canada. The zonal divisions about to be discussed are definable in terms of the relative frequency of the forest types. This important principle has only recently emerged as the basis of division in the boreal forest.

THE ZONAL DIVISIONS

We come now to the first of the two main purposes of this article—the definition of zonal divisions within the formation. The argument closely

TABLE I—PROPOSED ZONAL DIVISIONS OF THE BOREAL FOREST IN LABRADOR-UNGAVA

ZONAL DIVISION	HUSTICH'S TERM	DOMINANT FOREST TYPE
Forest-Tundra Ecotone	Forest-Tundra	Thin lichen-woodland in valleys; pure tundra on interfluves
Open Boreal Woodland	Taiga	Lichen-woodland
Main Boreal Forest	Southern Spruce Forests	Close-forest
Boreal–Mixed Forest Ecotone	——	Close-forest containing Great Lakes–St. Lawrence indicators

parallels that of Hustich, who laid down major forest regions for Labrador-Ungava in 1949.[7] The basis of definition and the precise limits of the divisions proposed here differ significantly from his. In the next section the climatic relations of each of the divisions are reviewed.

South of the tundra four zonal divisions are proposed. These are arranged in north-south sequence in Table I.

The proposed zonal boundaries in Labrador-Ungava are shown in Figure 4. Where these differ from those of Hustich, the differences are based on an inspection of aerial photographs, on flights across the boundary zones, and in a few cases on ground traverses. The map is in any case provisional and will demand continual revision.

The dominant forest types refer to areas of well-drained soil. Throughout the formation areas of poor drainage are covered by treeless swamps and muskegs that differ little from zone to zone. The detailed character of the cover in each zone is beyond the scope of this report, but some further description is necessary.

The *forest-tundra ecotone* extends across northern Labrador-Ungava from the Hudson Bay coast to the Atlantic. Here it is truncated by the pure coastal tundra, which runs along the Atlantic shore to the Strait of Belle Isle. Along the line of the Torngat uplift, running north-south just east of the George River, the ecotone is narrow and is displaced southward by the

[7] Hustich, *op. cit.*, pp. 47–53, Figs. 19 and 20. See also his "Phytogeographical Regions of Labrador." *Arctic*, Vol. 2, 1949, pp. 36–42, especially Fig. 4.

454

greater altitude. The forest-tundra ecotone[8] is the zone in which associations of the tundra and boreal forest formations intermingle. The boreal forest is represented by long strings of lichen woodland along the chief rivers, but the interfluves are covered by pure tundra entirely free of trees. Permafrost is widespread throughout the zone. The northern limit is the Arctic tree line. The southern, the line along which the lichen-woodland covers interfluves as well as valley floors, is known with some confidence from traverses by Rousseau on the George River,[9] Low on the Kaniapiskau River,[10] and Polunin at Lac Bienville.[11] The present author was also able to traverse the boundary by air near the headwaters of the Whale River.

The *open boreal woodland* as a term seems preferable to Hustich's "taiga," since the latter is applied by Russian ecologists to the entire formation and is so understood by geographers everywhere. As the present term implies, this zone is dominated by enormous stretches of the lichen-woodland forest type; tall and well-developed spruce (more rarely other conifers) stand several yards apart in a sea of *Cladonia*. On the wetter ground muskeg supervenes, with stunted trees, Labrador tea, and sphagnum. Close-forest types are absent over most of the zone but become abundant on steeply sloping ground near the southern boundary. This boundary—one of the most significant economic limits on the continent, as it is the virtual northern limit of lumbering—is defined as that along which close-forest exceeds lichen-woodland in area.

The open boreal woodland presents one of the most picturesque, colorful, and extensive landscapes of the continent and is equally important in the Eurasian boreal forest. The beauty of its *Cladonia* floor, which retains the impress of footprints for years and whose pastel shades defy the color film, is still largely unknown to North Americans, since convenient routes nowhere penetrate its solitudes.

The *main boreal forest* is far better known, for it yields more than 90 per cent of the pulpwood cut of eastern Canada. Along its entire length it is penetrated by railways, logging roads, and power-generating rivers. In

---

[8] The term "forest tundra" is a literal translation of the Russian term *lyesotundra* for the same belt in European Russia and Siberia. "Forest-tundra ecotone," a preferable form in English, was introduced by J. W. Marr: Ecology of the Forest Tundra Ecotone on the East Coast of Hudson Bay, *Ecological Monographs*, Vol. 17, 1948, pp. 117–144.

[9] J. J. Rousseau: The Vegetation and Life Zones of George River, Eastern Ungava and the Welfare of the Natives, *Arctic*, Vol. 1, 1948, pp. 93–96.

[10] A. P. Low: Report on Explorations in the Labrador Peninsula . . . , *Ann. Rept. Geol. Survey of Canada*, Vol. 8 (N.S.), Ottawa, 1895, Rept. L, p. 153.

[11] Nicholas Polunin: Report on Botanical Explorations in Arctic America, 1946–48, *Arctic*, Vol. 2, 1949, pp. 45–47.

eastern Canada it extends from north of Lake Superior across southern Labrador-Ungava to Anticosti Island and Newfoundland. Large outliers cover inland Gaspé, the highlands of New Brunswick, and parts of Maine.

This zone is largely covered by close-forest associations of black spruce and balsam fir east of Lake St. John, white spruce and balsam fir to the west, thus approaching the traditionally accepted boreal climax. Lichen-woodlands occur only on dry soils and appear to be a late stage of the xerosere.[12] Muskeg, with black spruce and tamarack as dominants, is again common, especially on the dreary plains south and west of James Bay (Fig. 10).

The northern limit of this zone was first defined by Halliday,[13] who consolidated traverse records from many transverse valleys crossing the boundary. Hustich accepted Halliday's line with few exceptions.[14] An accurate determination of its position on the Romaine River by H. N. Lash and N. Drummond showed, however, that Hustich's line was too far north.[15] The position given on Figure 4 incorporates their results.

An important outlier of the main boreal forest covers the lowlands around the head of Lake Melville and in the Hamilton Valley. This favored region of Labrador has much close-forest, though lichen-woodland (Figs. 8 and 9) is extensive on sand plains and gravels. It was formerly believed that the richness of this vegetation sprang from the deeper and more fertile soils developed on the Proterozoic sediments contained in the basin. It is now obvious, however, that this outlier is a climatic effect, a subject treated below. A revised version of Halliday's map[16] includes another outlier, the middle Kaniapiskau Valley, on the strongly folded Proterozoic sediments of the Labrador Trough. Here the vegetation consists of lichen-woodland and is included in the open boreal woodland of Figure 4.

The southern limit of the main boreal forest is the line along which the white pine–maple associations of the Great Lakes–St. Lawrence mixed forest formation replace the spruce-fir of the boreal forest. The position of this boundary as shown on Figure 4 is taken without change from "Native Trees of Canada."[17] The Lake St. John basin forms a conspicuous enclave of Great Lakes–St. Lawrence associations within the main boreal forest.

---

[12] The succession of covers achieved as the forest extends over dry surfaces like rocky outcrops or sand plains, which abound in this region.

[13] Halliday, op. cit., See map in folder.

[14] Hustich, On the Forest Geography of the Labrador Peninsula, op. cit., Figs. 19 and 20.

[15] Lash and Drummond made a traverse along Romaine River to determine ground control for the ecological interpretation of aerial photographs. The traverse, as yet unpublished, was carried out as part of a project directed by the present author. Mr. Lash has now assumed control of this project.

[16] Native Trees of Canada, Forest Service Bull. 61, 4th edit., Ottawa, 1949. See map inside covers.

[17] Ibid.

FIG. 10—Aerial view of the interminable muskegs south and west of James Bay.

457

The ecotone between these two formations is less easy to define than the forest-tundra. On Figure 4 the northern edge of the ecotone is taken as the tree line of white and red pine. However, certain elements of the Great Lakes–St. Lawrence forest, notably the white cedar and black ash, extend well beyond this line.

CLIMATIC RELATIONS

Climatic correlation has been impossible in the past because of the lack of inland climatological stations. Not until 1937 was a station established in the interior of Labrador-Ungava, a region equal in area to the United States east of the Mississippi and south of latitude 40° N. Since then, however, many stations have been opened by the Canadian Department of Transport and the United States Air Weather Service, and a rudimentary climatological network is now in operation. In 1947 the author began preparation of a report on the climatology of the region, and extensive use has been made below of materials gathered during this investigation.

Raw climatic data have little application in ecoclimatology. Effort must be made to find means of combining and integrating the elements into indices having a more direct applicability to ecological problems. The best available system is C. W. Thornthwaite's classification of 1948,[18] and it is used here. An account of the climates of Canada as a whole according to this new classification has already been published by Sanderson.[19] A considerably denser network of stations (see Appendix) has been used in the preparation of Figures 11 and 12, however, and these maps differ in detail from those of Sanderson.

Annual potential evapotranspiration is the function used by Thornthwaite to establish the degree of thermal efficiency possessed by a climate. It is an accumulating logarithmic function of monthly mean temperatures, regarded as expressing thermal efficiency on the basis of a presumed analogy with the control of growth rates by temperature.

Figure 11 shows annual potential evapotranspiration over eastern Canada and the boundaries of the thermal provinces suggested by Thornthwaite. The D'/C_1' boundary runs north of Baker Lake, across the Ungava Peninsula from Portland Promontory to Payne Bay, and across the northernmost part of the Torngat massif. The C_1'/C_2' boundary (separating cooler and

---

[18] C. W. Thornthwaite: An Approach Toward a Rational Classification of Climate, *Geogr. Rev.*, Vol. 38, 1948, pp. 55–94. A more general treatment of the climate is given by F. Kenneth Hare: The Climate of the Eastern Canadian Arctic and Sub-Arctic and Its Influence on Accessibility, 2 vols., Montreal, 1950. (Doctoral Diss., unpublished.)

[19] Marie Sanderson: The Climates of Canada According to the New Thornthwaite Classification, *Scientific Agric.*, Vol. 28, 1948, pp. 501–517.

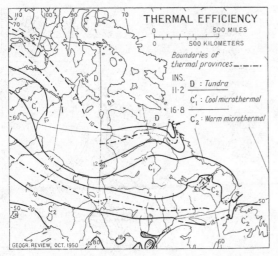

FIG. 11—Thermal efficiency, expressed in terms of potential evapotranspiration (in inches), according to Thornthwaite's classification of 1948.

warmer microthermal provinces) runs from the Hayes River near Gods Lake across James Bay to the northern tip of the Long Peninsula of Newfoundland. Thus the greater part of Labrador-Ungava falls into the cool microthermal province (C_1'). All the southern districts lie in the warm microthermal province (C_2'); mesothermal climates do not occur within the area of Figure 11, though they are found in the St. Lawrence lowlands near Montreal.

The records from Goose Bay airport show that an important outlier of warm microthermal climate occurs around the head of Lake Melville and the lower Hamilton Valley. Fragmentary records from North West River and the Hamilton Valley confirm that this is an extensive area, but its form can at present only be sketched in relation to the terrain (Fig. 11).

The moisture index, the other main element in Thornthwaite's classification, is shown in Figure 12. Labrador-Ungava, Newfoundland, and northern Ontario have an abundant well-distributed precipitation and rank almost exclusively as humid or perhumid. The southern half of Labrador-Ungava has indices of more than 100 (A; perhumid), as does most of Newfoundland. Highest values occur along the Laurentide scarp belt, just north of the Gulf of St. Lawrence, and in southern Newfoundland. Conspicuously drier areas include the structural depressions of Lake St. John and Lake Melville, and also the Atlantic coastal strip from Nain to Cape Harrison. Farther north and west indices are lower but everywhere exceed 20, except in the James Bay and Ungava Bay depressions. This is in striking contrast to the condition reported for the western boreal forest by Sanderson,[20] who found indices ranging from below −20 to about + 20, i.e. between arid and moist subhumid.

[20] Sanderson, Drought in the Canadian Northwest, op. cit.

There is some doubt about the extent of drought in the James Bay region. The isopleth of 20 in the center is based on values computed for Fort Albany (17), Moose Factory (19), and Fort George (33). It is possible, however, that these values are too low, perhaps because of faulty exposure of the snow-measuring site. More recent observations at Moos-onee, a first-order sta-

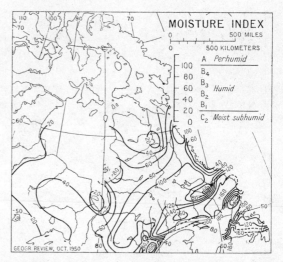

FIG. 12—Moisture index, according to Thornthwaite's classification of 1948. Note high values typical of southern Labrador-Ungava, low values along western margin.

tion staffed by trained professional observers, indicate a heavier winter snow-fall than at near-by Moose Factory, and the index stands at 74. The point is academic, since almost the entire district is covered by muskeg in which bad drainage upsets the normal moisture cycle.

CORRELATIONS BETWEEN CLIMATE AND THE ZONAL FOREST DIVISIONS

It now remains only to establish the relation between the climate distributions and the zonal divisions of the forest. Such attempts were previously made by Halliday[21] and Villeneuve[22] for various parts of the region, but in both cases before data were available from the interior of Labrador-Ungava and before Thornthwaite's new system was published. Villeneuve's maps do not extend beyond the 51st parallel.

Elsewhere, a good deal of work has been done on the growth conditions of the coniferous trees composing the boreal forest climax. With few exceptions, all these investigations have suggested that midsummer temperatures control growth rates and that precipitation is largely ineffective as a control. Thus Hustich reported that the width of annual rings in Scotch pine (*Pinus sylvestris*) at Utsjoki, Lappland, was closely correlated with July mean daily temperature; vertical growth of the trees was likewise

[21] Halliday, *op. cit.*, pp. 40–45.

[22] G. O. Villeneuve: Climatic Conditions of the Province of Quebec and Their Relationship to the Forests, *Forest Protection Service Bull. No. 6*, Quebec, 1946.

related to the July temperature of the previous year. Neither vertical nor radial growth was related to variations in summer precipitation.[23] Similar results were obtained by Erlandsson[24] and other Scandinavian workers for Scotch pine and other boreal forest conifers. Giddings stressed the dependence of the spruce on summer temperature in both Alaska[25] and the Mackenzie Valley.[26] The widely accepted view that the northern forests are governed in their growth by temperature, and that precipitation is every-

TABLE II—FOREST DIVISIONS AND POTENTIAL EVAPOTRANSPIRATION IN LABRADOR-UNGAVA

DIVISION	TYPICAL VALUE OF P-E ALONG BOUNDARIES (INCHES)	DOMINANT COVER TYPE
Tundra		Tundra
	12.0–12.5	
Forest-Tundra Ecotone		Tundra and lichen-woodland intermingled
	14.0–14.5	
Open Boreal Woodland		Lichen-woodland
	16.5–17.0	
Main Boreal Forest		Close-forest with spruce-fir associations
	18.5–19.0	
Boreal–Mixed Forest Ecotone		Close-forest with white and red pine, yellow birch, and other non-boreal invaders
	20.0	
Great Lakes–St. Lawrence Mixed Forest		Mixed forest

where adequate to supply the needs of the growth possible under such cool conditions, was also accepted by Thornthwaite in his earlier climatic classification.[27]

The present investigation amply confirms this view. A comparison of Figures 11 and 12 with Figure 4 shows at once that there is an obvious correlation between the zonal forest divisions and thermal efficiency (that is, potential evapotranspiration); the interdivisional boundaries tend to follow the isopleths of potential evapotranspiration. On the other hand, there is no obvious correlation between the moisture provinces and the forest divisions. No evidence whatever has been found to suggest any control of the forest structure by the moisture factor, other than the effects of poor drainage in the muskeg. Table II shows how close is the correlation between thermal efficiency and the forest divisions. With trifling exceptions, the

[23] I. Hustich: On the Correlation between Growth and the Recent Climatic Fluctuation, *in* Glaciers and Climate . . . dedicated to Hans W:son Ahlmann, *Geografiska Annaler*, Vol. 31, 1949, pp. 90–105.

[24] S. Erlandsson: Data 23, *Dendrochronological Studies*, Uppsala, 1936.

[25] J. L. Giddings, Jr.: Dendrochronology in Northern Alaska, *Univ. of Arizona Bull.*, Vol. 12, No. 4, 1941.

[26] *Idem:* Mackenzie River Delta Chronology, *Tree-Ring Bull.*, Vol. 13, 1947, pp. 26–29.

[27] C. W. Thornthwaite: The Climates of North America According to a New Classification, *Geogr. Rev.*, Vol. 21, 1931, pp. 633–655.

interdivisional boundaries follow closely the isopleths of potential evapotranspiration suggested in Table II.

The Arctic tree line, the southern limit of the tundra, nowhere reaches Thornthwaite's theoretical potential evapotranspiration value of 11.2 inches. Near the mouth of the George River, which affords a good migration route northward, a thin stand of black spruce and tamarack reaches the value 11.5 inches, but elsewhere the tree line lies between 12 and 12.5 inches. Marr has shown, however, that white spruce is actively invading the tundra near the Great Whale River, and it may well be that there has not been time since the Wisconsin glaciation for the forest to attain its climax tree line.[28]

Near Richmond Gulf on the Hudson Bay coast and south of Hebron on the Atlantic coast, well-developed black and white spruce groves stand well north of the isotherm of 10° C. (50° F.) for the warmest month.

The narrow strip of coastal tundra fringing the Atlantic coast of Labrador as far south as Belle Isle was formerly thought to be the reflection of the chilling effect of the Labrador Current and its pack ice. Climatological stations directly on this coastal tree line, however, show that the thermal efficiency is adequate to support lichen-woodland (Hopedale, 15.3 inches; Cartwright, 15.3 inches; Belle Isle, 14.5 inches). Evidently temperature is not alone responsible for the lack of trees.

The open boreal woodland extends between the potential evapotranspiration values of 14.0–14.5 and 16.5–17.0 inches. Its southern limit coincides with Thornthwaite's suggested divide between warmer and cooler microthermal climates (C_1'/C_2'). In other words, the forest-tundra ecotone and open boreal woodland correspond with the cool microthermal province.

Wide variations in moisture index occur within this division, without any apparent effect on the vegetation. Since moisture is abundant everywhere, it is of interest to speculate as to the origins of the curious structure of the dominant lichen-woodland, with its widely spaced but fully developed trees and its lichen floor that requires little moisture. Farther south lichen-woodland is definitely a drought type, confined to sandy or gravelly soils.

It may well be that the widespread character of this dry type in the open boreal woodland results from physiological drought, as Schimper has called it. Where frost in the soil is still unthawed in July, the season of peak growth, the trees can derive moisture only from the topmost layers of the soil and hence are driven to assume a horizontally developed root system. Competition between neighboring trees must then mean that the space between individuals has to be greater.

---

[28] Marr, *op. cit*

462

The main boreal forest occupies the range of potential evapotranspiration between 16.5–17.0 and 20.0 inches. It is invaded by indicators of the Great Lakes–St. Lawrence formation as far north as the 18.5- and 19.0-inch isopleths. The southern limit, 20.0 inches, is faithfully followed from Lake Superior to Gaspé; the 20.0-inch isopleth even curves around the Lake St. John lowland, with the little enclave of mixed forest mentioned above. It is to be noted that Thornthwaite's microthermal-mesothermal boundary (C'_2/B'_1) is 22.4 inches; the main boreal forest and the Great Lakes–St. Lawrence formation thus meet in the middle of the warm microthermal province.

The small outlier of warm microthermal climate in the Lake Melville–Hamilton River region coincides reasonably well with the detached area of main boreal forest in the same districts. Though poor in species, the well-developed close-forests of this region offer one of the largest untapped reserves of pulpwood in eastern North America. The region has a thermal efficiency similar to that of the forests now being cut near Clarke City and on Anticosti Island.

The Remaining Areas

Although the delimitation of zonal divisions has not yet been undertaken beyond Labrador-Ungava, a few comments may be made concerning other parts of eastern Canada.

"Native Trees of Canada" includes a revised version of the Halliday map of Canadian vegetation. It distinguishes between a "northern transition" zone and the main boreal forest; and in Labrador-Ungava the line very nearly coincides with the boundary between the open boreal woodland and the main boreal forest. From the vicinity of James Bay west to Manitoba the boundary continues to lie between the 16.5- and 17.0-inch isopleths of potential evapotranspiration. The regions farther north in the Hudson Bay lowland are too little known to permit further correlation.

The islands of Newfoundland and Anticosti lie wholly within the range of potential evapotranspiration found in the main boreal forest, with the solitary exception of the Long Peninsula of Newfoundland. Both islands are largely covered by close-forest, with the spruces and balsam fir as the dominants. There seems no doubt that they lie within the main boreal forest division. The warmest area of Newfoundland (potential evapotranspiration 19–20 inches) lies along the railway line from St. George Bay to the Avalon Peninsula. This thermal efficiency corresponds with the boreal–mixed forest ecotone on the mainland, and it is interesting to note that many non-boreal trees occur in isolated localities (for example, white pine and red maple, *Acer rubrum*). The south coast of Newfoundland is chilled by the onshore prevailing winds crossing the offshoot of the Labrador Current that moves westward along the coast. Much of the high ground of the south is covered by treeless moss barrens. In many cases the lack of trees is an effect of altitude, but moss barrens occur also at low altitudes in regions where the thermal efficiency is ample to support high forest. Their origin has not been explained.

A preliminary glance at the Russian taiga has shown that zonal divisions comparable with those defined above for Labrador-Ungava have almost identical relationships with climate. This encourages the hope that it will ultimately be possible to extend the present review to the entire extent of the boreal forest formation. It will be of particular interest to see whether anything of the same zonal structure is revealed in the boreal forest of western Canada, where Sanderson has reported the retarding effects of drought. It may well be that the dependence of growth on thermal efficiency so strikingly confirmed in the humid east breaks down in the drier west.

APPENDIX—LIST OF CLIMATOLOGICAL STATIONS

The following list includes all stations to whose detailed records access was obtained. In certain areas beyond the southern margin of the subarctic the high station density has made it necessary to omit some points from the maps and appendix. Within the region itself the list is effectively complete. The dates given do not necessarily indicate the complete period of record: they show only the years used by the author in the statistical analysis. It was sometimes necessary to reject records of certain months or years because they were vitiated, or because of changes in observational practice or large gaps in daily sequences. "B" indicates a broken record. The international index numbers of telegraphic reporting stations are taken from the Department of Transport's *Circular 1521*, January 1, 1949.

STATION	INDEX NO.	LATITUDE N.	LONGITUDE W.	ELEVATION (*feet*)	PERIOD
Albanel, Que.	—	48°53′	72°27′	635	1922–48
Amos, Que.	—	48°36′	78°07′	1002	1913–48
Anticosti, East Point, Que.	—	49°12′	61°40′	—	—
Arctic Bay, N.W.T.	918	73°16′	84°17′	36	1937–48
Armstrong, Ont.	841	50°18′	88°55′	1065	1925–48
Arvida, Que.	—	48°28′	71°10′	335	1931–48
Ashuanipi, Lab.	817	52°32′	66°14′	1790	1948
Bagotville, Que.	727	48°20′	71°00′	536	1943–48
Baie Comeau, Que.	720	49°12′	68°16′	177	1939–48B
Belle Isle, Nfld.	809	51°53′	55°22′	426	1874–1948
Bersimis, Que.	—	48°55′	68°37′	—	1923–48
Bonavista, Nfld.	—	48°38′	53°05′	—	1934–38B
Botwood, Nfld.	808	49°09′	55°21′	31	1938–48B
Buchans, Nfld.	804	48°51′	56°50′	894	1934–48
Cambridge Bay, N.W.T.	925	69°07′	105°01′	45	1929–48B
Cape Harrison, Lab.	181	54°44′	58°19′	65	1943–48
Cape Hopes Advance, Que.	900	61°03′	69°36′	240	1929–48B

STATION	INDEX NO.	LATITUDE N.	LONGITUDE W.	ELEVATION (*feet*)	PERIOD
Cape Race, Nfld.	800	46°39'	52°04'	99	1920–48
Cartwright, Lab.	818	53°42'	57°00'	34	1935–48
Channel, Nfld.	—	47°37'	59°09'	50	1893–1918B
Chesterfield Inlet, N.W.T.	916	63°20'	90°43'	13	1921–48
Chibougamau, Que.	821	49°54'	74°18'	1234	1937–48
Chicoutimi, Que.	—	48°25'	71°05'	150	1893–1948B
Churchill, Man.	913	58°47'	94°11'	44	1908–48
Chute à Murdock, Que.	—	48°31'	71°15'	300	1921–48
Chute aux Galets, Que.	—	48°39'	71°12'	500	1920–48
Clarke City, Que.	812	50°12'	68°38'	186	1906–47
Clyde River, N.W.T.	090	70°25'	68°17'	10	1942–46B
Colinet, Nfld.	—	—	—	—	1938–48B
Coral Harbour, N.W.T.	915	64°11'	83°17'	193	1943–48
Corner Brook, Nfld.	—	48°57'	57°57'	40	1933–48
Daniels Harbour, Nfld.	185	50°14'	57°35'	49	1946–48
Deer Lake, Nfld.	—	49°06'	57°29'	185	1933–48
Doucet, Que.	—	48°13'	76°37'	1236	1922–39
Ellis Bay, Que.	—	49°50'	64°25'	28	1936–45B
Fogo, Nfld.	806	49°43'	54°17'	25	1910–48B
Fort Chimo, Que.	906	58°05'	68°25'	112	1919–48B
Fort George, Que.	—	53°50'	79°05'	—	1915–44B
Fort McKenzie, Que.	901	56°53'	68°25'	250	1938–48
Fort Ross, N.W.T.	919	72°02'	94°03'	50	1938–47B
Frobisher Bay, N.W.T.	909	63°44'	68°33'	54	1942–48
Gander, Nfld.	803	48°57'	54°34'	482	1937–48
Gillam, Man.	912	56°21'	94°46'	454	1942–48
Glenwood, Nfld.	—	48°59'	54°52'	93	1936–48
Gods Lake, Man.	—	54°40'	94°10'	585	1938–44
Goose Bay, Lab.	816	53°20'	60°24'	144	1941–48
Gouin Dam, Que.	—	48°23'	74°00'	1325	1915–48
Grand Bank, Nfld.	802	47°06'	55°46'	19	1934–48
Grand Falls, Nfld.	—	48°55'	55°40'	200	1913–48B
Great Whale River, Que.	905	55°17'	77°46'	50	1925–48B
Haileybury, Ont.	—	47°27'	79°38'	707	1902–48
Harrington Harbour, Que.	814	50°34'	59°30'	˙25	1912–48
Hebron, Lab.	—	58°12'	62°37'	49	1883–1910
Hopedale, Lab.	—	55°27'	60°14'	35	1867–1902B
					(Moravian Record)
Hopedale, Lab.	900	55°27'	60°14'	35	1942–46
Howley, Nfld.	—	49°11'	57°06'	384	1934–48B
Ile Maligne, Que.	—	48°40'	71°45'	390	1924–38
Indian House Lake, Que.	098	56°02'	64°44'	1044	1944–48
Kapuskasing, Ont.	831	49°25'	82°28'	752	1920–48
Kenora, Ont.	850	49°48'	94°22'	1345	1898–1948
Knob Lake, Que.	828	54°50'	66°42'	1550	1948
Lake Edward, Que.	—	47°39'	72°16'	1195	1910–23B
Lake Harbour, N.W.T.	095	62°50'	69°55'	54	1884–1938B
Lake Manuan, Que.	820	50°38'	70°32'	1625	1942–48
Lake Norman, Que.	817	52°08'	63°49'	1625	1942–45
Lake Onatchiway, Que.	—	49°00'	71°02'	1050	1920–48
Lansdowne House, Ont.	846	52°14'	88°00'	840	1938–48

STATION	INDEX NO.	LATITUDE N.	LONGITUDE W.	ELEVATION (feet)	PERIOD
Millertown, Nfld.	—	49°00′	56°21′	692	1934–48
Mingan, Que.	188	50°17′	64°09′	76	1943–48
Mistassini Post, Que.	—	50°30′	73°55′	1235	1915–48
Moose Factory, Ont.	—	51°16′	80°40′	20	1891–1937
Moosonee, Ont.	836	51°16′	80°39′	34	1933–48
Morhiban, Que.	182	51°50′	62°53′	1720	1943–48
Nain, Lab.	—	56°33′	61°40′	13	1883–1902
Nakina, Ont.	840	50°11′	86°42′	1065	1938–47
Natashquan, Que.	813	50°12′	61°49′	18	1914–48
Nitchequon, Que.	826	53°12′	70°35′	1690	1942–48
Nottingham Is., N.W.T.	908	63°07′	77°56′	54	1928–48
Okak, Lab.	—	57°34′	62°03′	16	1876–89B
Padloping Is., N.W.T.	911	67°06′	62°21′	130	1941–48
Pagwa, Ont.	833	50°02′	85°16′	620	1923–48
Pangnirtung, N.W.T.	—	66°09′	65°30′	50	1925–47B
Parent, Que.	726	47°55′	74°37′	1405	1943–48
Pickle Lake, Ont.	845	51°28′	90°18′	1245	1930–48
Pond Inlet, N.W.T.	—	72°43′	78°30′	13	1921–48B
Port Burwell, Que.	—	60°25′	64°46′	—	1928–34B
Port Harrison, Que.	907	58°25′	78°08′	20	1921–48
Port Nelson, Man.	—	57°10′	92°30′	25	1903–14
Ramah, Lab.	—	58°23′	62°21′	10	1872–89
Ramea-Burgeo, Nfld.	—	47°32′	57°31′	—	1934–48B
Red Lake, Ont.	854	51°03′	93°50′	1250	1938–47
Resolution Is., N.W.T.	903	61°18′	64°53′	127	1928–48
Roberval, Que.	—	48°31′	72°13′	532	1913–26
St. Andrews, Nfld.	197	47°46′	59°20′	35	1944–48
St. Anthony, Nfld.	819	51°25′	55°30′	45	1944–48B
St. Félicien, Que.	729	48°39′	72°27′	366	1938–48
St. Georges, Nfld.	—	48°28′	58°25′	10	1902–45B
St. Johns, Nfld.	—	47°34′	52°42′	125	1875–1948
Sandgirt Lake, Lab.	827	53°50′	65°30′	1435	1942–47
San Maur, Que.	—	47°53′	73°48′	1170	1930–48
Senneterre, Que.	728	48°24′	77°15′	1038	1940–48
Seven Islands, Que.	811	50°13′	66°16′	190	1943–48
Sioux Lookout, Ont.	842	50°07′	91°54′	1227	1915–48
Southwest Point, Que.	810	49°24′	63°33′	24	1881–1948
Stephenville, Nfld.	815	48°32′	58°33′	44	1943–48
Tadoussac, Que.	—	48°10′	69°40′	25	1913–48
Torbay, Nfld.	801	47°37′	52°44′	463	1942–48
Trout Lake, Ont.	848	53°50′	89°52′	720	1938–48
Zoar, Lab.	—	56°07′	61°22′	33	1883–1902B